Rapid Electrical Estimating and Pricing

Rapid Electrical Estimating and Pricing

A HANDY, QUICK METHOD OF DIRECTLY DETERMINING THE SELLING PRICES OF ELECTRICAL CONSTRUCTION WORK

C. Kenneth Kolstad, P. E.
Gerald V. Kohnert, P. E.

Fifth Edition

McGraw-Hill Inc. New York St. Louis San Francisco Auckland Bogotá Caracas Lisbon London Madrid Mexico Milan Montreal New Delhi Paris San Juan São Paulo Singapore Sydney Tokyo Toronto

Library of Congress Cataloging-in-Publication Data

Kolstad, C. Kenneth.
Rapid electrical estimating and pricing : a handy, quick method of directly determining the selling prices of electrical construction work / C. Kenneth Kolstad, Gerald V. Kohnert.—5th ed.
p. cm.
Includes index.
ISBN 0-07-035523-1
1. Electrical engineering—Estimates. I. Kohnert, Gerald V.
II. Title
TK435.K6 1993
621.319'24'0299—dc20 92-34066
CIP

3456789 KPKP 9987654

ISBN 0-07-035523-1

The sponsoring editor for this book was Harold B. Crawford, the editing supervisor was Kimberly A. Goff, and the production supervisor was Pamela A. Pelton. This book was set in Times Roman Italic.

Printed and bound by Halliday Lithograph.

Contents

Preface

During our years in the electrical contracting industry and as consulting engineers, we realized that a method for establishing a cost estimate which was both reasonably accurate and quick was needed. Such a method of working out engineering estimates would be of considerable value to contractors, architects, engineers, physical-plant superintendents, and others.

Previously, a proper estimate would require more time than was economically feasible—the only accurate method demanded an estimate similar to the one used by contractors. A takeoff of the items required with the labor units assigned to the various pieces, and finally, a summary of the estimate would be necessary. Since this was time-consuming and costly and did not necessarily result in a sale, the time spent was often wasted. But this was about the only accurate method available.

For an estimate to be of value to the contractor or engineer, it should be possible to prepare it rapidly and with a reasonable degree of accuracy. A departure from the conventional material and labor-hour columns with the additions of overhead, labor, taxes, profit, etc., is necessary. All these items have to be in the "rapid" price. Thus, the qualified observer will notice that the graphs in this book show neither material prices nor labor hours, so that a quick accurate price in dollars can be determined.

The prices shown on the graphs include contractors' material costs, labor hours for installation at an overall national average of $17 per hour (not including benefits), overhead at an average of 102% on labor, direct job expenses of 12% on labor, and 5% profit on prime costs (materials + labor + overhead + direct job expenses). Overhead includes administrative salaries, rent, bookkeeping, telephones, insurance, promotional expenses, etc., and costs not associated with a specific job, which generally vary inversely with the size of the firm. Direct job expenses as indicated here include time estimating, field shop, field telephone, job tools used and depreciated, job supervision, and freight and truck expenses relating to the specific job. As a consequence of adding these costs to the material and labor, graph prices reflect the total installed selling price by the electrical contractor.

A Total Price Adjustment Chart which deals with the mechanics of adjusting labor rates and material prices is shown on page xiv. This is an extremely important aspect of estimating prices that must be understood by the user of this book before establishing any firm estimate.

This book will be of considerable value and assistance to many technical people involved in electrical construction work. Consulting engineers, electrical contractors, general contractors, architects, physical-plant superintendents, electrical equipment manufacturers, and electrical wholesale representatives serving smaller contractors will find the book useful, as will engineers in such government agencies involved in construction as the Army, Navy, Air Force, General Services Administration, and state and municipal engineering departments, and, finally, industrial, college, and university physical-plant administrators.

Since the first four editions of this book have been so widely accepted, many new items have been added and existing ones updated as seemed appropriate. Owing to technological progress, a number of items which are obsolete have been deleted. The book should prove to be as satisfactory a working tool for the user as it has been for those of us who have been using this method over the years.

The book is organized into sections corresponding to the same general categories as an electrical construction project. These categories are: Lighting, Circuit Protection, Services, Grounding, Feeders, Branch Circuits, Control Equipment, Transformers, Auxiliary Systems, Electric Heating, Power Distribution above 600 Volts, and Miscellaneous. The Appendix contains four typical problems with their complete solution to demonstrate the manner of rapidly finding the job selling price.

It has been found that a job can be taken off and priced in about one-fifth the time required by the conventional system with the same degree of accuracy as you find between bidders. It might be pointed out that it is rather difficult to evaluate bids correctly when there are only two bidders, particularly if one is not familiar with the bidding situation in the areas involved at the time of bidding. Five bidders provide a much clearer picture. When one is familiar with conditions in an area, the total price adjustment multiplier that is more accurate for one's use can be easily found. We have also found that on big jobs where there are large open spaces or much repetition of lighting luminaries and panelboards, there is often competition between manufacturers and wholesalers, which affects the accuracy of estimates from this book. The estimator must be aware of this situation and adjust for it as he or she sees fit.

We would like to express our appreciation to the following well-qualified people who, through their own specialized knowledge, have given much help and suggestions for the project:

Clarence (Clancy) O. Bader, Electrical Construction Co., Colorado Springs, CO
Al Bolger, Adams Excavating Co., Colorado Springs, CO
Dale Chase, Berwick Electric Co., Colorado Springs, CO
Gregg Cloos, Gregg Cloos Co., Denver, CO
Robert E. Cripe, President, Independent Protection Co., Goshen, IN
G. (Jerry) T. Daveline, American Electric Co., Colorado Springs, CO
Bill Duffus, Electro-Media of Colorado, Denver, CO
David Evancheck, Simplex Time Recorder Co., Denver, CO
Dallas Huscher, American Electric Co., Colorado Springs, CO
Jim Leach, Berwick Electric Co., Colorado Springs, CO
Marvin Logan, Lithonia Products, Monument, CO
David Marquardt, Marquardt/Herbert Co., Denver, CO
Joe Mihelich, All Phase Electric Supply Co., Colorado Springs, CO
Lynne Morey, Lumen Power Sources, Inc., Denver, CO
Victor Palazzini, Wiremold Co., Denver, CO
Keith Severson, E & M Sales Inc., Denver, CO
Philip Smith, Performance Lighting Products Co., Denver, CO
Donna Sus, Electrical Agencies, Denver, CO
Barry Walsh, Blazer Electric Supply Co., Colorado Springs, CO
Craig Whitney, President, Whitney Electric Co., Colorado Springs, CO

How to Use This Book

The basic concept of this book of graphs is to provide a means of quickly pricing a job with a reasonable degree of accuracy. The use of assemblies, as developed by the Estimatic Corporation, was followed and modified where required. For example, a 60-ampere, 250-volt, three-phase, four-wire safety switch, NEMA 1, in place ready for use, consists of:

1. One 60-ampere safety switch
2. Three fuses (Fusetrons are used here)
3. Four wall fastenings (toggle bolts are used here on the assumption of mounting to a masonry wall).
4. Twelve feet of #8 THHN wire (copper) in the switch and eight wire terminations
5. Two 1-inch galvanized rigid conduit terminals, which include cutting and threading the conduit and installing two locknuts and a metal-insulated bushing on each conduit terminal.

Obviously a number of the items indicated could be changed, using the same switch, but the price change would be insignificant in relation to the whole assembly price, including labor, overhead, direct job expense, and profit; hence an average finite value can be used with reasonable accuracy.

Since the above is typical of assemblies, it is important that you become familiar with the description of each graph in order to understand all that each graph implies. Since these graphs are not intended to furnish a job, as a NECA of Estimatic takeoff, certain liberties can be taken in the interest of speed. If a contractor should sell a job from these graphs, he or she can then make a material takeoff to furnish the job, since he or she can then afford the time to do this work.

The use of these graphs can be hazardous for the inexperienced estimator because they are based upon average conditions. Job factors must be considered and applied as required. For example, labor units are not the same when conduit must be installed for a 25-foot-high ceiling as for a 12-foot-high ceiling. Labor units for installing fixtures from a raw dirt floor will not be the same as from a clean concrete slab. The estimator must be cognizant of the many pitfalls that can turn an average job into a loser. Some geographical areas also seem to have a planned productivity control which must also be evaluated by the estimator.

Occasionally, the contractor is required to relocate existing equipment such as safety switches, panelboards, feeder, or plug-in busway. Fixtures are sometimes supplied by the owner to the contractor. In these cases it is necessary to deduct only the cost of the equipment. Fastening devices, lamps, connectors, wires, hangers, etc., and their associated labor as well as overhead and direct job expense are still required. In order to separate out the cost of equipment items, it is only necessary to procure costs of materials from a wholesaler or a catalog, then deduct this amount for the equipment only. The other costs will remain in the estimate, as they should. A departure from the normal pricing method has been introduced on pages A-22, A-23, and A-24 relating to residential fixtures. It has been our experience that many residential jobs are done with an allowance provided for the cost of fixtures. Obviously, the owner can select residential fixtures with a wide cost variation. However, the installation cost will not vary greatly in most instances. The customer is allowed to provide whatever he or she wants, and you, the contractor, are expected to install the fixtures. Therefore, we have selected a few typical residential fixtures, assigned labor units and lamps, then determined the selling price for installation only, which recovers direct labor, overhead, direct job expense, and some profit.

The sections of the book have been arranged so that an orderly progression through a complex job can be made with ease and with some semblance of order. There are many ways to make a takeoff, all of which are satisfactory; the following is just one suggestion. On pricing and summary sheets like those shown in the examples in the Appendix:

1. List quantity of each type of fixture.
2. List distribution equipment and panelboards.
3. List service equipment.
4. List feeder conduits, conductors, fittings, etc.
5. List branch circuit outlets, receptacles, switches, conduits, wire, etc.
6. List motor feeder disconnects, starters, controllers, connections to motors and appliances, dry transformers, etc.
7. List auxiliary system equipment such as telephone panels, fire alarm equipment, audible signals, sound system, etc.
8. With equipment and other items listed on the pricing sheets, look up the item costs, extend, and summarize.
9. After summarizing the costs on the summary sheet, apply the price adjustment multiplier as determined from the Total Price Adjustment Chart. Apply the multiplier to come up with a total selling price shown at the bottom of the summary sheet. (See Appendix.)

Occasionally you will not be able to locate an item in REEP that is required on the job (refer to "Pricing Sheets for Items Not Included in REEP" in the Appendix). To handle this sort of problem, insert the item on the Pricing Sheet provided for items not included in REEP. Insert the appropriate labor hours, material dollars, and labor rate *including benefits* (see Total Hourly Labor Cost on page xv), and complete the calculation.

The reader is referred to examples of pricing in the Appendix. Example 1 illustrates pricing of a distribution system from a one-line diagram which was made up for illustrative purposes only. Example 2 illustrates the pricing of a main distribution panel and motor control center. Example 3 illustrates the pricing of a small job, a kitchen addition at a scout camp. Example 4 illustrates the pricing of a clock/sound system installed in an existing school.

Two types of blank pricing sheets and a summary sheet are included in the Appendix. Parts of the pricing sheets are included here for illustrative purposes. The pricing sheet subtitled "Pricing Sheet" has a column labeled "Mult." The Total Price Multiplier generated in the next section can be entered here for each line item so that the "Extended Price" column reflects the adjusted price, item by item. If including the multiplier here is not appropriate, it can be entered once on the summary sheet on the line labeled "Price Adjustment Multiplier."

REEP

PRICING SHEET

JOB ______ SHEET NO. ______

WORK ______ OF ______

PRICED BY DATE

DESCRIPTION	REMARKS OR DEVIATIONS	QTY.	UNIT PRICE	MULT	EXTENDED PRICE
SHEET TOTAL					

REEP

PRICING SHEET FOR ITEMS NOT INCLUDED IN REEP

JOB ______ SHEET NO. ______

WORK ______ OF ______

PRICED BY DATE

DESCRIPTION	QTY.	UNIT LABOR	EXTENDED HOURS	UNIT MAT'L	EXTENDED PRICE
TOTAL LABOR HOURS & MATERIAL DOLLARS				—	$
LABOR RATE PER HOUR INCLUDING BENEFITS			x		
TOTAL LABOR DOLLARS			$		
OVERHEAD & D.J.E. MULTIPLIER			x 2.14		
TOTAL LABOR, OVERHEAD & D.J.E DOLLARS			$	→	
TOTAL GROSS COST					$
NET PROFIT					x 1.05
SHEET TOTAL					$

How to Adjust for Labor and Material Price Changes

Probably the most generally asked question regarding the previous editions has been related to compensation for labor and material price changes in the marketplace. The method we have developed has worked quite well.

Since we are dealing with averages in the establishment of the unit costs, we must be able to adjust for specific geographical areas. To do this, we make the assumption that the amount the worker is paid does not influence the worker's productivity—that the worker installs about the same amount of material regardless of his or her compensation. If the quantity of work installed in a day is further controlled, the labor productivity factor should be adjusted up. The authors have assumed and corroborated that journeymen require about 30 minutes of nonproductive time in the morning and afternoon for coffee breaks, relief time, tool and material acquisition, and cleanup. Since this time totals an hour per day, it is necessary to add this cost, which amounts to a 12-1/2% addition, to determine the total hourly labor cost.

To use the Total Price Adjustment Chart properly, it is necessary to compensate for both labor and material. First, fill out the table on page xv; next, obtain the current Producer Price Index, which is found in Table 33 of the *Monthly Labor Review*, published by the U.S. Department of Labor, Bureau of Labor Statistics. This publication can be obtained by subscription or found in your local library. Tracking the "Finished Goods" row (bold print) over several years shows a close relationship between wholesale prices for electrical construction materials and this row. A partial copy of the April 1992 Table 33 appears below.

Next, simply draw a line from your current labor cost, including fringe benefits, to the current price index. The resulting Total Price Multiplier can be applied item by item, or once to the total cost.

Adjustment is usually only required annually unless a rapid rise in inflation causes a significant material cost change or a change in geographical location requires a significant change in labor rate (including benefits).

Current Labor Statistics:* *Price Data

33. Producer Price Indexes, by stage of processing

(1982 = 100)

Grouping	Annual average		1991										1992	
	1990	1991	Mar.	Apr.	May	June	July	Aug.	Sept.	Oct.	Nov.	Dec.	Jan.	Feb.
Finished goods	119.2	121.7	120.9	121.1	121.8	121.9	121.6	121.7	121.4	122.2	122.3	121.9	121.7	121.9
Finished consumer goods	118.2	120.5	119.6	119.8	120.6	120.7	120.4	120.4	120.2	120.8	120.9	120.3	120.0	120.2
Finished consumer foods	124.4	124.1	125.2	125.3	125.8	125.3	124.5	123.3	122.7	123.0	123.1	122.2	122.5	123.5
Finished consumer goods excluding foods	115.3	118.7	117.0	117.2	118.2	118.6	118.4	119.0	119.0	119.7	119.7	119.3	118.7	118.6
Nondurable goods less food	111.5	115.0	112.8	113.2	114.6	115.2	115.0	115.8	116.1	115.6	115.7	115.2	114.2	114.2
Durable goods	120.4	123.9	124.0	123.7	123.2	123.1	123.1	122.9	122.1	126.0	126.0	125.6	125.9	125.7
Capital equipment	122.9	126.7	126.2	126.2	126.5	126.5	126.6	126.5	126.2	127.9	127.9	128.0	128.3	128.3

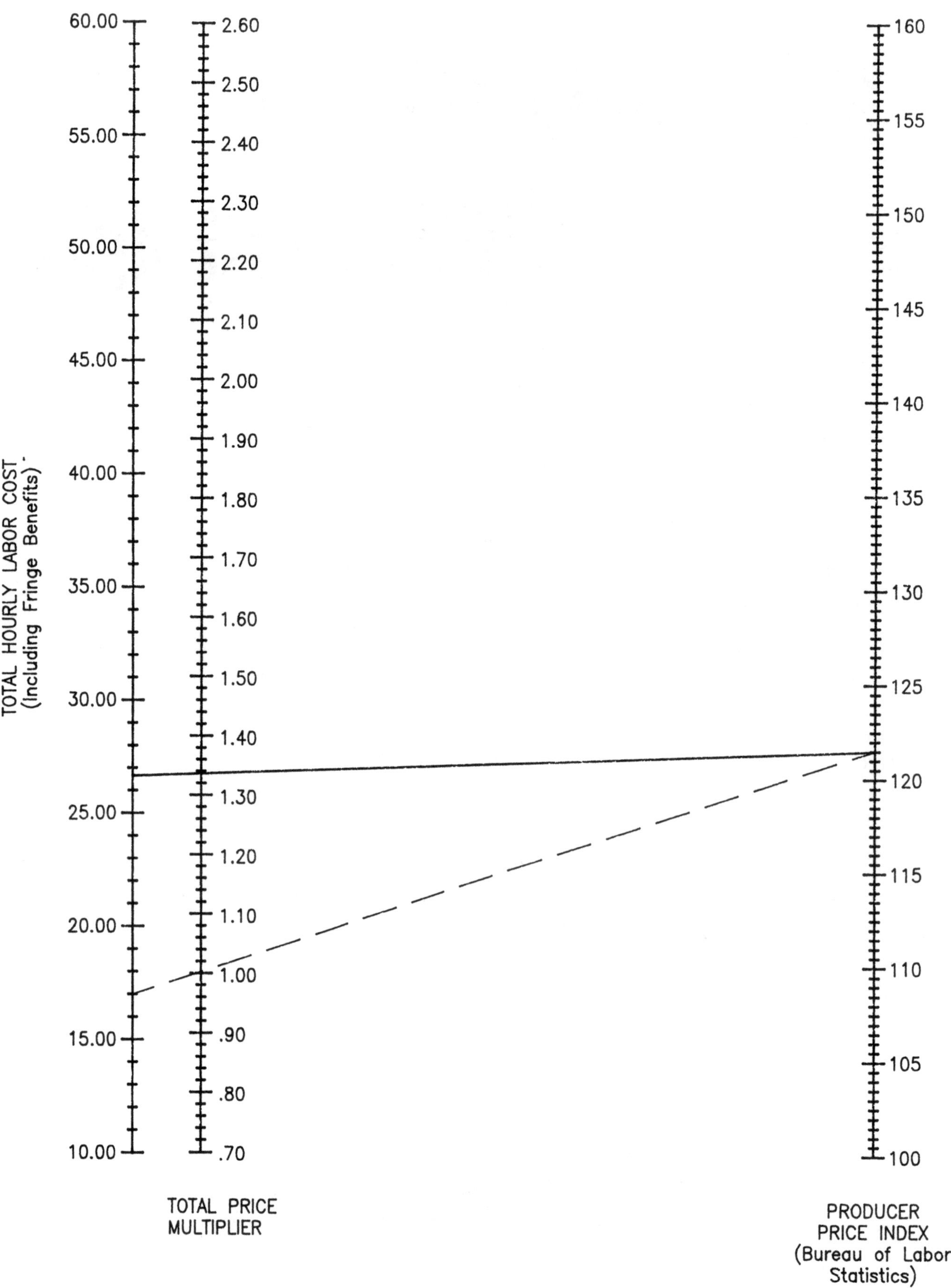

TOTAL PRICE ADJUSTMENT CHART
TOTAL HOURLY LABOR COST
(Including Fringe Benefits)
60.00
55.00
50.00
45.00
40.00
35.00
30.00
25.00
20.00
15.00
10.00
2.60
2.50
2.40
2.30
2.20
2.10
2.00
1.90
1.80
1.70
1.60
1.50
1.40
1.30
1.20
1.10
1.00
.90
.80
.70
160
155
150
145
140
135
130
125
120
115
110
105
100
TOTAL PRICE
MULTIPLIER
PRODUCER
PRICE INDEX
(Bureau of Labor
Statistics)

TOTAL HOURLY LABOR COST

	Typical		Commercial industrial labor rate, your area		Light commercial labor rate, your area		Residential labor rate, your area	
	Percent	Dollars	Percent	Dollars	Percent	Dollars	Percent	Dollars
Base rate per hour	–	17.50						
FICA (social security)	7.65	1.34						
State unemployment tax	4.50	0.79						
Federal unemployment tax	0.80	0.14						
State workman's compensation insurance & general liability insurance	5.65	0.99						
Health and Welfare Fund	–	1.50						
Pension Fund	–	1.00						
National Electrical Benefit Fund	3.00	0.53						
National Electrical Contractors Association	1.80	0.32						
Apprentice Fund (JATC)	–	0.10						
National Electrical Industry Fund	2.00	0.35						
Labor productivity factor (two coffee breaks, tool acquisition, reliefs, etc.)	12.50	2.19						
Total hourly labor cost	---	26.73	---		---		---	

Labor adjustment: Fill in the appropriate figures in the above list to determine the total hourly labor cost to the specific job at hand. Bear in mind that these items change with area and time. Use this value on the left "ladder" of the adjustment chart

Material adjustment: Look in the Monthly Labor Review, Activity, Monthly Indicators, Producer Prices, Finished Goods, Published by the Bureau of Labor Statistics, and find the latest price index. Use this value on the right "ladder" of the chart.

Draw a line between the two and find the equivalent total price multiplier.

Index to Sections

Lighting

INTERIOR/COMMERCIAL FLUORESCENT

INTERIOR/INDUSTRIAL FLUORESCENT

INTERIOR/COMMERCIAL—INDUSTRIAL HID

INTERIOR/COMMERCIAL INCANDESCENT

VAPORTIGHT/EXPLOSION PROOF

COST OF FLUORESCENT TROFFERS – SPEC. GRADE ON GRID CEILING

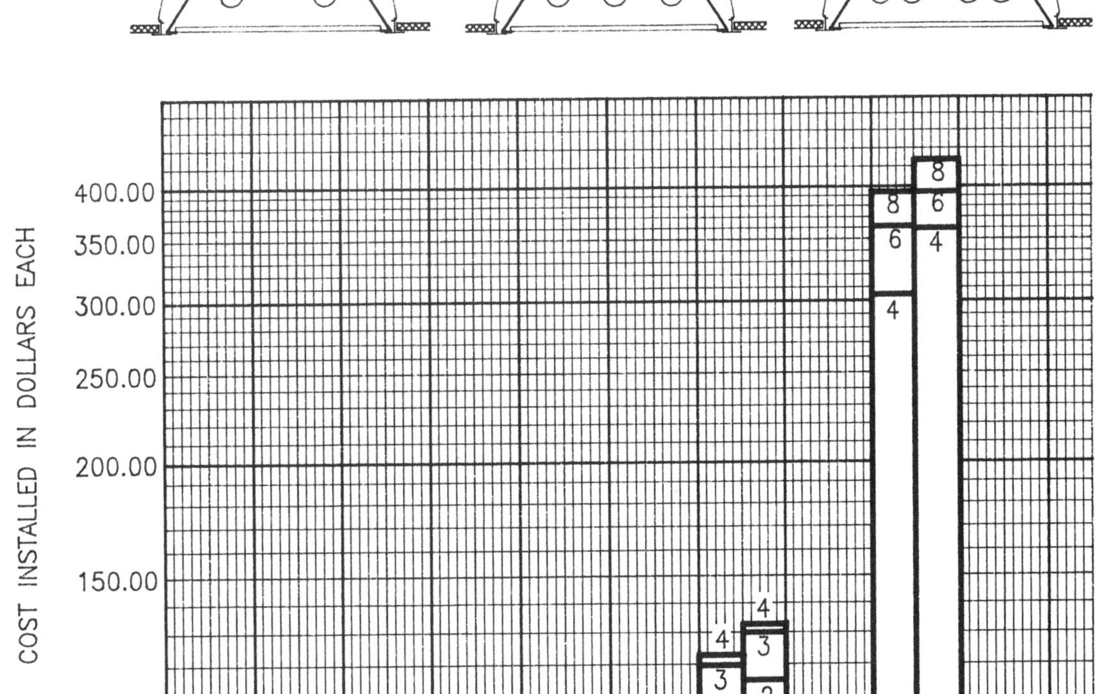

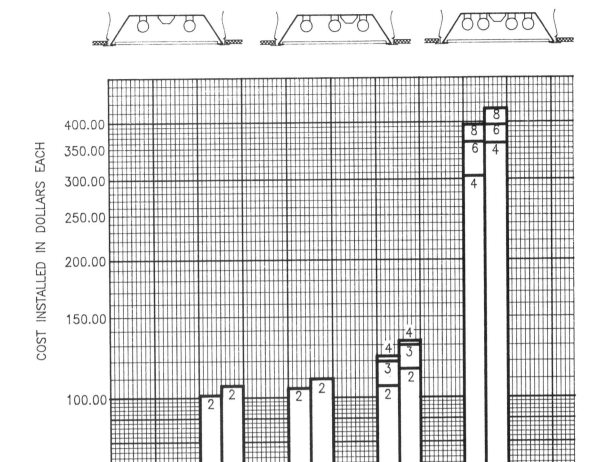

NUMBERS DENOTE NUMBER OF LAMPS
A – .125" EXTRUDED ACRYLIC LENS
B – INJ. MOLDED ACRYLIC LENS

The costs shown for these fixtures consist of the published contractors' book price for the fixtures with the lenses shown, the number of lamps shown, and the labor required, including flexible cable. If an outlet for the fixture is required, see Section F for a ceiling outlet recessed above the ceiling.

COST OF FLUORESCENT TROFFERS – SPEC. GRADE – FLANGE TYPE

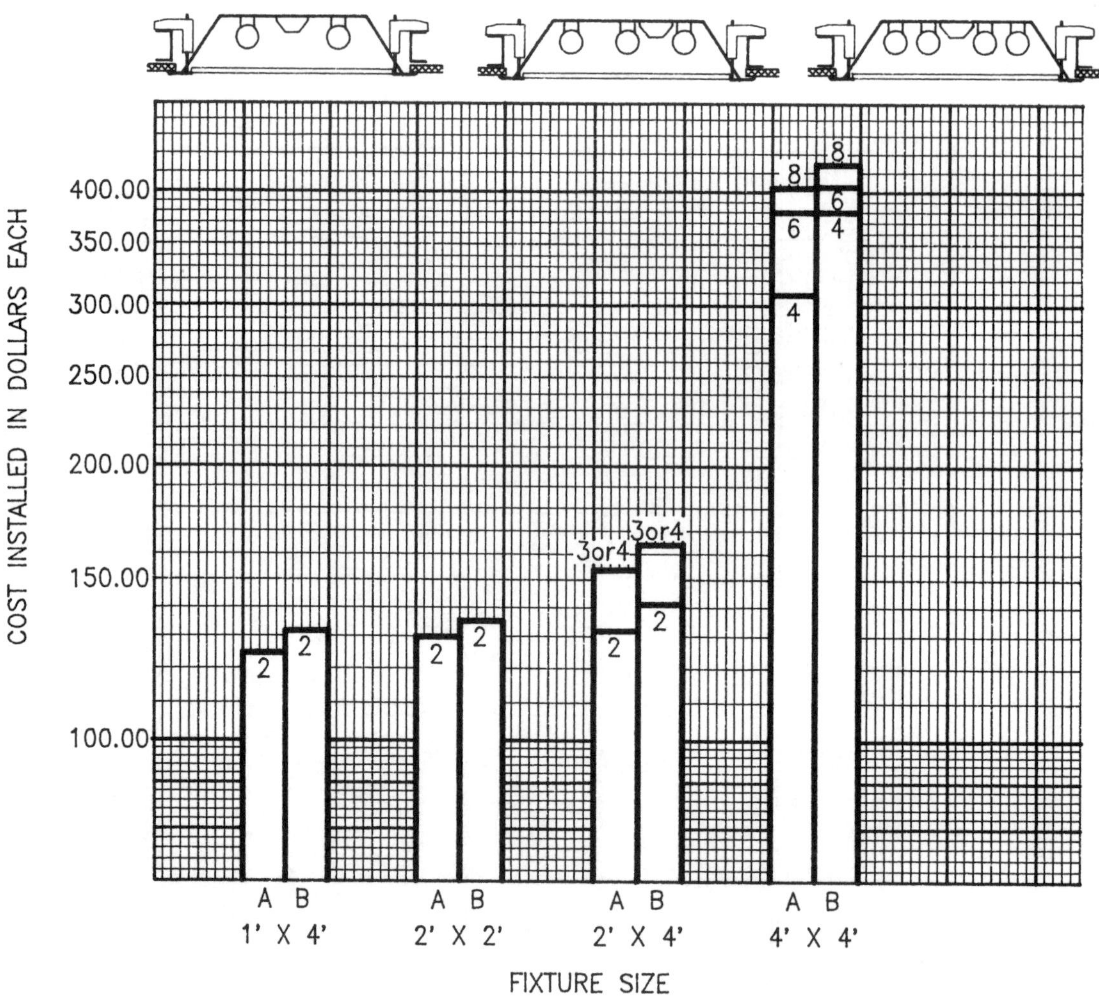

NUMBERS DENOTE NUMBER OF LAMPS
A – .125" EXTRUDED ACRYLIC PRISMATIC LENS
B – INJ. MOLDED ACRYLIC MALE PRISM LENS

ADD FOR PLASTER FRAMES

1x4	$42.25
2x2	36.50
2x4	48.00
4x4	65.00

The costs shown for these fixtures consist of the published contractors' book price for the fixtures with the lenses shown, the number of lamps shown, and the labor required, including flexible cable. If an outlet for the fixture is required, see Section F for a ceiling outlet recessed above the ceiling.

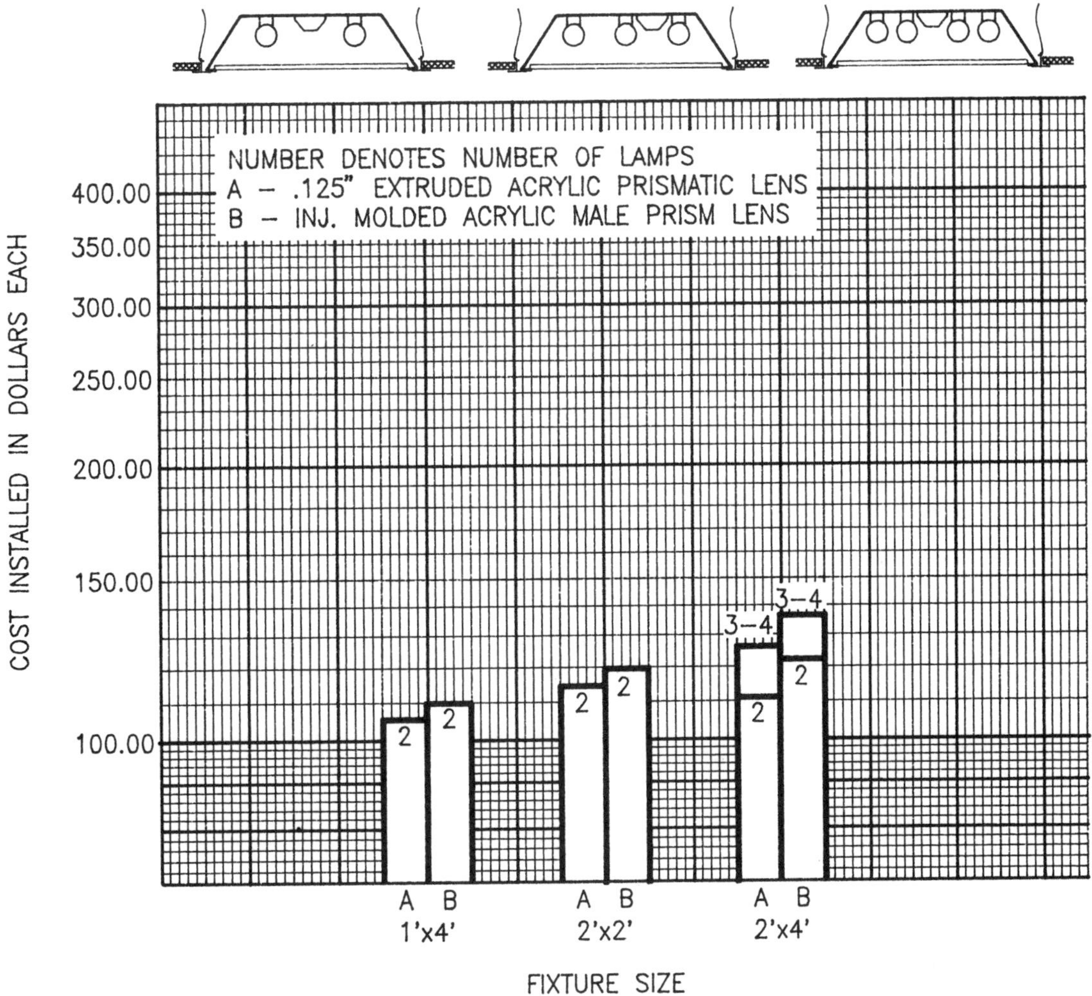

The costs shown for these fixtures consist of the published contractors' book price for the fixtures with the lenses shown, the number of lamps shown, and the labor required, including flexible cable. If an outlet for the fixture is required, see Section F for a ceiling outlet recessed above the ceiling.

COST OF FLUORESCENT AIR–HANDLING TROFFERS – SPEC. GRADE – FLANGE TYPE

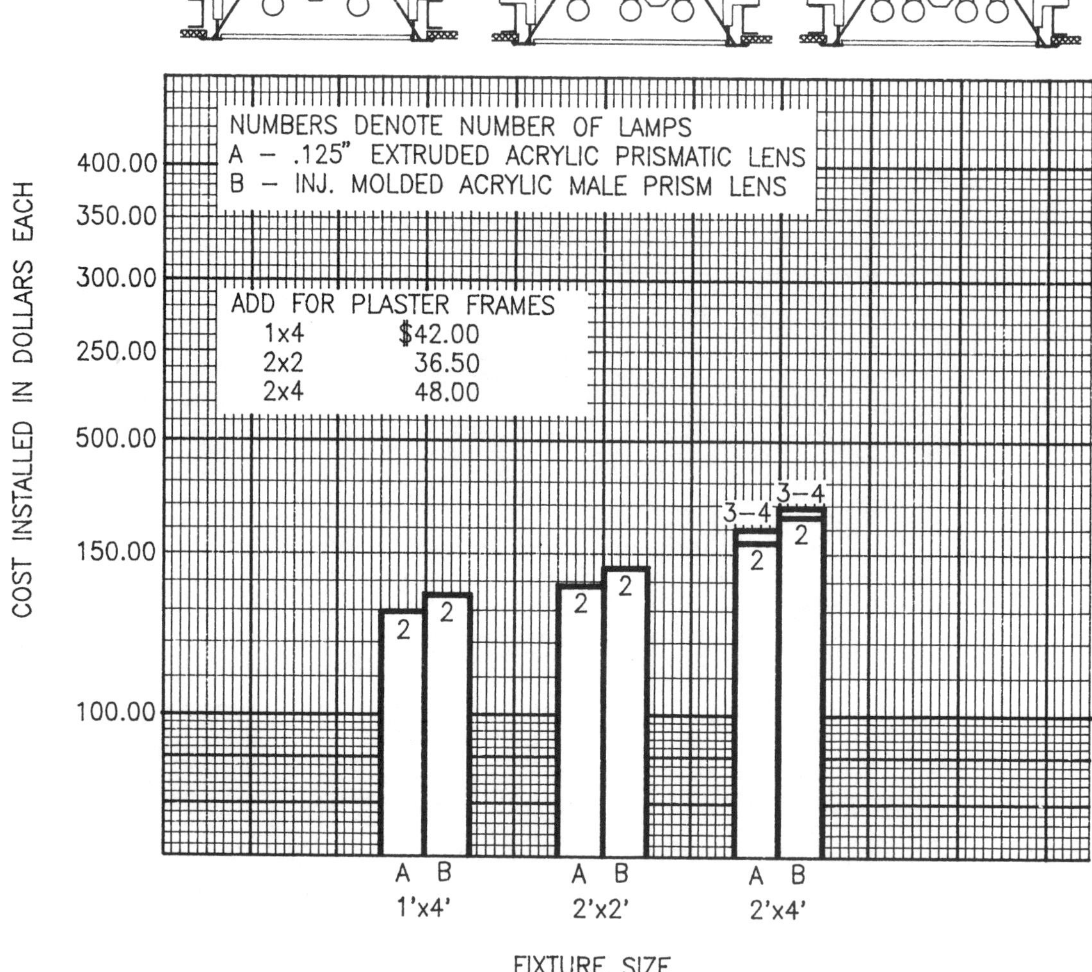

The costs shown for these fixtures consist of the published contractors' book price for the fixtures with the lenses shown, the number of lamps shown, and the labor required, including flexible cable. If an outlet for the fixture is required, see Section F for a ceiling outlet recessed above the ceiling.

COST OF PARABOLIC LOUVER FLUORESCENT AIR–HANDLING TROFFER

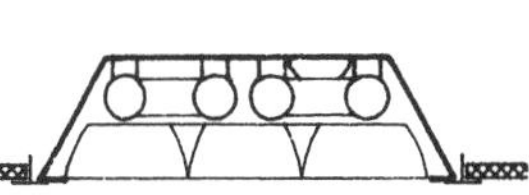

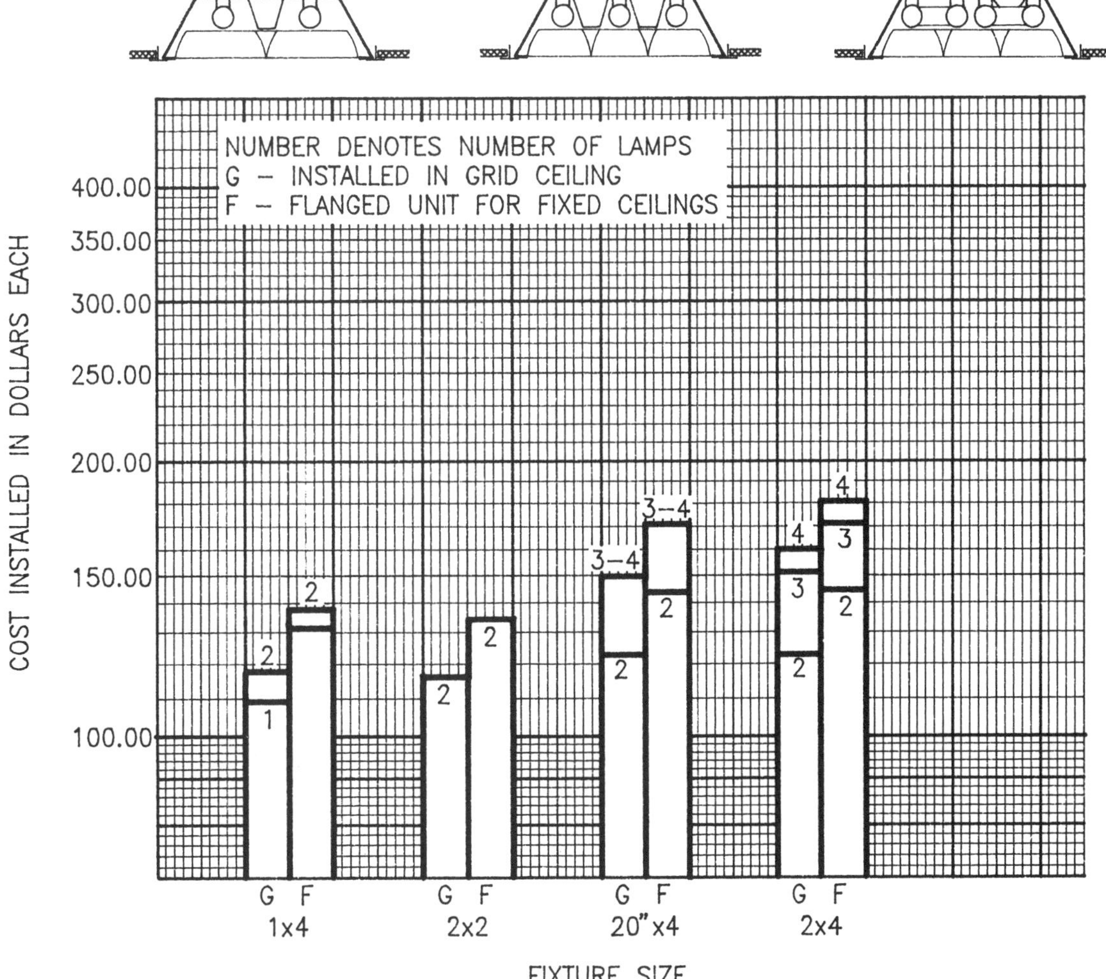

The costs shown for these fixtures consist of the published contractors' book price for the fixtures with the lenses shown, the number of lamps shown, and the labor required, including flexible cable. If an outlet for the fixture is required, see Section F for a ceiling outlet recessed above the ceiling.

COST OF METAL–SIDED SURFACE–MOUNTED FLUORESCENT FIXTURES – SPEC. GRADE

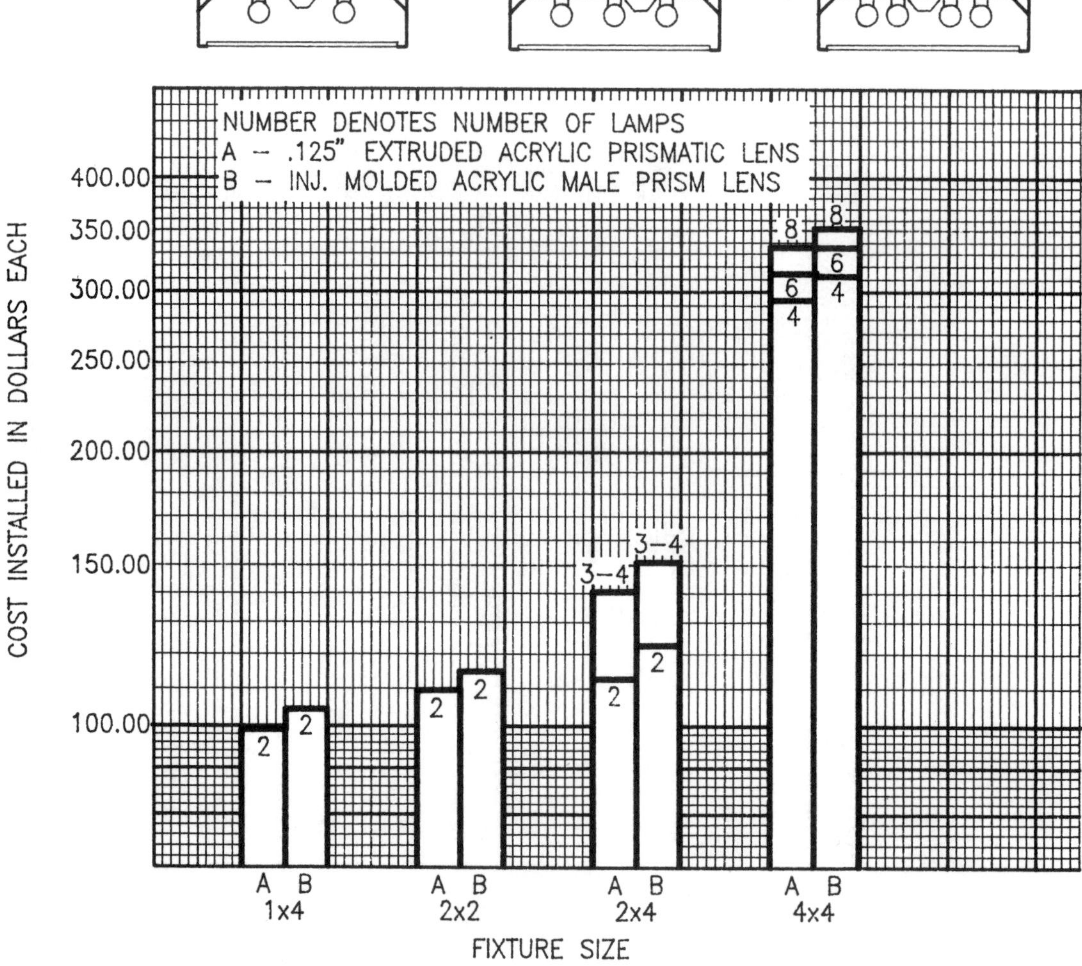

The costs shown for these fixtures consist of the published contractors' book price for the fixtures with the lenses shown, the number of lamps shown, and the labor required. If an outlet for the fixture is required, see Section F for the proper type of outlet.

The 2' x 2' fixture is considered to use U lamps instead of 20-watt trigger start lamps.

TYPE OF UNIT	MANUFACTURER'S CATALOGUE NO.	DESCRIPTION	INSTALLED COST
DAYBRITE HALLMARK	SURFACE MOUNT		
	#45257-4	2 LT. – 4 FT.	$118.00
	#45257-8	4 LT. – 8 FT.	221.50
	#45457-4	4 LT. – 4 FT.	175.75
	PENDANT MOUNT		
	#45267-4	2 LT. – 4 FT.	140.25
	#45267-8	4 LT. – 8 FT.	241.75
	#45467-4	4 LT. – 4 FT.	196.00
FOR 24" SINGLE STEM HANGERS–ADD	CS500/CS24		23.50
DAYBRITE VANDAL–RESIST.	SURFACE MOUNT		
	#VR2224-4	2 LT.–4 FT. R.S.	130.75
	#VR7244-4	4 LT.–4 FT. R.S.	177.25
DAYBRITE VAPORLUME	SURFACE MOUNT		
	#VR2-4D	2 LT.–4 FT. R.S.	118.00
	#VR2-4W	4 LT.–4 FT. R.S.	124.50
	#VS2-8D	2 LT.–8 FT. S.L.	208.50
	#VS2-8W	2 LT.–8 FT. S.L.	215.00
	#VH2-8D	2 LT.–8 FT. H.O.	245.75
	#VH2-8W	2 LT.–8 FT. H.O.	252.50
	#TVR2-4D	2 LT.–4 FT. R.S.	130.75
	#TVR2-4W	4 LT.–4 FT. R.S.	177.25
DAYBRITE UTILITY UNIT	WALL MOUNT		
	CZW2222- 2	2 LT.–2 FT. T.S.	114.50
	CZW2223- 3	2 LT.–3 FT. R.S.	124.50
	CZW2224- 4	2 LT.–4 FT. R.S.	117.50
	CZX2222- 2	2 LT.–2 FT. T.S.	114.50
	CZX2223- 3	2 LT.–3 FT. R.S.	124.50
	CZX2224- 4	2 LT.–4 FT. R.S.	117.50

The costs shown for these fixtures consist of the published contractors' book price for the fixtures with the lenses shown, the number of lamps shown, the necessary fastening devices and wiring connections, and the labor required. All fixtures are priced with virgin acrylic lenses. If an outlet is required, see Section F for the proper type.

TYPE OF UNIT		FIXTURE LENGTH	LAMP NUMBER & LENGTH	INSTALLED COST
LITECONTROL 1-lamp Biax	BIAX LAMPED	3'	2–18"	$331.50
		4'	2–24"	338.00
		6'	4–18"	518.50
		8'	4–24"	524.50
3-lamp T8	T8 LAMPED	3'	1–3'	300.50
		4'	1–4'	360.50
		6'	2–3'	456.00
		8'	2–4'	423.00
		3'	2–3'	295.00
		4'	2–4'	288.00
		6'	4–3'	463.50
		8'	4–4'	442.00
		3'	3–3'	332.00
		4'	3–4'	331.50
		6'	6–3'	509.50
		8'	6–4'	505.00
	RAPID START LAMPED	3'	1–3'	280.50
		4'	1–4'	272.00
		6'	2–3'	421.00
		8'	2–4'	403.00
		3'	2–3'	306.00
		4'	2–4'	274.50
		6'	4–3'	438.50
		8'	4–4'	431.00
		3'	3–3'	321.00
		4'	3–4'	313.50
		6'	6–3'	513.50
		8'	6–4'	505.50

The costs shown for these indirect pendant-mounted fixtures consist of the published contractors' book price for the fixtures with the number and type of lamps shown, the suspension hangers, and the labor for the installation. To select the necessary outlet, see Section F.

TYPE OF UNIT	MANUFACTURER	DESCRIPTION	INSTALLED COST
RECESSED IN GRID W/ .110" PRISMATIC ACRYLIC LENS	DAYBRITE DAYLINE	STATIC UNIT	
	#CG242G02D	2 X 4 – 2 LT. R.S.	$81.75
	#CG243G02D	2 X 4 – 3 LT. R.S.	119.75
	#CG242G02D	2 X 4 – 4 LT. R.S.	103.00
WRAPAROUND–ACRYLIC LENS	LITHONIA		
	#WA240A	2 LT. – 4 FT. R.S.	116.00
	#8TWA240A	#4 LT. – 8 FT. R.S.	207.25
	#WA440A	#4 LT. – 4 FT. R.S.	167.50
SHALLOW PARABOLIC FLUORESCENT TROFFER	DAYBRITE DESIGNER		
	#FGS222–APF12C	2 X 2 – 2 LT. /U	123.75
	#FGS223–APF12C	2 X 2 – 3 LT. /U	153.00
	#FGS242–APF24D	2 X 4 – 2 LT. R.S.	146.00
	#FGS243–APF24D	2 X 4 – 3 LT. R.S.	159.75
	#FGS244–APF24D	2 X 4 – 4 LT. R.S.	161.75
	#FFS222–APF12C	2 X 2 – 2 LT. /U	148.75
	#FFS223–APF12C	2 X 2 – 3 LT. /U	178.00
	#FFS242–APF24D	2 X 4 – 2 LT. R.S.	173.00
	#FFS243–APF24D	2 X 4 – 3 LT. R.S.	186.50
	#FFS244–APF24D	2 X 4 – 4 LT. R.S.	188.75

The costs shown for these fixtures consist of the published contractors' book price for the fixtures with the lenses shown, the number of lamps shown, and the labor required, including flexible cable. If an outlet is required, see Section F for the proper type.

The illustrations shown are only to give a general idea of the type of fixture represented on the chart. These fixtures are all of competitive grade.

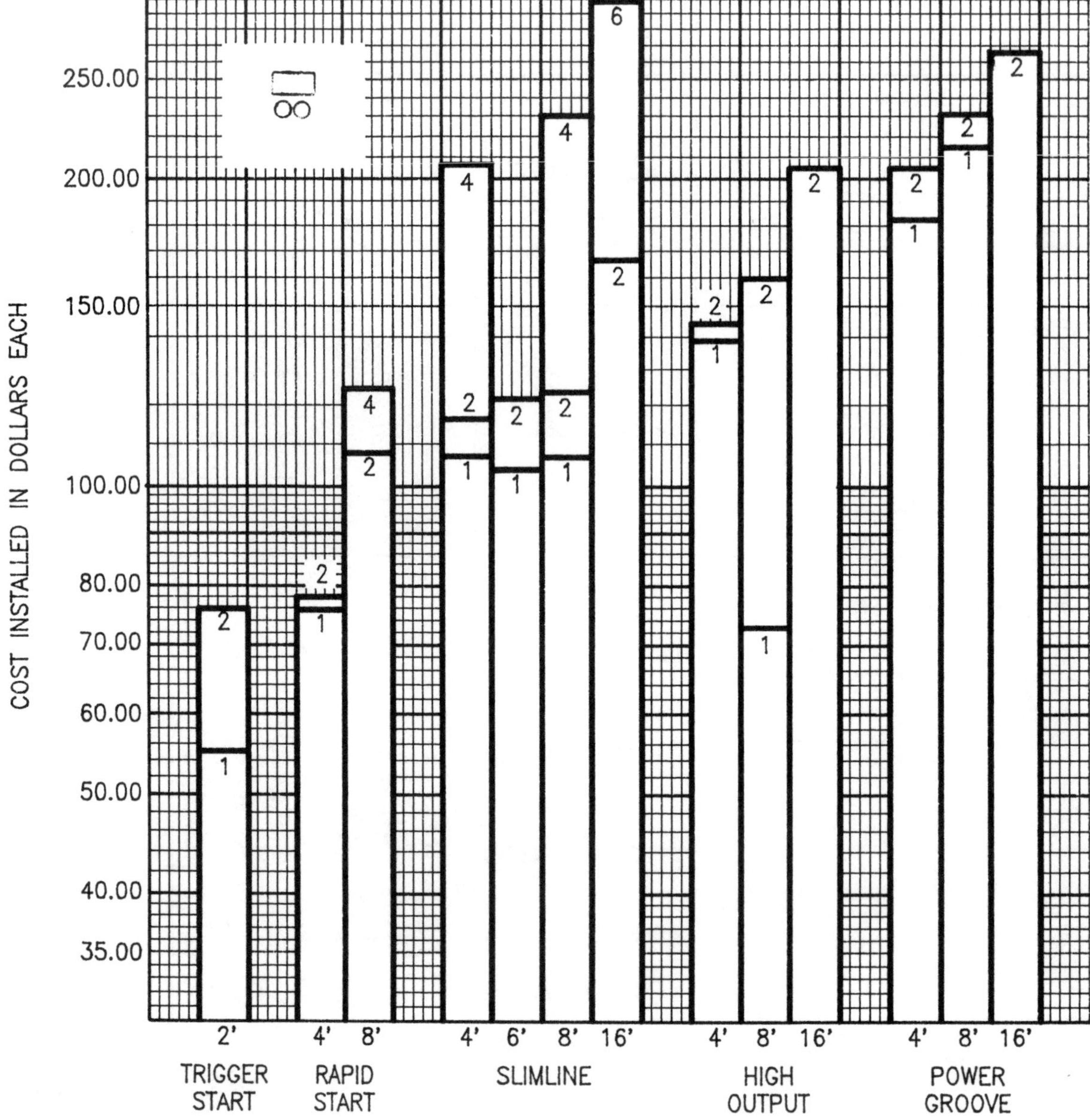

The costs shown for these fixtures consist of the published contractors' book price for the fixtures with the number of lamps shown, and the labor required for installation. If an outlet is required, see Section F for the proper type.

TYPE OF UNIT	MANUFACTURER'S CATALOG NUMBER	TYPE OF UNIT	INSTALLED COST
SPECIFICATION GRADE DAYBRITE FLB SERIES POLYESTER ENAMEL	FLB-2124-4U	2 LT. – 4 FT. R.S.	$99.00
	FLB-2124-8U	4 LT. – 8 FT. R.S.	172.50
	FLB-2021-8U	2 LT. – 8 FT. S.L.	176.00
	FLB-2025-4U	2 LT. – 4 FT. H.O.	140.50
	FLB-2025-8U	2 LT. – 8 FT. H.O.	185.75
	FLB-2026-4U	2 LT. – 4 FT. P.G.	181.25
	FLB-2026-8U	2 LT. – 8 FT. P.G.	228.00
HINGED LOUVERS – WITH 30C & 20L SHIELDING IN WHITE ENAMEL	FL143	4 FT. UNIT	42.25
	(2)FL-143	8 FT. UNIT	84.25
COMPETITIVE GRADE DAYBRITE DAYLINE BAKED WHITE ENAMEL	#FKR-1224-4U	2 LT. 4 FT. R.S.	71.25
	FKR-1224-8U	4 LT. 8 FT. R.R.	125.00
	FKR-1121-8U	2 LT. 4 FT. S.L.	111.75
FOR 120 VOLT HYDEE HANGER – ADD $30.00			

The costs shown for these fixtures consist of the published contractors' book price for the fixture with the number of lamps indicated. No hanging or fastening materials are included for the suspension system, which must be priced separately. For the proper outlet box, see Section F.

TYPE OF UNIT	CATALOGUE NUMBER	WATTAGE & LAMP TYPE	INSTALLED COST
HOLOPHANE PRISMATIC GLASS PENDANT REFRACTOR	CL1A100MH–12–36–BWH	100 M.H.	$516.00
	CL1A175MH–12–36–CWH	175M.H.	516.00
	CL1A175MH–12–36–DWH	175 M.H.	516.00
ENCLOSED & GASKETED PETROLUX REFRACTOR FOR WET/HAZARDOUS LOCATIONS (CLASS 1 – DIV 2)	PTA–050HP–12–L–P–25C	50 HPS	426.50
	PTA–070HP–12–L–P–25C	70 HPS	436.00
	PTA–100HP–12–L–P–25C	100 HPS	446.50
	PTA–150HP–12–L–P–25C	150 HPS	460.50
	PTA–175MH–12–L–P–25C	175 MH	455.00
SPEC GRADE ALUMINUM REFLECTOR GENERAL ELECTRIC "DURAGLOW"	DGS25SOM514V7	250 HPS	386.00
	DGS40SOM514V7	400 HPS	396.00
	DGS01SOM514V2	1000 HPS	615.00
	DGS25MOM514V7	250 M.H.	383.50
	DGS40MOM514V7	400 M.H.	371.00
	DGS01MOM514V2	1000 M.H.	554.00
ECON. GRADE ALUMINUM REFLECTOR GENERAL ELECTRIC "GHB" SERIES	GHBA25SOA5V6	250 HPS	331.00
	GHBA40SOA5V6	400 HPS	316.00
	GHBA25MOA5V6	250 M.H.	317.00
	GHBA25MOA5V6	400 M.H.	310.00

The costs for these fixtures consist of the published contractors' book price. These fixtures are as manufactured by Holophane or General Electric, and include the ballast for pendant mounting. See Section F for the proper outlet box. Lamps are included. Labor includes assembly, hanging, and connection.

TYPE OF UNIT	CATALOGUE NUMBER	WATTAGE & LAMP TYPE	INSTALLED COST
OPEN APERTURE WITH CLEAR REFLECTOR	PRESCOLITE		
	1224H7–75MV–362	75W M.V.	$256.00
	1226H5–100MV–662	100W M.V.	301.50
	1238H9–175MV–850	175W M.V.	357.00
	1238H10–250MV–850	250W M.V.	386.50
	1224M1–32MHFE–M362	32W M.H.	321.50
	1290M5–100MHFE–992	100W M.H.	309.00
	1238H9–175MH–B850	175W M.H.	377.00
	1238H9–250MH–B850	250W M.H.	406.00
	1226S6–70HPS–B652	70W HPS	391.00
	1226S5–100HPS–B652	100W HPS	394.00
	1226S8–150HPS–B652	150W HPS	411.00
	1238S10–250HPS–B862	250W HPS	471.50
OPEN APERTURE WITH CLEAR REFLECTOR & DOUBLE ENDED LAMP	70MHFE–382L	70W M.H.	355.00
	100MHFE–382L	100W M.H.	355.00
	150MHFE–382L	150W M.H.	378.50
OPEN APERTURE WITH CLEAR ELLIPTICAL REFLECTOR	1057H5–100MV–734	100W M.V.	314.00
	1060H9–175MV–744	175W M.V.	342.00
	1060H10–250MV–744	250W M.V.	349.50
	1062H11–400MV–846	400W M.V.	478.00
	1061M9–175MH–835	175W M.H.	398.00
	1062M11–400MH–846	400W M.H.	505.50
	1057S6–70HPS–734	70W HPS	382.00
	1057S5–100HPS–734	100W HPS	384.50
	1057S8–150HPS–734	150W HPS	402.00
	1061S10–250HPS–835	250W HPS	477.50

The costs shown for these fixtures consist of the published contractors' book price. These fixtures are manufactured by Prescolite and include potted ballast, prewired junction box, and the appropriate lamp.

TYPE OF UNIT	CATALOGUE NUMBER	WATTAGE & LAMP TYPE	INSTALLED COST
ROUND OR SQUARE W/REGRESSED LENS & HORIZONTAL LAMP	PRESCOLITE		
	91H5100FE–M8	100 M.V.	$264.00
	1391H9–175FE–M8	175 M.V.	300.00
	1391M9–155MHFE–M8	175 M.H.	350.00
	91S6–70HPSFE–M8	50 OR 70 HPS	354.50
ROUND VERTICAL LAMP UNIT WITH REGRESSED LENS	PRESCOLITE		
	90H5–100FE–M8	100 M.V.	292.00
	93057H9–175FE–M8	175 M/V/	330.00
	93057H10–250FE–M8	250 M.V.	356.00
	93057M9–175MH–M8	175 M.H.	380.00
	93057M10–250MH–M8	250 M.H.	397.00
	90S6HPS–M8	50 OR 70 HPS	405.00
	93057S5–100HPS–M8	100 HPS	422.50
	93057S8–150HPS–M8	150 HPS	430.00
SURFACE & PENDANT CYLINDERS	PRESCOLITE		
	HD10C08	50 HPS	452.00
	HD10C09	70 HPS	456.00
	HD10C010	100 HPS	460.00
	HD10C03	100 M.V.	373.00
	HD13C02	175 M.V.	465.00
	HD13C005	250 M.V.	463.50
	HD13C006	175 M.H.	469.00
	HD13C007	250 M.H.	498.50
	HD13C011	150 HPS	537.00
	HD13C012	250 HPS	574.00
2' X2' GRID MOUNTED UNIT	HOLOPHANE		
	MULTI175MH	175 M.H.	497.00
	MULTI250MH	250 M.H.	490.00
	MULTI400MH	400 M.H.	510.00
	MULTI250HP	250 HPS	519.00

The costs for these fixtures consist of the published contractors' book price for the fixtures shown. These fixtures are manufactured by Prescolite and Holophane and include potted ballasts, prewired junction boxes, and the appropriate lamp.

TYPE OF UNIT	CATALOGUE NUMBER	WATTAGE & LAMP TYPE	INSTALLED COST
RECESSED ROUND WITH BLACK MILLIGROVE BAFFLE	PRESCOLITE		
	1204–900	30–50W R20	105.50
	1212–910	75W R30	108.50
	1220–920	150PAR38	57.00
	1227–980	150W R40	188.00
RECESSED ROUND "A" LAMP DOWNLIGHT	1222–262	100A	117.00
	1224–362	150A	129.50
	1225–462	200A	146.00
RECESSED SQUARE RELAMPALITE TRIM	488HF–7	100A	101.00
	1015–HF–7	150A	116.00
	1313H2F–7	200A	166.00

The costs shown for these fixtures consist of the published contractors' book price. Included are prewired junction boxes, the lamps indicated, and the labor for installation.

TYPE OF UNIT	CATALOGUE NUMBER	WATTAGE & LAMP TYPE	INSTALLED COST
CEILING MOUNT	PRESCOLITE		
	1102–910	75W R30	$87.00
	1105–92	150W R40	96.58
	1108–93	300W R40	175.00
	1122–910	75W R30	133.00
	1125–920	150W R40	147.00
	1128–930	300W R40	230.00
	1170–900	2–50W R20	162.50
	1172–910	2–75W R40	164.00
	1175–920	2–150W R40	194.50
	1178–932	2–300W R40	275.50
WALL BRACKET	WB–2	100A	40.50
	WB–28	200A	71.00
LITE–FORM	4040	1–100A	36.00

The costs for these fixtures consist of the published contractors' book price for the fixtures shown. Included are the required lamps and the labor for installation. If an outlet is required, see Section F for the appropriate type.

TYPE OF UNIT	DESCRIPTION	INSTALLED COST	
		SURFACE MOUNT	RECESSED
PRESCOLITE TWO–CIRCUIT	4' STARTER TRACK W/ LIVE–END FEED–IN	$58.00	$126.50
	8' STARTER TRACK W/ LIVE–END FEED–IN	83.50	182.50
	BASIC PAR LAMP LAMPHOLDER WITH 150 PAR/FL LAMP (UPPER ILLUS.)	66.00	---
	WHITE CYLINDRICAL FIXTURE WITH 300PAR56 LAMP (MIDDLE ILLUS.)	117.00	---
	WALL WASHER WITH Q250DC QRZ. LAMP (LOWER ILLUS.)	197.00	---
SURFACE/PENDANT EXIT SIGN THINLINE – PROFILE SERIES WITH 50,000–HOUR LAMPS	PRESCOLITE		
	#75221 WITH LAMPS TOP OR END MOUNT	69.00	---
	PENDANT MOUNTED	104.00	---
	REPLACEMENT LAMP 20T6–1/2 DC/IF	5.00	---

The costs shown consist of the published contractors' book price for the track and the fixtures shown, including the labor for installation. Any single run of track must also be provided with an outlet box. See Section F for the type required, and add to the cost shown. Each separate run must have a starter track section, as it provides the branch circuit connection capability which the joiner track section does not have. Add the track cost to the total fixture cost to find the system cost.

The exit sign shown is a standard, non-self-powered unit and includes two lamps. For self-powered signs, see page A-21.

TYPE OF UNIT	CATALOGUE NUMBER	WATTAGE & LAMP TYPE	INSTALLED COST
VAPORTITE CLEAR GLOBE & GUARD	APPLETON		
	VPOBW20G	60–200W	$106.50
	VPOBW20G	200–300W	111.00
E & G FLUORESCENT CLASS 1, DIV. 2	VRS240–120NESB	2–40W R.S.	490.00
	VRS340–120NESD	3–40W R.S.	542.00
	VRS260–120N	2–60W H.O.	563.00
EXPLOSION PROOF INCANDESCENT CLASS 1, DIV. 1 OR 2	AC1050G	100W	292.00
	AC1550G	150–300W	292.50
	AC2050G	200–300W	666.00
	AC5050G	300–500W	634.00
EXPLOSION PROOF METAL HALIDE CLASS 1, DIV. 1 OR 2	CHP1775	175W M.H.	714.00
	CHP2575	250W M.H.	845.00
	CHP4075	400W M.H.	884.00
EXPLOSION PROOF FLUORESCENT CLASS 1, DIV. 1 OR 2	ARS240–118	2040W R.S.	1465.00
	ARS340–118	3–40W R.S.	2148.00
	ARS440–118	4–40W R.S.	2759.00
	ARS260–118	2–60W H.O.	1738.00
	ARS360–118	3–60W H.O.	2564.00
	ARS460–118	4–60W H.O.	3300.00

The costs for these fixtures consist of the published contractors' book price for the fixtures shown. Included are the lamps indicated and the labor for installation. No outlet is included. See Section F for the appropriate type of outlet.

COST OF BATTERY POWERED EMERGENCY LIGHTING UNITS

TYPE OF UNIT	CATALOGUE NUMBER	PRO-RATA GUARANTEE	INSTALLED COST
GENERAL PURPOSE	DUALLITE STANDARD		
	ALA-30-SB	10 YEAR	$496.00
	ALC-X-30	15 YEAR	447.00
	AS-145	20 YEAR	705.00
	DUALLITE SPECTRON		
	AS-80-BCI	15 YEAR	530.00
	AS-145I	20 YEAR	628.00
SELF-CONTAINED EMERGENCY WALL OR CEILING MOUNTED	DUALLITE STANDARD		
	EDC104	5 YEAR	208.00
	EDC204	5 YEAR	269.00
	ESC1-1	15 YEAR	302.00
	ESC2-1	15 YEAR	408.00
	DUALLITE SPECTRON		
	EIC-1-I	10 YEAR	237.00
	EIC-2-I	10 YEAR	284.00
	ESC1-1-I	15 YEAR	338.50
	ESC21-0-I	15 YEAR	435.00
SELF-CONTAINED EMERGENCY CEILING MOUNTED	DUALLITE STANDARD		
	EDS	5 YEAR	131.00
	DUALLITE SPECTRON		
	ESS-I	15 YEAR	220.00
SEMI-RECESS MTG KIT	F-SRM	———	36.00
FULL-RECESS MTG KIT	FRM	———	69.00
LOW VOLTAGE FIXTURES			
	EXT123S	———	103.00
	EXT130	———	99.00
	NF500	———	97.00

The costs shown for these battery-operated emergency lighting units consist of the published contractors' book price for the units shown. They are manufactured by Dual-Lite Inc. of Newtown, Conn. The prices are influenced by the battery life, and there are mainly three types used—lead-acid, lead-calcium, and nickel-cadmium.

ENCLOSURE ARRANGEMENT	BATTERY	WATTAGE STANDARD SERIES	INSTALLED COST	WATTAGE SPECTRON SERIES	INSTALLED COST
One Cabinet	LONG LIFE LEAD ACID WITH 15 YEAR PRORATED GUARANTEE	500 750 1000 1250 1500	$4021 4490 4553 4738 5795	1000 1250 1500 1800 2000	$6868 7874 8712 9630 10315
Two Cabinets		1800 2400 3000 3600 4500	7583 8310 9445 10504 11879	2500 3000 3500 4000 4500	10441 10912 12577 13632 15416
Three Cabinets		5500 6500 8000 10000 12000	16747 19783 21320 22850 31120	5000 6000 7500 10000 12000	16419 17070 19487 22124 30221
One Cabinet	NICKEL–CADMIUM BATTERY WITH 20 YEAR PRORATED GUARANTEE	500 750 1000 1250 1500	9204 10345 10417 10832 13323	1000 1250 1500 1800 2000	15930 19802 20273 22351 23848
Two Cabinets		1800 2400 3000 3600 4500	17368 19098 21699 24112 27228	2500 3000 3500 4000 4500	23964 25195 29052 31402 35471
Three Cabinets		5500 6500 8000 10000 12000	38663 45813 49442 53006 72301	5000 6000 7500 10000 12000	37891 39366 45125 51291 70283

The costs shown for these units consist of the published contractors' book price for the units illustrated, which are manufactured by Dual-Lite Inc. of Newtown, Conn. They include the necessary batteries to satisfy Article 700 of the NEC (87-1/2% of the normal voltage maintained for 1-1/2 hours under full-load conditions). See page A-21 for accessories.

TYPE OF UNIT	CATALOGUE NUMBER	CAPACITY	INSTALLED COST
ACCESSORIES FOR AC SYSTEMS	DUALLITE		
STANDARD REMOTE MONITOR	RAP–2	-----	473.00
SPECTRON REMOTE MONITOR	RMAP–2	-----	237.00
INPUT OR OUTPUT TRANSFORMERS		750VA	416.00
		1500VA	499.00
		2400/3000VA	631.00
		4500VA	1256.00
		5500/6000VA	1256.00
		8000VA	1275.00
		15000VA	1845.00
SELF–POWERED EXIT SIGN	DUALLITE EXCITE SERIES		
SINGLE FACE	STANDARD	-----	283.00
DOUBLE FACE	SPECTRON	-----	284.00
SINGLE FACE	STANDARD	-----	362.00
DOUBLE FACE	SPECTRON	-----	363.00

The costs of the units shown consist of the published contractors' book price for the units and the labor for the installation. Wiring between monitor units and the central equipment is not included.

The self-powered signs contain a hermetically sealed battery in a recessed box for mounting in the ceiling or wall. The fixtures have six-inch-high letters. Back boxes in this case are included as part of the fixture, as it is a special.

Although most residential fixtures are furnished and selected by the building owner, they are expected to be installed by the contractor; consequently no fixture prices are considered here, but installation costs are included.

The costs shown for the Post Light does not include the cost of the pole or the fixture; however, it does include the cost of hand excavation, concrete base, conduit elbow, wire in the pole, and the lamp.

The costs shown for the other fixtures do not include the cost of the fixture, but do include the required lamps and the labor for the fixture installation.

COST OF RESIDENTIAL INCANDESCENT FIXTURE – INSTALLATION ONLY

TYPE OF UNIT	WATTAGE	INSTALLATION COST
POST LIGHT 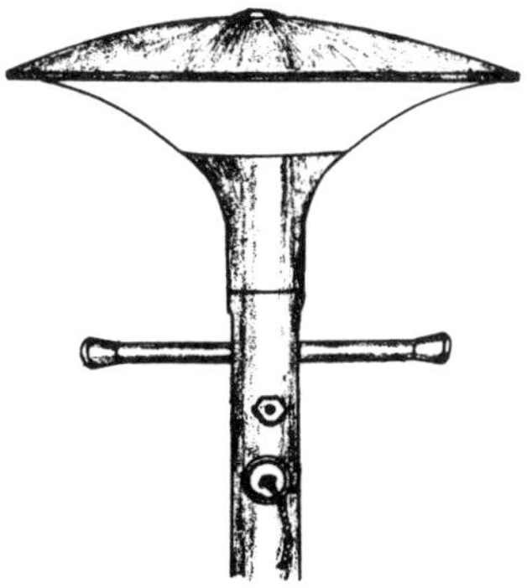	1–100	$96.25
PORCH LIGHT 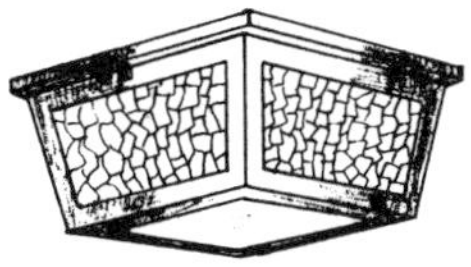	2–60	14.00
EXTERIOR WALL BRACKET 	1–100	12.25
PORCH OR CORRIDOR 	1–100	14.00

TYPE OF UNIT	WATTAGE	INSTALLATION COST
CHANDELIER 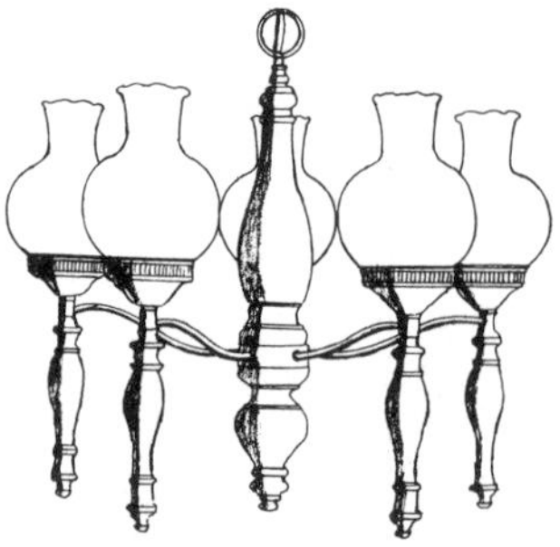	5–60	$51.00
WALL BRACKET 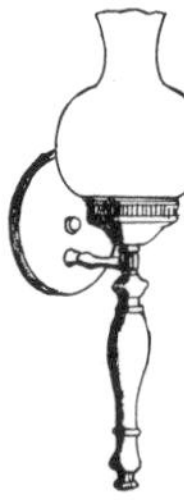	1–60	19.75
KITCHEN ETC. 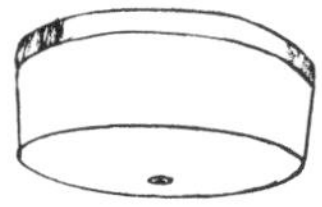	2–100	14.75
HALL OR CLOSET 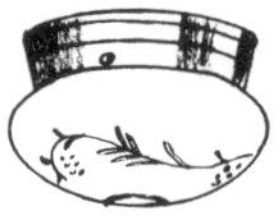	1–60	14.00

The costs shown for these fixtures do not include the cost of the fixture, but do include the required lamps and the labor for the installation.

COST OF RESIDENTIAL INCANDESCENT FIXTURE – INSTALLATION ONLY

TYPE OF UNIT	WATTAGE	INSTALLATION COST
GENERAL USE 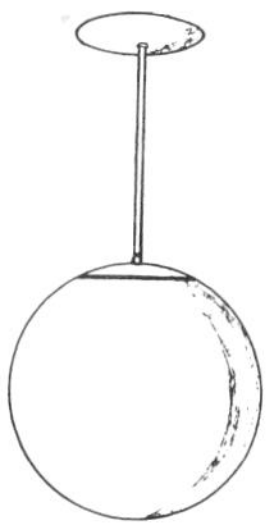	1–100	$29.50
RECESSED 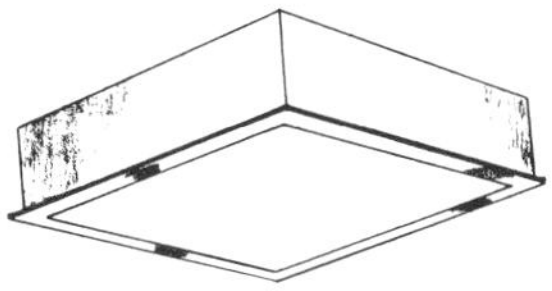	1–100	46.50
BATH 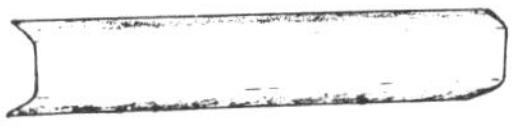	1–60	21.25
BEDROOM 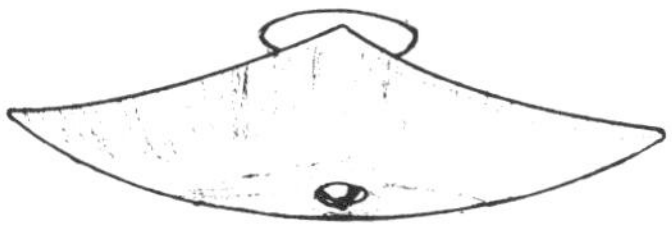	4–60	18.00

The costs shown for these fixtures do not include the cost of the fixture, but do include the required lamps and the labor for the installation.

TYPE OF UNIT	CATALOGUE NUMBER	WATTAGE & LAMP TYPE	INSTALLED COST
WALL MOUNTED AREA LIGHT	CROUSE HINDS		
	WAC70SP2FC	70W HPS	$409.00
	WAC100SP2FC	100W HPS	416.00
	WAC150SP2FC	150W HPA	422.00
	WAC175MW2FC	175W M.H.	423.00
WALL MOUNTED AREA LIGHT	SYLVANIA		
	ALLEY KAT SERIES	50W HPS	268.00
		70W HPS	268.00
		100W HPS	274.00
		150W HPS	298.00
PAR LAMPHOLDERS	STONCO		
	150L	1–150PAR/FL	30.00
	6700S/67–1S	1–150PAR/FL	71.00
	6700S/67–2S	2–150PAR/FL	104.00
AREA FLOODLIGHT	SYLVANIA		
	MSK70HPS	1–70W HPS	224.00
	MSK100HPS	1–100W HPS	238.00
	MSK150HPS	1–150W HPS	252.00
POWER BEAM FLOODLIGHT	STONCO		
	4600E	200 PAR46	133.50
	5600E	300 PAR56	146.00
	6400E	500 PAR64	214.00
	Q6400AH	1000 PAR (QTZ)	388.00

The costs shown for these fixtures consist of the published contractors' book price for the fixtures shown. Included are the required lamps, and the labor for fixture installation; however, no outlet is included. See Section F for the appropriate type of outlet

COST OF FLOODLIGHTING POLES

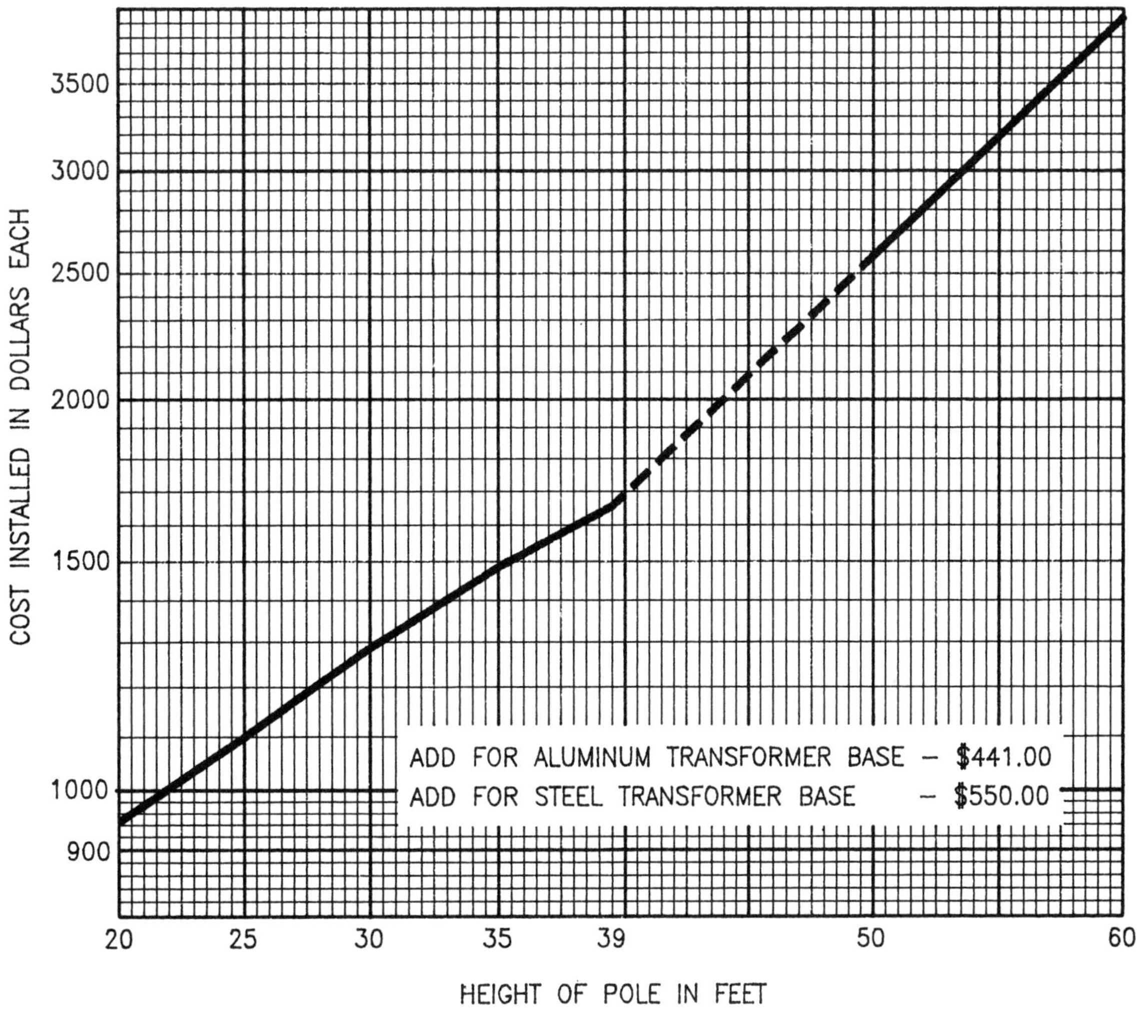

3500
3000
2500
2000
1500
1000
900
COST INSTALLED IN DOLLARS EACH
ADD FOR ALUMINUM TRANSFORMER BASE – $441.00
ADD FOR STEEL TRANSFORMER BASE – $550.00
20
25
30
35
39
50
60
HEIGHT OF POLE IN FEET

NOMINAL MOUNTING HEIGHT

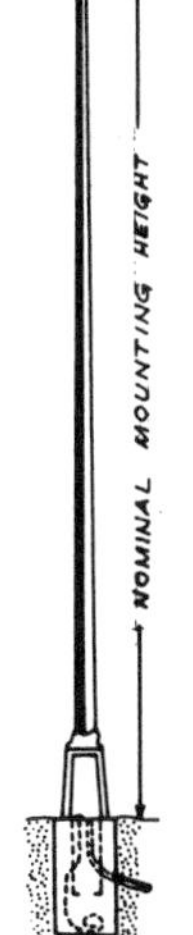

The costs shown for these poles consist of the contractors' book prices with a shoe base and are as manufactured by Valmont Industries, Inc. For a transformer base, add as indicated.

Included: (material and labor)

1. *Cost of pole including freight*
2. *Hand excavation in normal soil*
3. *Cost of concrete installed*
4. *Anchor bolts*
5. *2-1" GRC elbows*
6. *Grounding stud*
7. *Wire from base of pole to luminaire*

Excluded: Arms, fittings, and luminaire

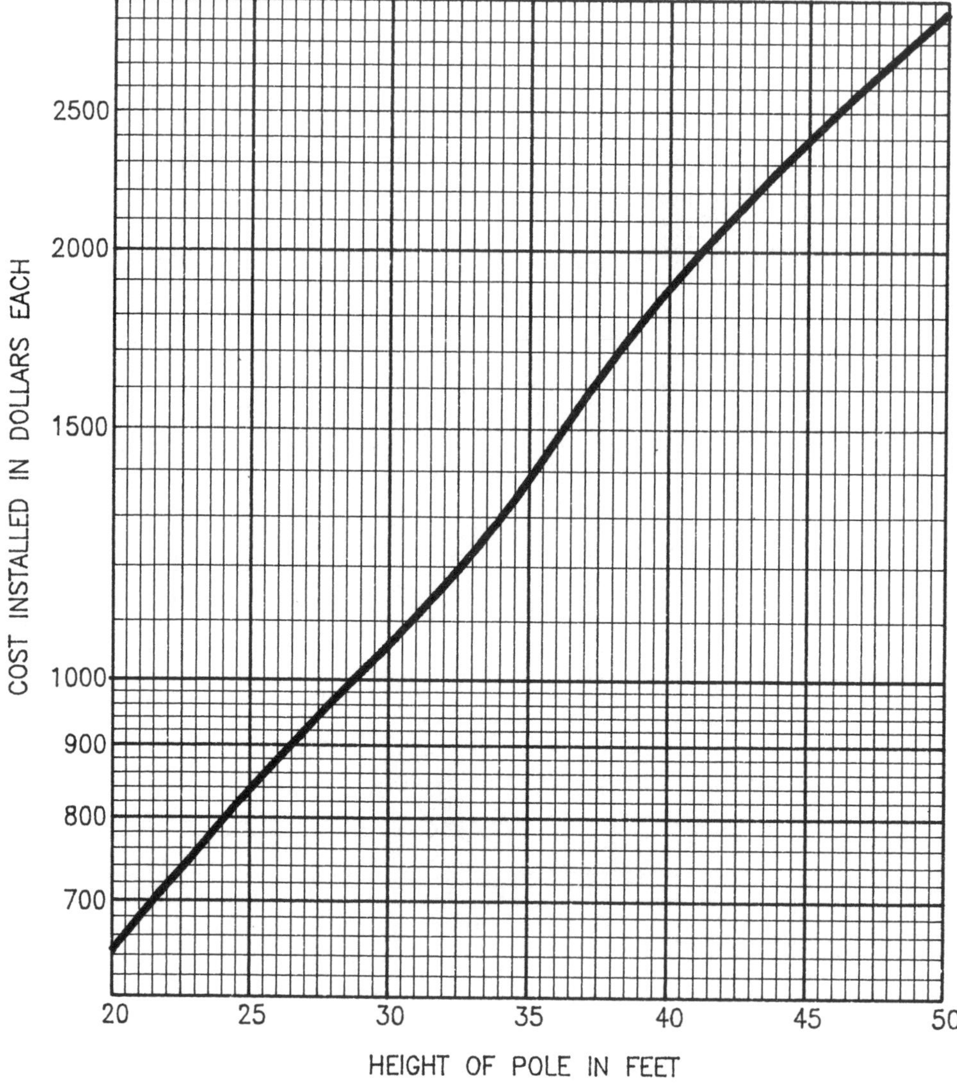

The costs shown for these poles consist of the published contractors' book prices with a shoe base and are as manufactured by Lexington, Inc.

Included: (material and labor)

1. *Cost of pole including freight*
2. *Hand excavation in normal soil*
3. *Cost of concrete installed*
4. *Anchor bolts*
5. *2-1" GRC elbows*
6. *Grounding stud*
7. *Wire from base of pole to luminaire*

Excluded: Arms, fittings, and luminaire

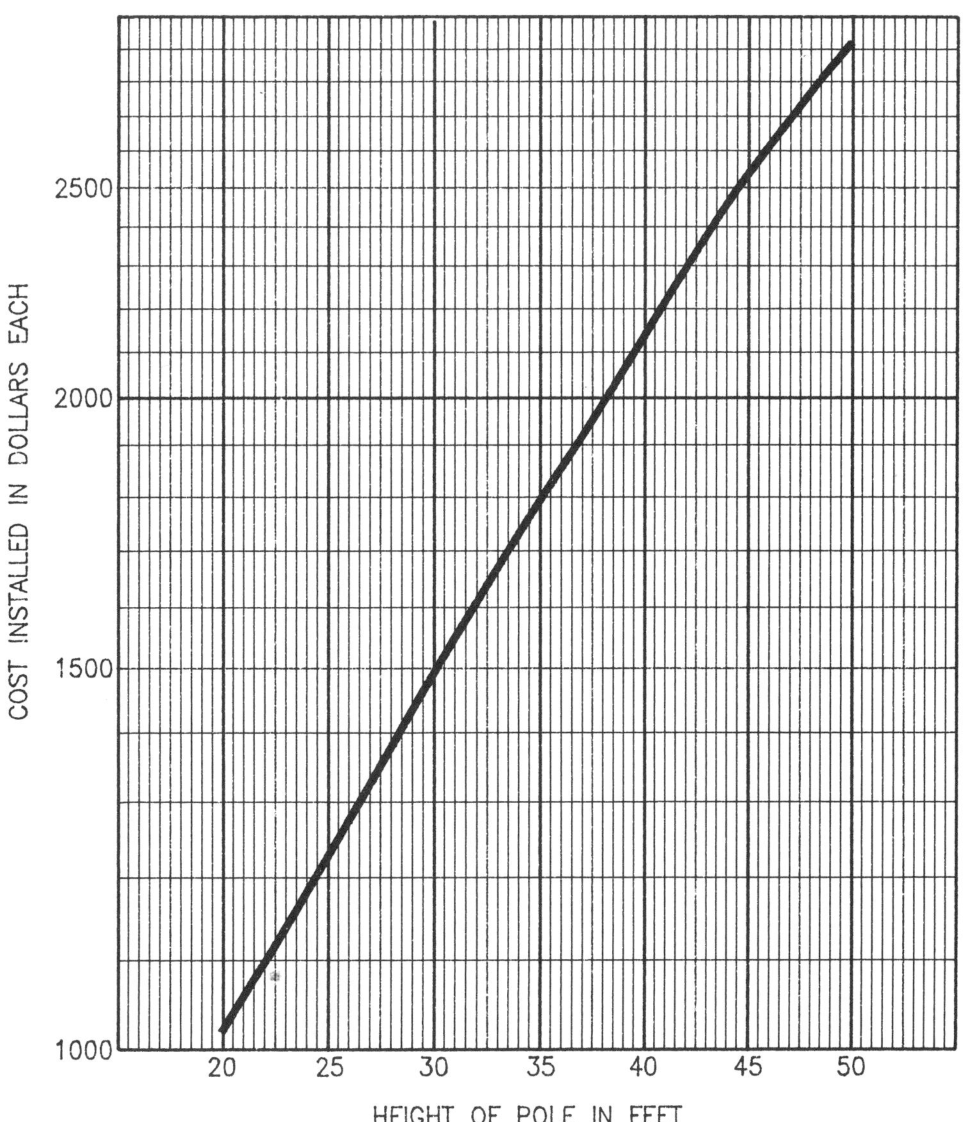

The costs shown for the poles consist of the published contractors' book prices with a shoe base and are as manufactured by Valmont Industries, Inc. For a transformer base, add as indicated on page A-26.

Included: (material and labor)

1. *Cost of pole including freight*
2. *Hand excavation in normal soil*
3. *Cost of concrete installed*
4. *Anchor bolts*
5. *2-1" GRC elbows*
6. *Grounding stud*
7. *Wire from base of pole to luminaire*

Excluded: Arms, fittings, and luminaire

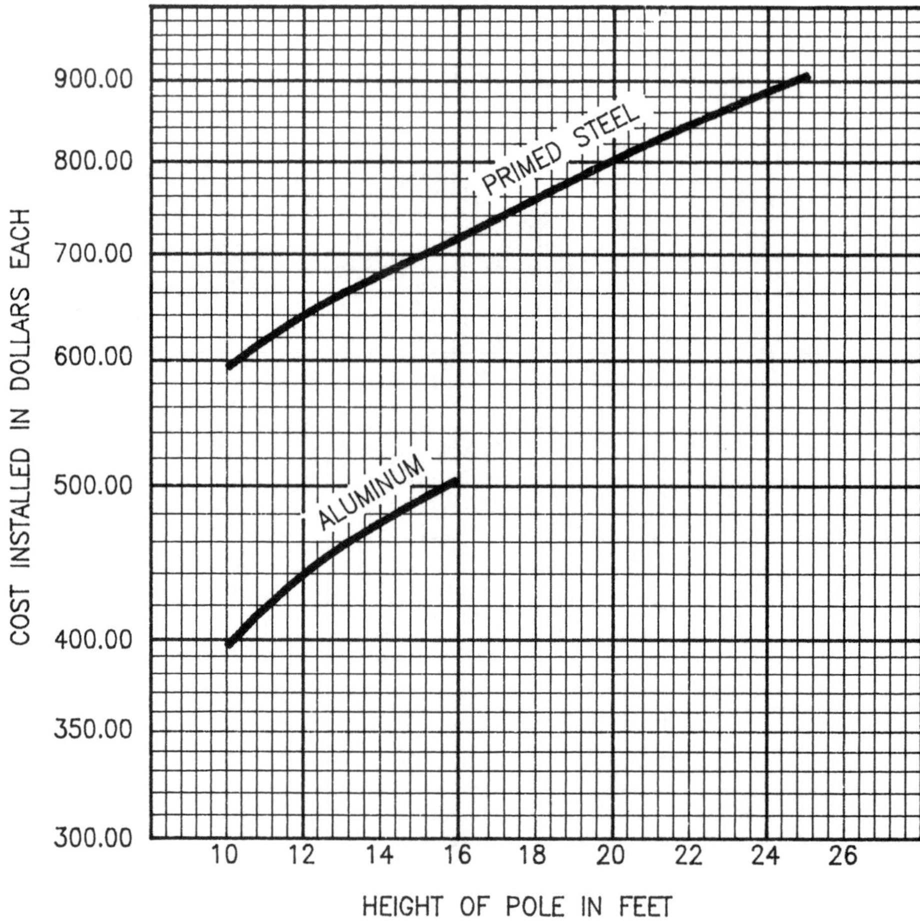

The costs shown for these poles consist of the published contractors' book prices with a shoe base and are as manufactured by Lexington, Inc. and Valmont Industries, Inc.

Included: (material and labor)

1. *Cost of pole including freight*
2. *Hand excavation in normal soil*
3. *Cost of concrete installed*
4. *Anchor bolts*
5. *2-1" GRC elbows*
6. *Grounding stud*
7. *Wire from base of pole to luminaire*

Excluded: Arms, fittings, and luminaire

COST OF STREET–LIGHTING POLES WITH PIPE ARMS

COST INSTALLED IN DOLLARS EACH

LUMINAIRE MOUNTING HEIGHT IN FEET		ARM LENGTH IN FEET		
		4	6	8
GALVANIZED STEEL	20	790.00	790.00	828.00
	25	883.00	883.00	921.00
	30	956.00	956.00	994.00
	40	1243.00	1243.00	1243.00
	ADD FOR SECOND ARM	100.00	110.00	120.00

The costs shown for these poles consist of the published contractors' book prices with a shoe base and are as manufactured by Lexington, Inc. and Valmont Industries, Inc.

Included: (material and labor)

1. *Cost of pole including freight*
2. *Hand excavation in normal soil*
3. *Cost of concrete installed*
4. *Anchor bolts*
5. *2-1" GRC elbows*
6. *Grounding stud*
7. *Wire from base of pole to luminaire*

Excluded: Luminaires

The costs shown for these brackets consist of the published contractors' book prices for the brackets shown and are as manufactured by Valmont Industries, Inc.

Included: (materials and labor)

1. *Cost of bracket and freight*
2. *Fastening bracket to pole*

Excluded: Luminaire

COST OF POLETOP BRACKETS

2 LIGHT

3 LIGHT

COST INSTALLED IN DOLLARS EACH

ARM LENGTH	1 LIGHT	2 LIGHT	3 LIGHT	4 LIGHT
4 FT.	100.00	150.00	196.00	234.00
6 FT.	113.00	163.00	——	——

3 LIGHT

4 LIGHT

COST INSTALLED IN DOLLARS EACH

2 LIGHT	88.00
3 LIGHT IN LINE	121.00
3 LIGHT @120 DEG.	130.50
4 LIGHT @ 90 DEG.	146.00

The costs shown for these luminaires consist of the published contractors' book prices for the luminaires illustrated.

Included: (material and labor)

1. *Luminaire with slip fitter, if required*
2. *Lamp of size and type required*
3. *Ballast of size required, if necessary*
4. *Mounting and connecting*

Excluded: Poles and brackets

COST OF EXTERIOR LUMINAIRES

TYPE OF UNIT	WATTAGE	INSTALLED COST IN DOLLARS	
		METAL HALIDE	HIGH-PRESSURE SODIUM
CROUSE-HINDS GAL SERIES	150	—	—
	250	674.00	—
	400	804.00	777.00
	1000	1082.00	1707.00
CROUSE-HINDS RMF SERIES	150	—	512.00
	250	498.00	526.00
	400	493.00	534.00
	1000	692.00	837.00
APPLETON GEN.PURP. SPORTSLIGHTER	400	381.00	382.00
	1000	477.00	567.00
	1500	535.00	—
APPLETON QUARTZLITE			TUNGSTEN HALOGEN
	500		89.00
	1000/1500		113.00

A-33

TYPE OF UNIT	WATTAGE	COST INSTALLED IN DOLLARS EACH		
		MERCURY VAPOR	METAL HALIDE	HIGH–PRESSURE SODIUM
SPAULDING PEACHTREE SERIES	70	———	———	397.00
	100	353.00	———	416.00
	150	———	———	419.00
	175	354.00	373.00	———
	250	380.00	391.00	———
	400	377.00	381.00	344.00
SPAULDING NEW YORKER SERIES	70	———	———	472.00
	100	———	———	491.00
	150	———	———	494.00
	175	———	466.00	———
	250	———	483.00	———
SPAULDING MIAMI ENCLOSED UNIT		800MA	1500MA	
	4 FT.	158.00	185.00	
	6 FT.	181.00	224.00	
	8 FT.	209.00	265.00	
SPAULDING PHILADELPHIA SERIES	4 FT.	267.00	297.00	
	6 FT.	285.00	315.00	
	8 FT.	296.00	327.00	

The costs shown for these luminaires consist of the published contractors' book prices for the luminaires illustrated.

Included: (material and labor)

1. *Luminaire with slip fitter, if required*
2. *Lamp of size and type required*
3. *Ballast of size required, if necessary*
4. *Mounting and connecting*

Excluded: Poles and brackets

COST OF EXTERIOR LUMINAIRES

TYPE OF UNIT	WATTAGE	COST INSTALLED IN DOLLARS EACH		
		MERCURY VAPOR	METAL HALIDE	HIGH-PRESSURE SODIUM
HOLOPHANE PARKLANE SERIES	150	———	———	1464.00
	175	———	———	———
	250	1337.00	1351.00	1462.00
	400	1335.00	1338.00	1473.00
GARDCO FORM 10H SERIES	70	———	———	517.00
	100	442.00	472.00	523.00
	150	———	———	526.00
	175	435.00	459.00	———
	250	562.00	576.00	645.00
	400	568.00	571.00	646.00
	1000	853.00	951.00	1144.00
DEVINE COVERED GARAGE FIXTURE	75	245.00	———	———
	100	245.00	307.00	276.00
	150	———	———	276.00
CROUSE-HINDS STREET LIGHTING FIXTURE	250	———	———	385.00
	400	———	377.00	397.00

The costs shown for these luminaires consist of the published contractors' book prices for the luminaires illustrated.

Included: (material and labor)

1. *Luminaire with slip fitter, if required*
2. *Lamp of size and type required*
3. *Ballast of size required, if necessary*
4. *Mounting and connecting*

Excluded: Poles and brackets

TYPE OF UNIT	WATTAGE	COST INSTALLED IN DOLLARS EACH		
		MERCURY VAPOR	METAL HALIDE	HIGH-PRESSURE SODIUM
GARDCO 8" DIA. ROUND BOLLARD	35	———	———	517.00
	50	442.00	472.00	523.00
	70	———	———	526.00
	75	435.00	459.00	———
	100	562.00	576.00	645.00
GARDCO 8" SQUARE BOLLARD	35	———	———	517.00
	50	442.00	472.00	523.00
	70	———	———	526.00
	75	435.00	459.00	———
	100	562.00	576.00	645.00

TYPE OF UNIT	CONFIGURATION	LAMPS	COST
PRESCOLITE FLUORESCENT BOLLARD	SINGLE SIDED	2–F15T8	315.00
	DOUBLE SIDED	2–F15T8	340.00

The costs shown consist of the published contractors' book prices for the units shown, including the lamps required and the labor for installation. The labor includes excavation and compaction where required or concrete base where required.

Circuit Protection

B

CIRCUIT-BREAKER INTERRUPTING RATINGS

ENCLOSED CIRCUIT BREAKERS

ENCLOSED MOLDED-CASE SWITCHES

COST OF BOLTED PRESSURE SWITCHES

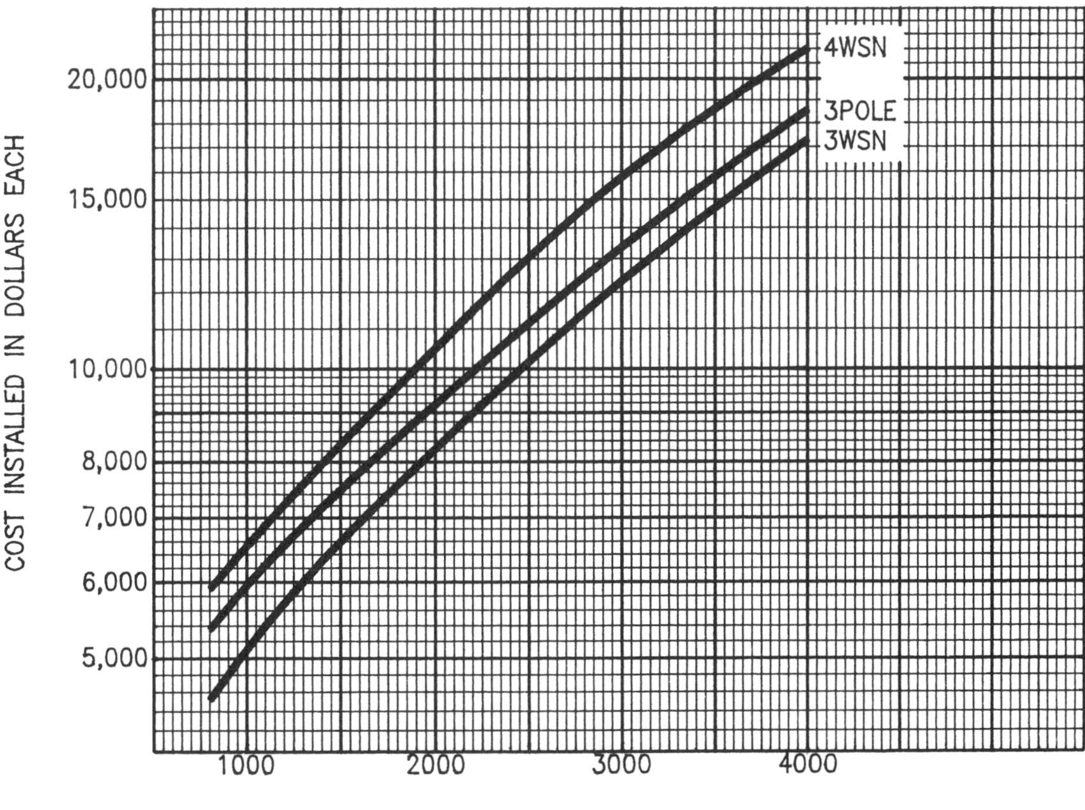

The costs shown for these bolted pressure switches consist of the published contractors' book price. The switches used here are Square D-Bolt Loc, contained in a NEMA 1 enclosure, and include Buss Hi-Cap fuses to match the switch. Also included is a necessary amount of copper conductor sized to match the switch, by paralleling with wire terminals and connecting to the bus. Labor includes placing and connecting the switch and installing fuses.

ADDERS	
BLOWN MAIN–FUSE DETECTOR	$1805.
RAINTIGHT ENCLOSURE	
800–2500 AMP	$1355.
3000–4000 AMP	$1355.
ELECTRIC TRIP MECHANISM	$1265.
GROUND FAULT PROTECTION (INCL SENSOR, SOLID STATE RELAY, CONTROL TRANS., WIRED TO ELECTRIC TRIP MECHANISM.	
800–2000 AMP	$4435.
2500–4000 AMP	$5035.

B-2

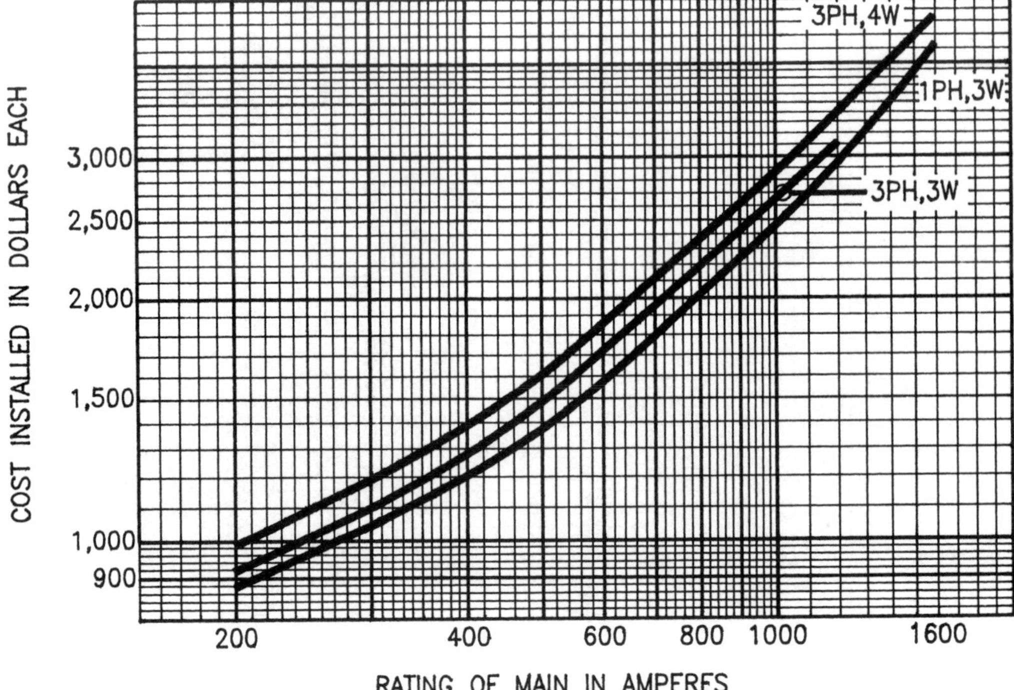

In order to determine the price of a switch or a circuit-breaker type of distribution panel, it is necessary to determine from the one-line diagram the type of cabinet, which has either main lugs, main switch, or main breaker, to which will be added the costs of the cable interconnect and the costs of the switches or circuit breakers.

The cost of the cabinet shown above includes the following:

1. *Cost of cabinet with main lugs and labor for installation*
2. *Terminal time and conductor for main connections*
3. *A grounding bar*

Not included:

1. *Cable interconnect to next section*
2. *Switches or circuit breakers*

ADDERS						
TYPE OF FITTING	NO. OF POLES	AMPACITY OF PANEL MAINS				
		225	400	600	800	1000
SUBFEED LUGS	2	52.00	96.00	193.00	268.50	320.50
	3	69.50	114.50	210.75	282.75	354.50
SPLIT BUS	2	137.50	162.75	193.25	168.50	324.50
	3	162,75	193.25	210.75	304.00	354.50

FUSIBLE-TYPE PANELBOARD – CABINET ONLY WITH MAIN LUGS ONLY 240/600 VOLT

COST OF FUSIBLE–TYPE DISTRIBUTION PANELS

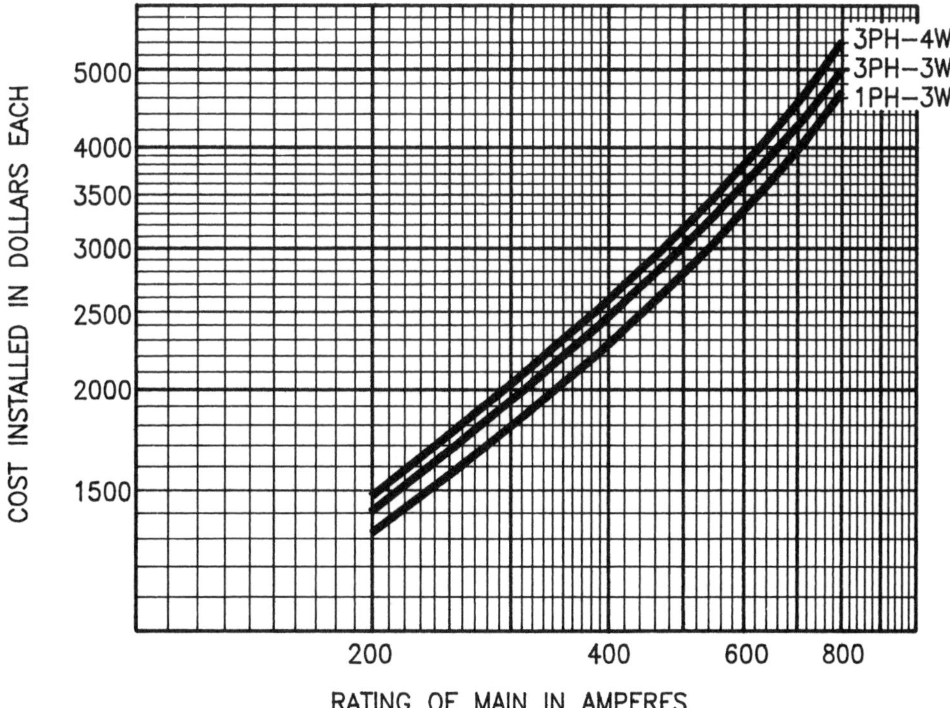

In order to determine the price of a switch or a circuit-breaker type of distribution panel, it is necessary to determine from the one-line diagram the type of cabinet, which has either main lugs, main switch, or main breaker, to which will be added the costs of the cable interconnect and the costs of the switches or circuit breakers.

The cost of the cabinet shown above includes the following:

1. *Cost of cabinet with switch and fuses as selected and labor for installation*
2. *Terminal time and conductor for main connections*
3. *A grounding bar*

Not included:

1. *Cable interconnect to next section*
2. *Branch circuit switches*

ADDERS					
TYPE OF FITTING	NO. OF POLES	AMPACITY OF PANEL MAINS			
		225	400	600	800
SUBFEED LUGS	2	52.00	96.00	193.00	268.50
	3	69.50	114.50	210.75	282.75
SPLIT BUS	2	137.50	162.75	193.25	168.50
	3	162.75	193.25	210.75	304.00

COST OF FUSIBLE–TYPE DISTRIBUTION PANELS

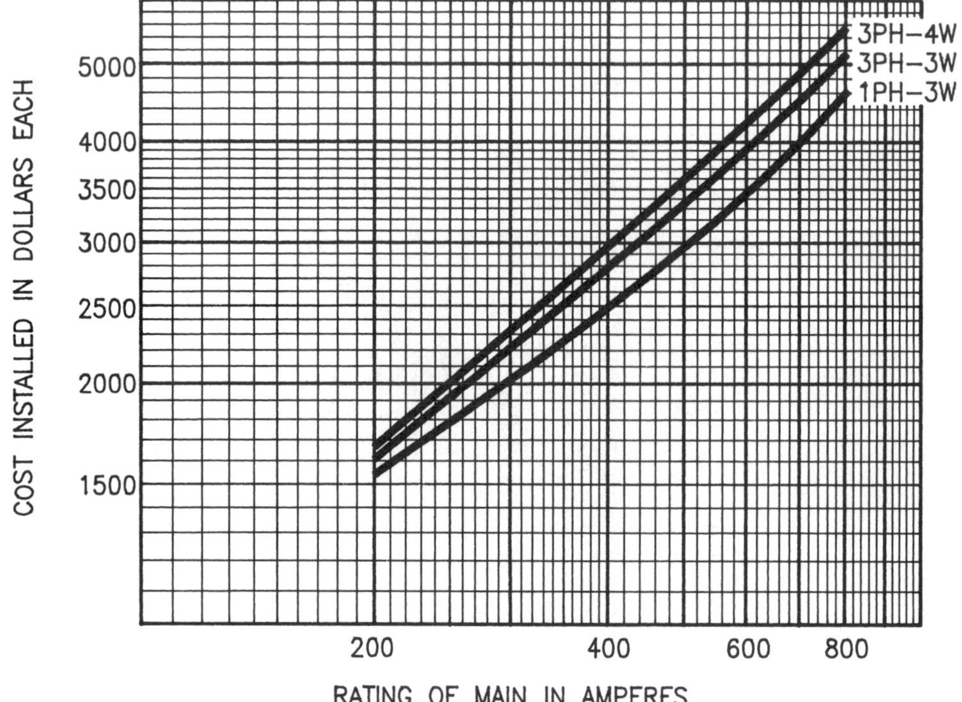

In order to determine the price of a switch or a circuit-breaker type of distribution panel, it is necessary to determine from the one-line diagram the type of cabinet, which has either main lugs, main switch, or main breaker, to which will be added the costs of the cable interconnect and the costs of the switches or circuit breakers.

The cost of the cabinet shown above includes the following:

1. *Cost of cabinet with switch and fuses as selected and labor for installation.*
2. *Terminal time and conductor for main connections*
3. *A grounding bar*

Not included:

1. *Cable interconnect to next section*
2. *Branch circuit switches*

ADDERS
FOR SUB–FEED LUGS OR SPLIT BUS, SEE PAGE B–3

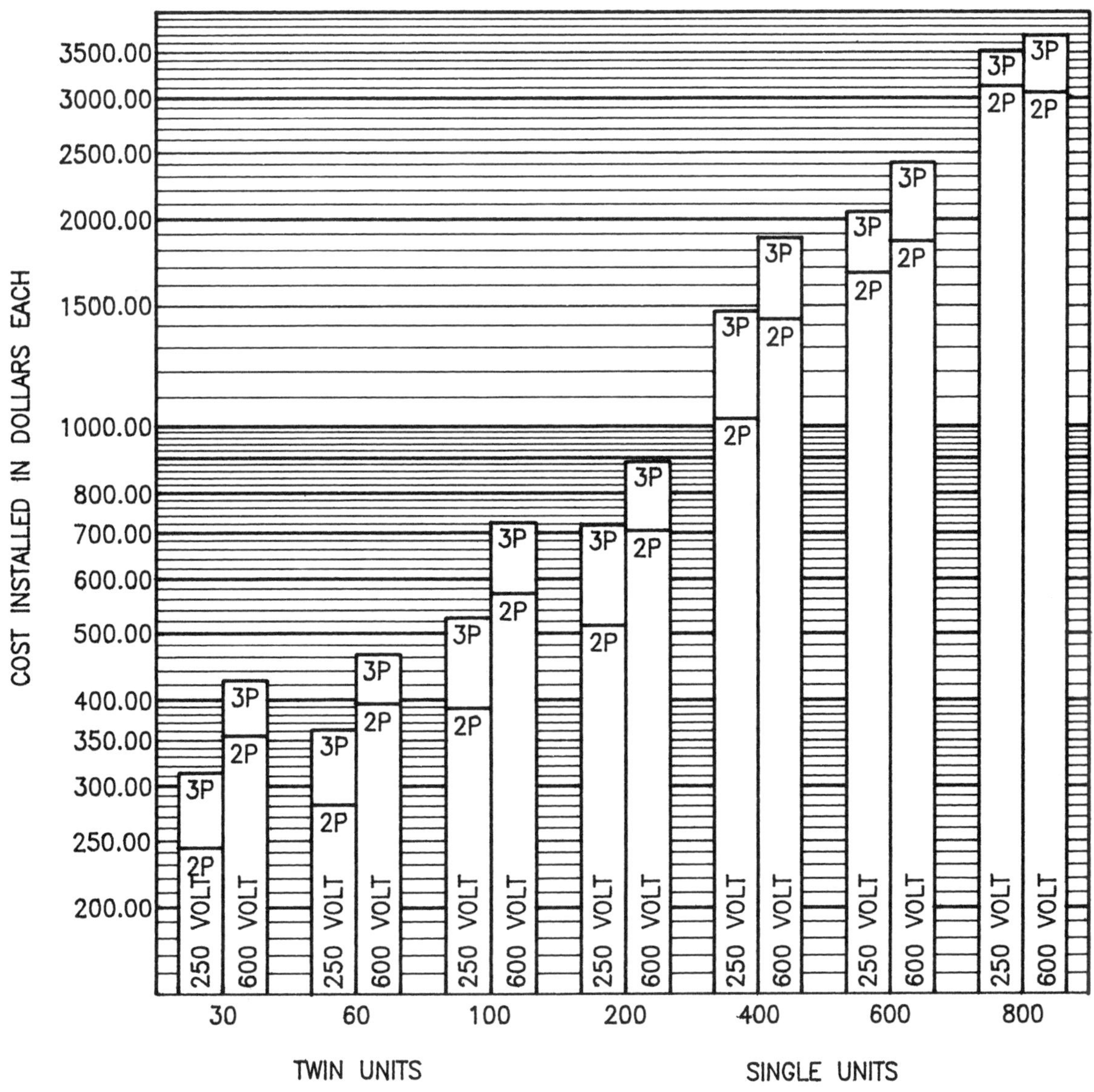

ADDER FOR 3-POLE SPACES ONLY		
AMPACITY	240 VOLT	600 VOLT
30–30	75	75
60–60	75	100
100–100	95	115
200	145	145
400	215	215
600	215	215
800	215	215

After the price of the cabinet and cable interconnect costs are determined, the number of switches of the proper class and number of poles must be added for the total installed cost of the distribution panel. Each switch includes the cost of the conductors, terminal make-up time, and time for a neutral connection, as well as cabinet time. No cost of cutting holes in steel panels for conduit terminals has been provided. Add as needed.

COST OF CIRCUIT–BREAKER DISTRIBUTION PANEL

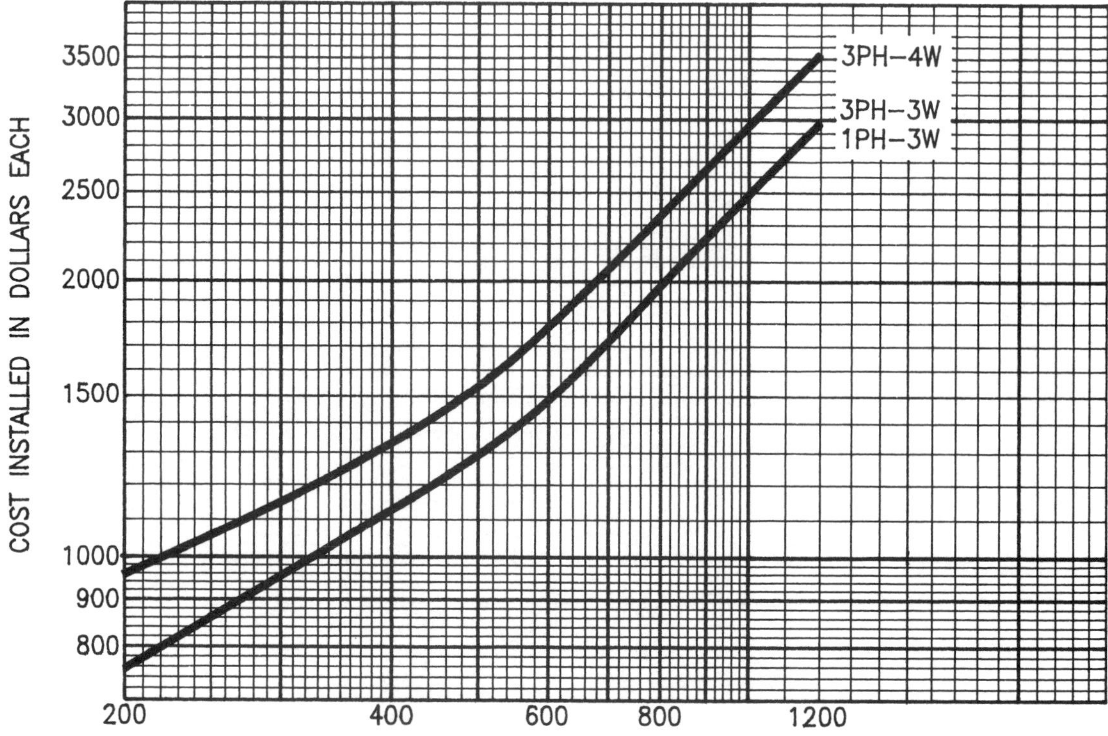

ADDERS
FOR SUBFEED LUGS OR SPLIT BUS, SEE PAGE B–3

In order to determine the price of a switch or a circuit-breaker type of distribution panel, it is necessary to determine from the one-line diagram the type of cabinet, which has either main lugs, main switch, or main breaker, to which will be added the costs of the cable interconnect and the costs of the switches or circuit breakers.

The cost of the cabinet shown above includes the following:

1. *Cost of cabinet with main lugs and labor for installation*
2. *Terminal time and conductor for main connections*
3. *A grounding bar*

Not included:

1. *Cable interconnect to next section*
2. *Branch circuit breakers*

COST OF CIRCUIT–BREAKER TYPE DISTRIBUTION PANELS

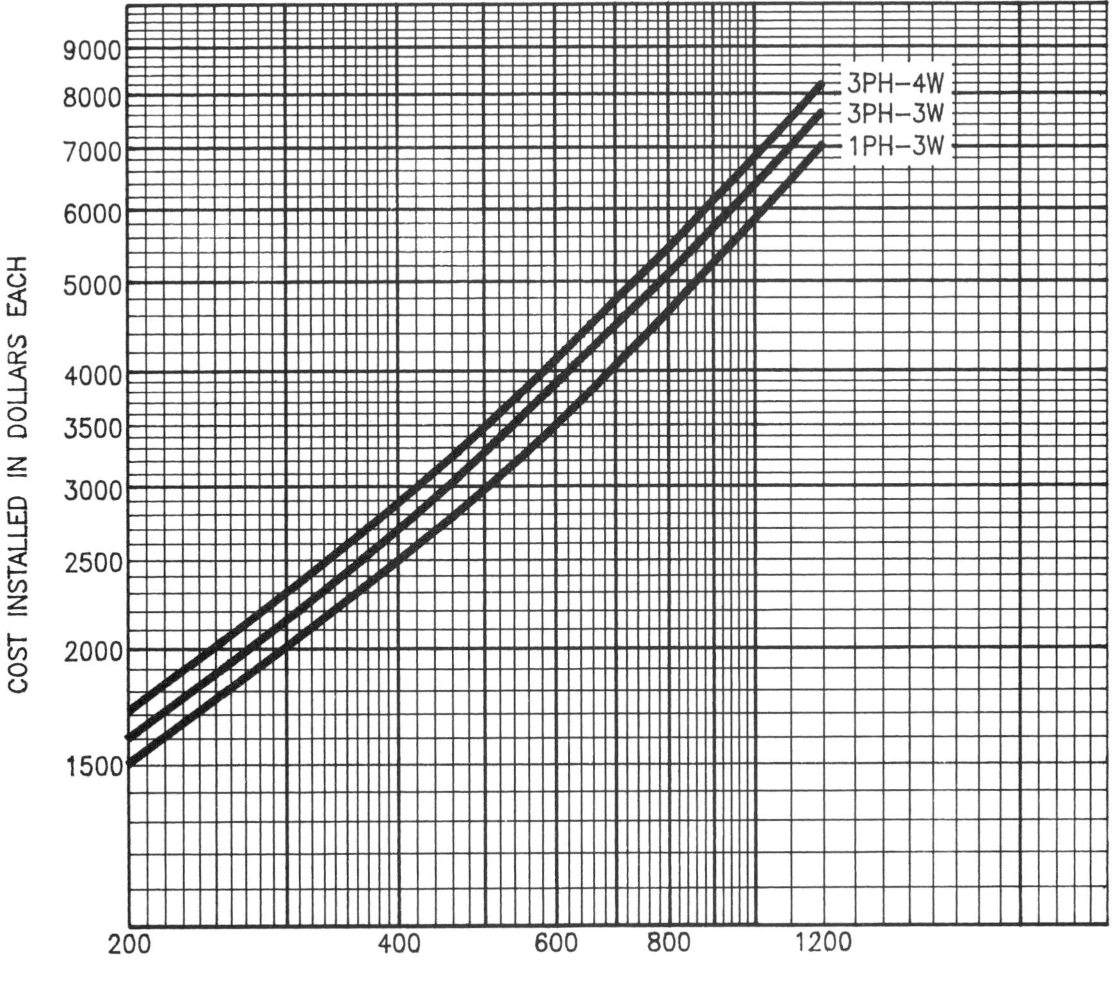

In order to determine the price of a switch or a circuit-breaker type of distribution panel, it is necessary to determine from the one-line diagram the type of cabinet, which has either main lugs, main switch, or main breaker, to which will be added the costs of the cable interconnect and the costs of the switches or circuit breakers.

The cost of the cabinet shown above includes the following:

1. *Cost of cabinet with main circuit breaker as selected and labor for installation.*
2. *Terminal time and conductor for main connections*
3. *A grounding bar*

Not included:

1. *Cable interconnect to next section*
2. *Branch circuit breakers*

FOR ADDERS FOR SUBFEED LUGS OR SPLIT BUS, SEE PAGE B–2.

COST OF DISTRIBUTION PANEL CIRCUIT BREAKER BRANCHES

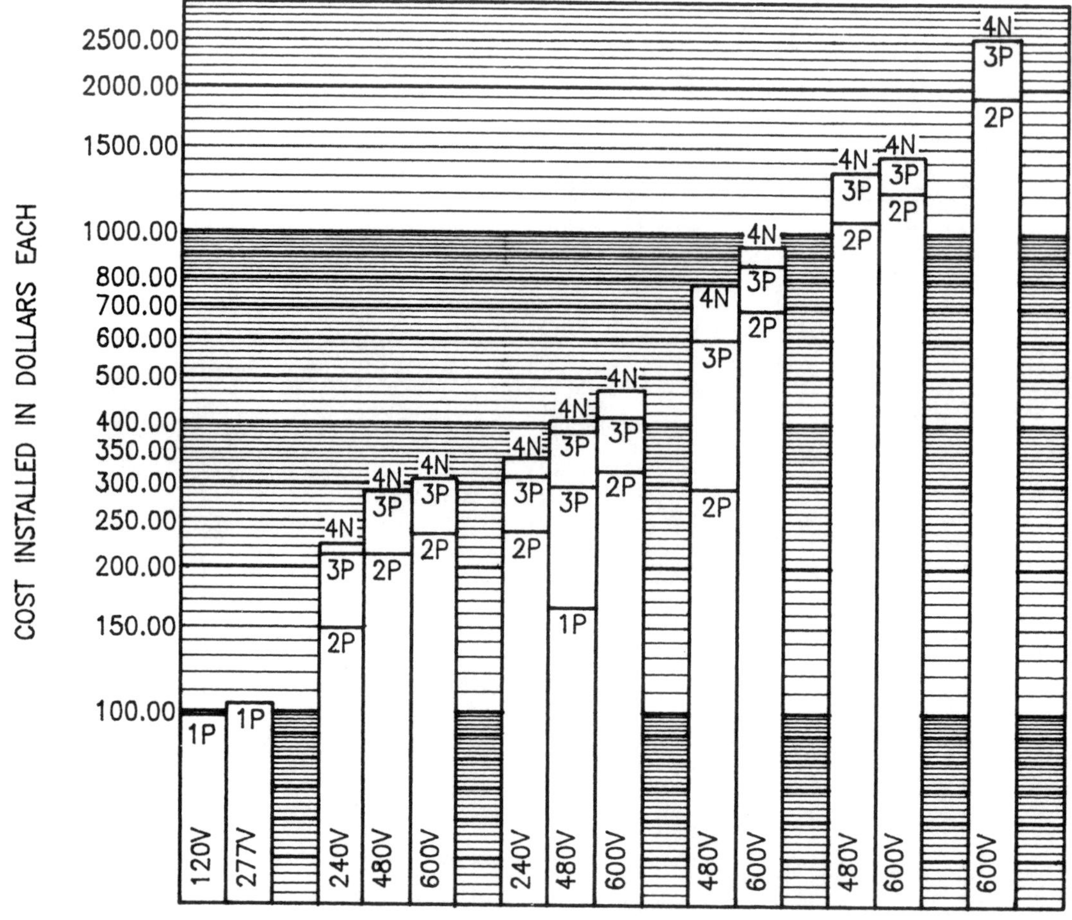

CIRCUIT BREAKER RATING IN VOLTAGE, AMPACITY, & POLES

ADDER FOR SPACES ONLY			
AMPACITY	1 POLE	2 POLE	3 POLE
15–100	17.50	20.25	24.00
100–225	N.A.	61.75	61.75
250–400	N.A.	105	105
450–800	N.A.	110	110

After the price of the cabinet and cable interconnect costs are determined, the number of circuit breakers of the proper class and number of poles must be added for the total installed cost of the distribution panel. Each circuit breaker includes the cost of the conductors, terminal makeup time, and time for a neutral connection, as well as cabinet time. No cost of cutting holes in steel panels for conduit terminals has been provided. Add as needed.

COST OF PANEL INTERCONNECT (CABLE)

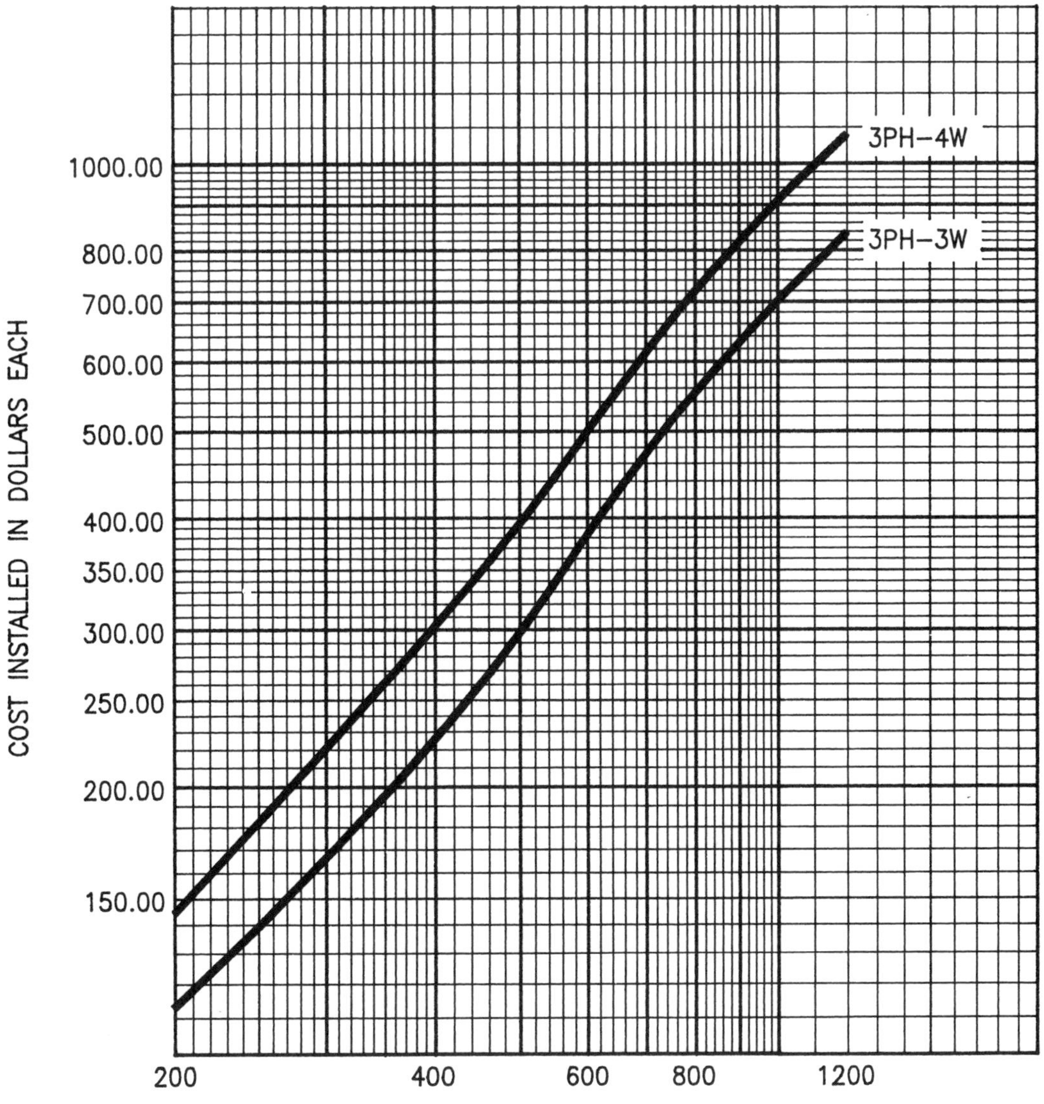

The cable interconnect consists of copper conductors for the ampacities shown, the necessary conductor terminals, and the labor for installation. It is used when cross-busing is not provided by the manufacturer.

COST OF PANELBOARDS

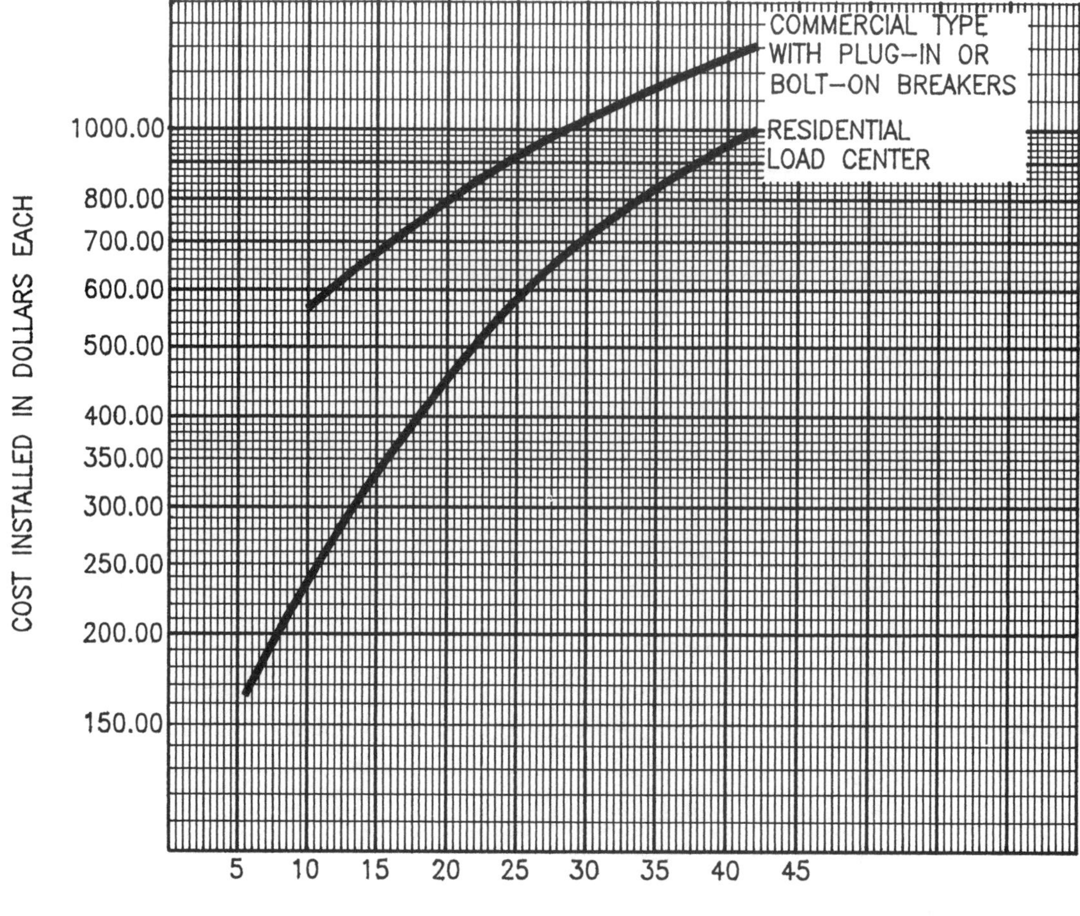

The costs shown for these panelboards consist of the published contractors' book price, and also include wire terminals for the number of breakers provided. The branch circuit conduit terminals are not included here since they are provided with the outlet boxes. A feeder conduit and feeder wire terminal, however, are provided, of a size adequate to feed the panel with the number of branch circuits provided. Also provided is sufficient conductor for connections to the main buses.

The residential panel referenced would be the equivalent of the Square D QO Load Center with single-pole circuit breakers, plug-in type, rated at 10,000 A. I. C.

The commercial panels referenced would be equivalent to the Square D type NQO and NQOB, factory-assembled with single-pole plug-in or bolt-on breakers rated at 10,000 A. I. C.

ADDERS

FOR MAIN BREAKERS, SEE "ENCLOSED BREAKERS" IN THIS SECTION

SUBFEED LUGS, $31.50 SPLIT BUS, $73.50

PANELBOARDS – 120/240 VOLT – 1 PHASE, 3 WIRE – MAIN LUGS ONLY

COST OF PANELBOARDS

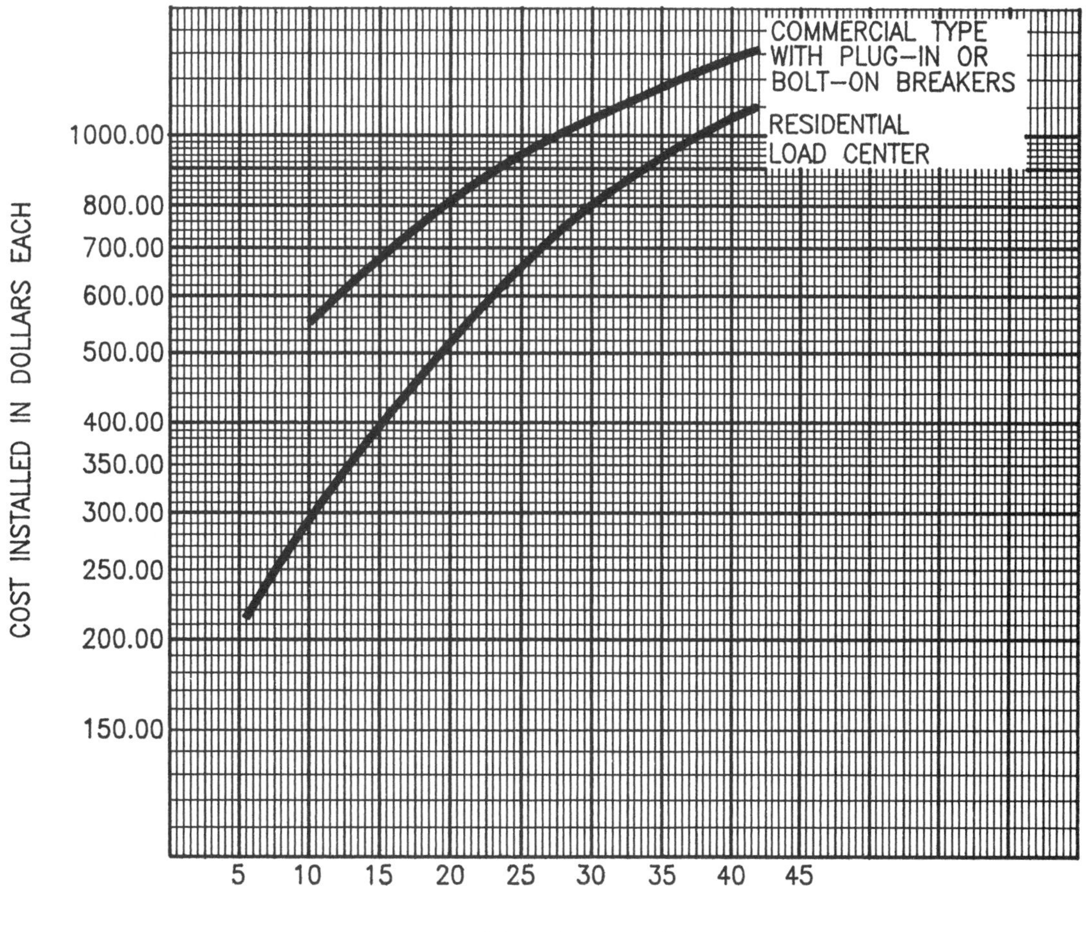

The costs shown for these panelboards consist of the published contractors' book price, and also include wire terminals for the number of breakers provided. The branch circuit conduit terminals are not included here since they are provided with the outlet boxes. A feeder conduit and feeder wire terminal, however, are provided, of a size adequate to feed the panel with the number of branch circuits provided. Also provided is sufficient conductor for connections to the main buses.

The residential panel referenced would be the equivalent of the Square D QO Load Center with single-pole circuit breakers, plug-in type, rated at 10,000 A. I. C.

The commercial panels referenced would be equivalent to the Square D type NQO and NQOB, factory-assembled with single-pole plug-in or bolt-on breakers rated at 10,000 A. I. C.

ADDERS

FOR MAIN BREAKERS, SEE "ENCLOSED BREAKERS" IN THIS SECTION

SUBFEED LUGS $31.50 SPLIT BUS $73.50

120/240 VOLT QO(PLUG–IN), QOB(BOLT–ON)			
SIZE	1 POLE	2 POLE	3 POLE
10,000 A.I.C (QO)			
10–60A	25.35	42.40	95.75
70A	34.25	60.40	113.75
80–100A	17.50	78.25	128.00
GFI 15–30A	70.50	119.75	----
22,000 A.I.C.(QO–VH)			
10–60A	32.60	61.50	129.55
70A	73.50	91.40	152.00
80–100A	-----	119.70	157.75
GFI 15–30A	129.25	----	----
65,000 (QH)			
15–30A	51.25	109.50	195.30

The costs shown for circuit breakers only consist of the published contractors' book prices and the labor for installing in an existing panelboard with spaces available. Installation of branch circuit conductor terminations is also provided.

COST OF PANELBOARDS

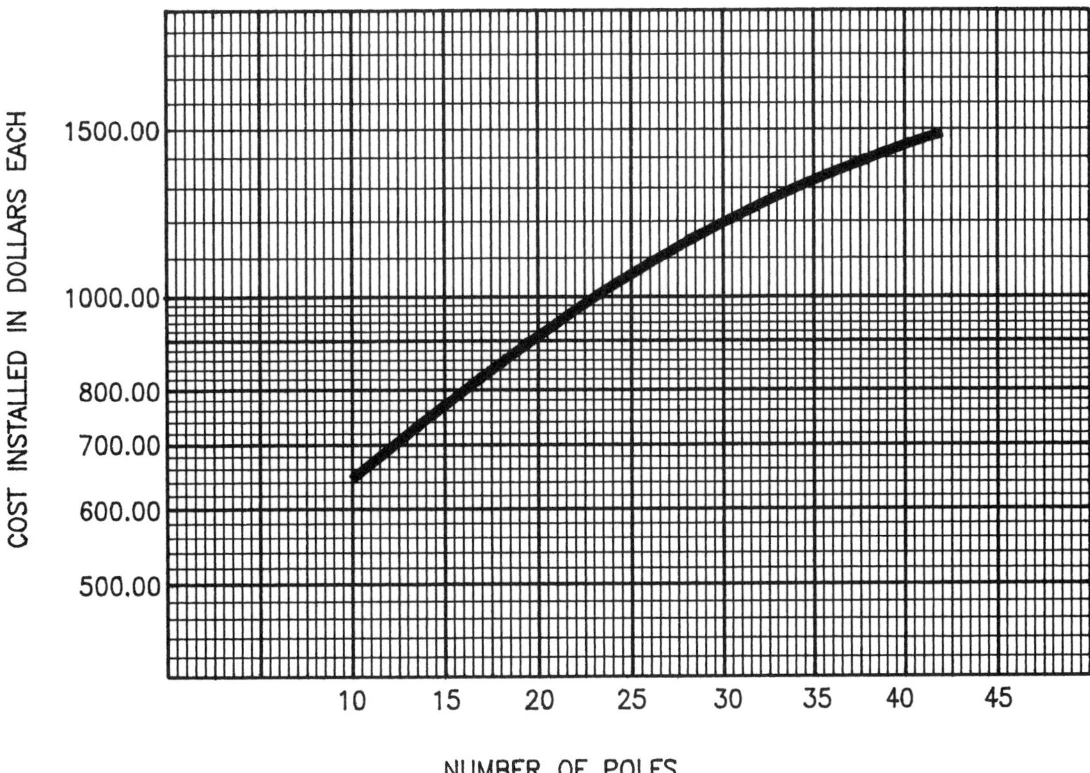

NUMBER OF POLES

The costs shown for these panelboards consist of the published contractors' book price, and also include wire terminals for the number of breakers provided. The branch circuit conduit terminals are not included here since they are provided with the outlet boxes. A feeder conduit and feeder wire terminal, however, are provided, of a size adequate to feed the panel with the number of branch circuits provided. Also provided is sufficient conductor for connections to the main buses.

The panels referenced would be the equivalent of the Square D type NEHB, factory-assembled with single-pole plug-in or bolt-on breakers. Single-pole breakers for this panel are rated at 14,000 A. I. C. at 277 volts.

ADDERS

FOR MAIN BREAKERS, SEE "ENCLOSED BREAKERS" IN THIS SECTION

SUBFEED LUGS $31.50 SPLIT BUS $110.00

COST OF 1 PHASE, 3 WIRE – SAFETY SWITCHES

B-14

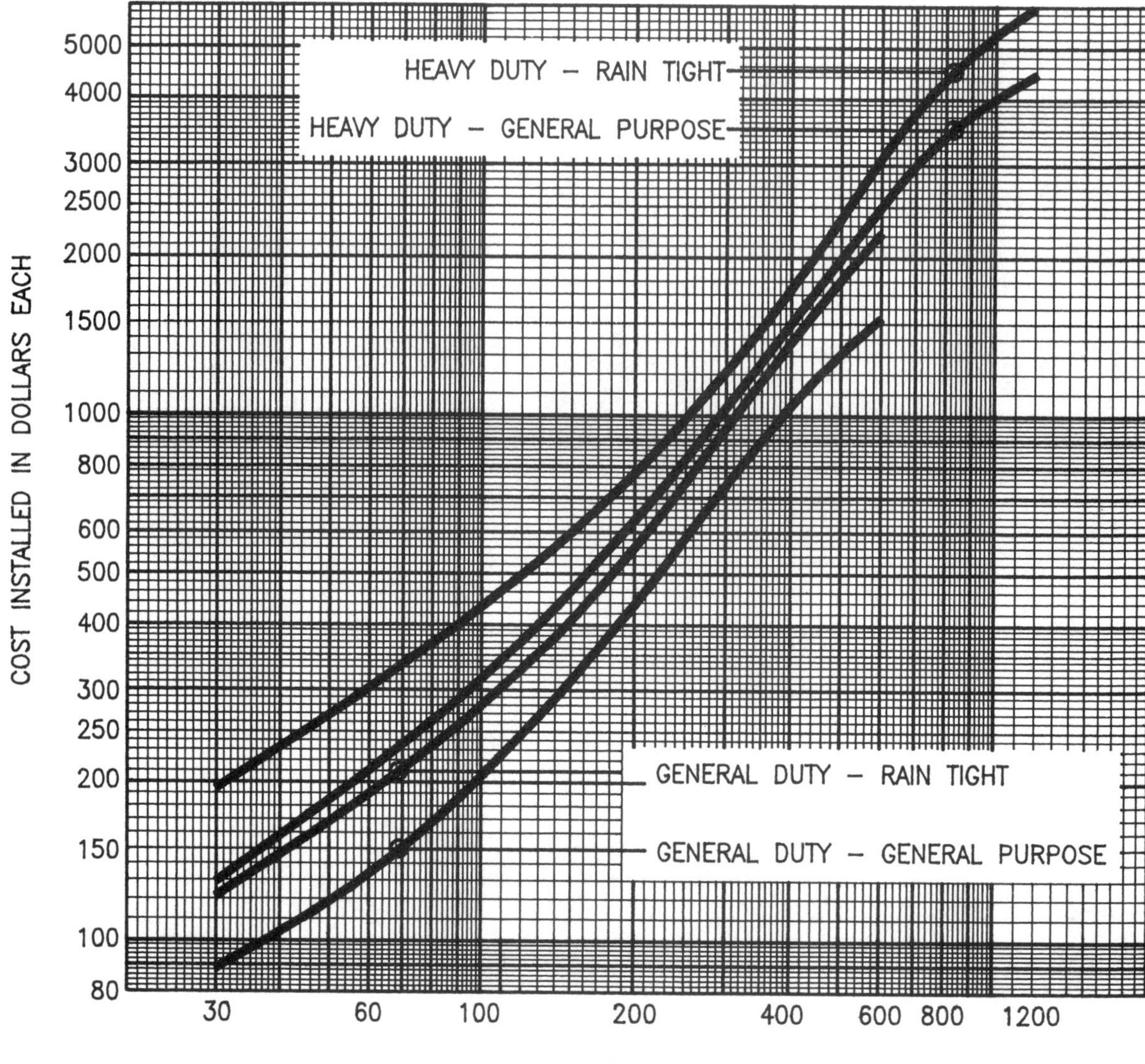

The costs shown for the safety switches consist of the published contractors' book prices and further include the following:

1. *Fuses where required*
2. *Fastening devices for mounting to a masonry wall*
3. *A conduit terminal for the conduit size required*
4. *Wire required inside the enclosure*
5. *Terminations*
6. *Labor for complete installation of switch, conduit terminal, wire, and fuses*

FUSIBLE SAFETY SWITCH – 240 VOLT – SINGLE PHASE, 3 WIRE

COST OF 3 POLE SAFETY SWITCHES

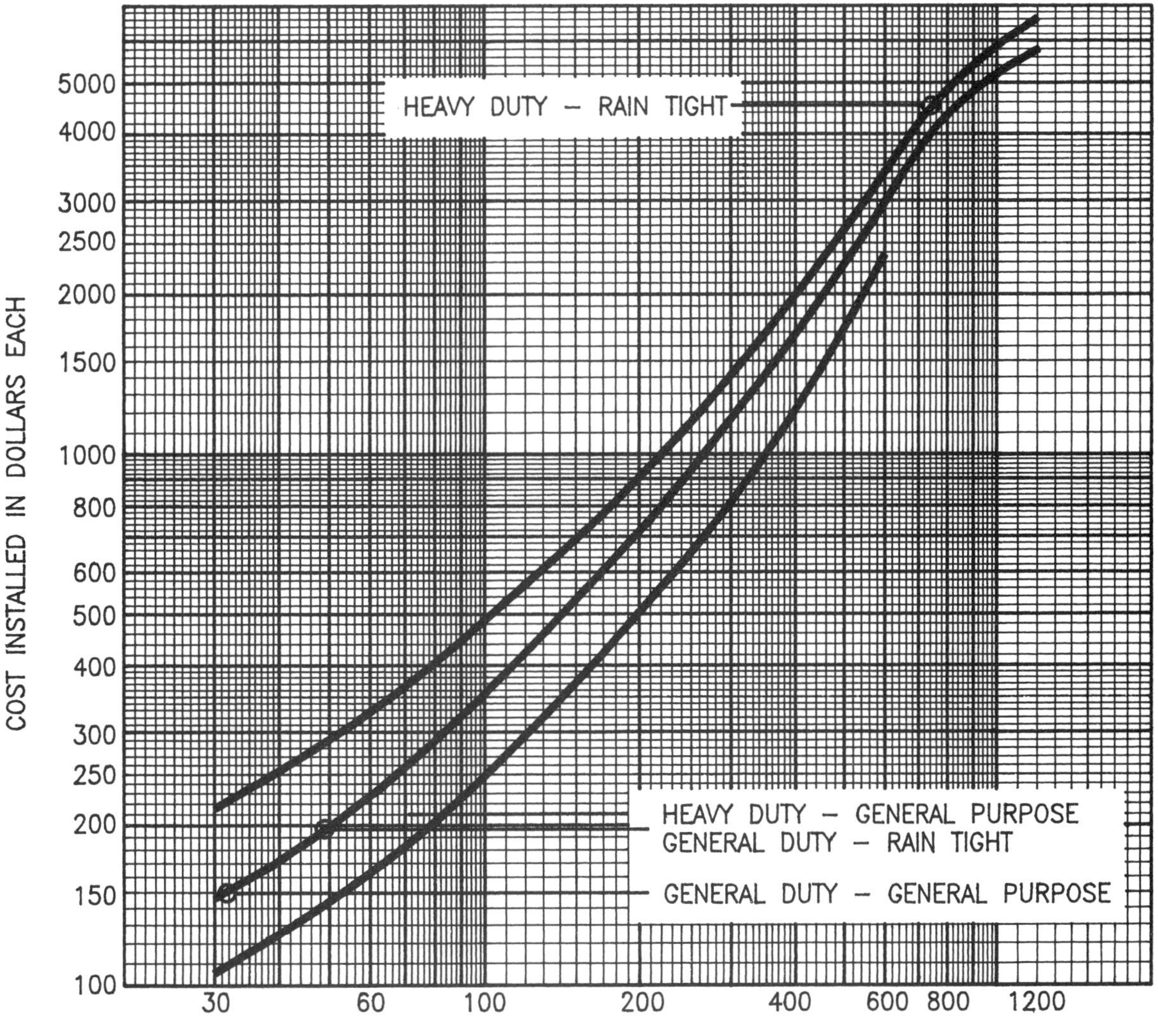

The costs shown for the safety switches consist of the published contractors' book prices and further include the following:

1. *Fuses where required*
2. *Fastening devices for mounting to a masonry wall*
3. *A conduit terminal for the conduit size required*
4. *Wire required inside the enclosure*
5. *Terminations*
6. *Labor for complete installation of switch, conduit terminal, wire, and fuses*

COST OF 3 PHASE, 4 WIRE – SAFETY SWITCHES

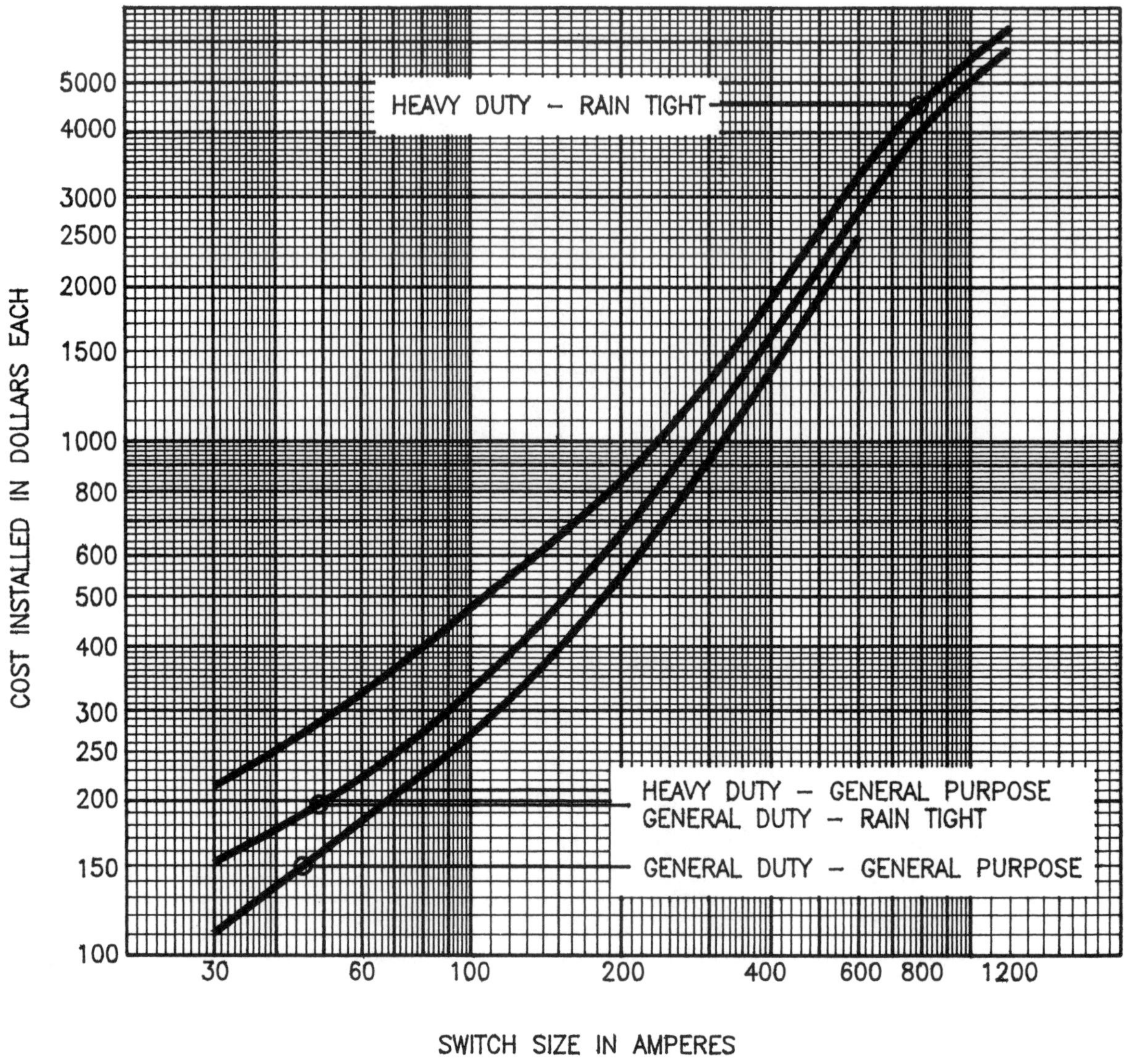

The costs shown for the safety switches consist of the published contractors' book prices and further include the following:

1. *Fuses where required*
2. *Fastening devices for mounting to a masonry wall*
3. *A conduit terminal for the conduit size required*
4. *Wire required inside the enclosure*
5. *Terminations*
6. *Labor for complete installation of switch, conduit terminal, wire, and fuses*

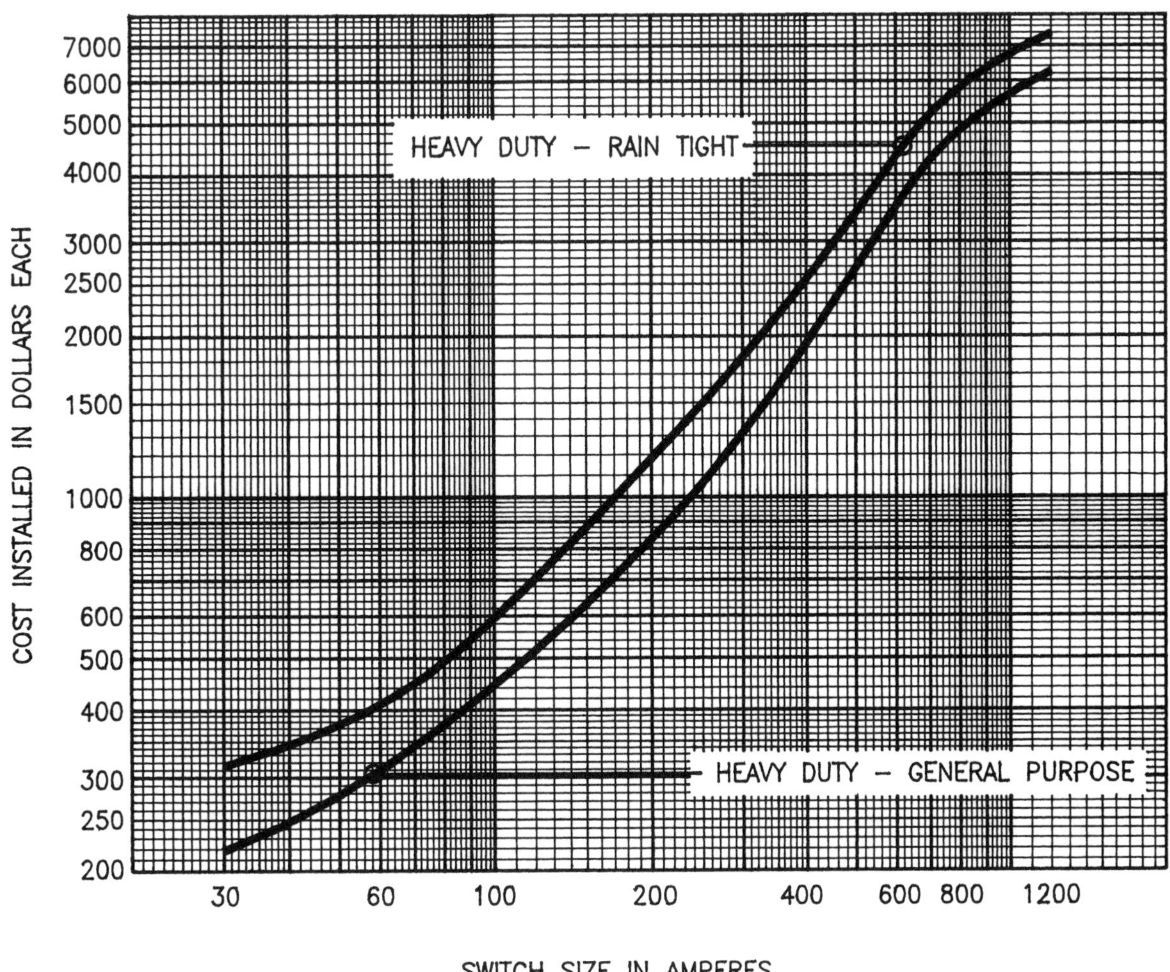

The costs shown for the safety switches consist of the published contractors' book prices and further include the following:

1. *Fuses where required*
2. *Fastening devices for mounting to a masonry wall*
3. *A conduit terminal for the conduit size required*
4. *Wire required inside the enclosure*
5. *Terminations*
6. *Labor for complete installation of switch, conduit terminal, wire, and fuses*

COST OF 3 POLE SAFETY SWITCHES

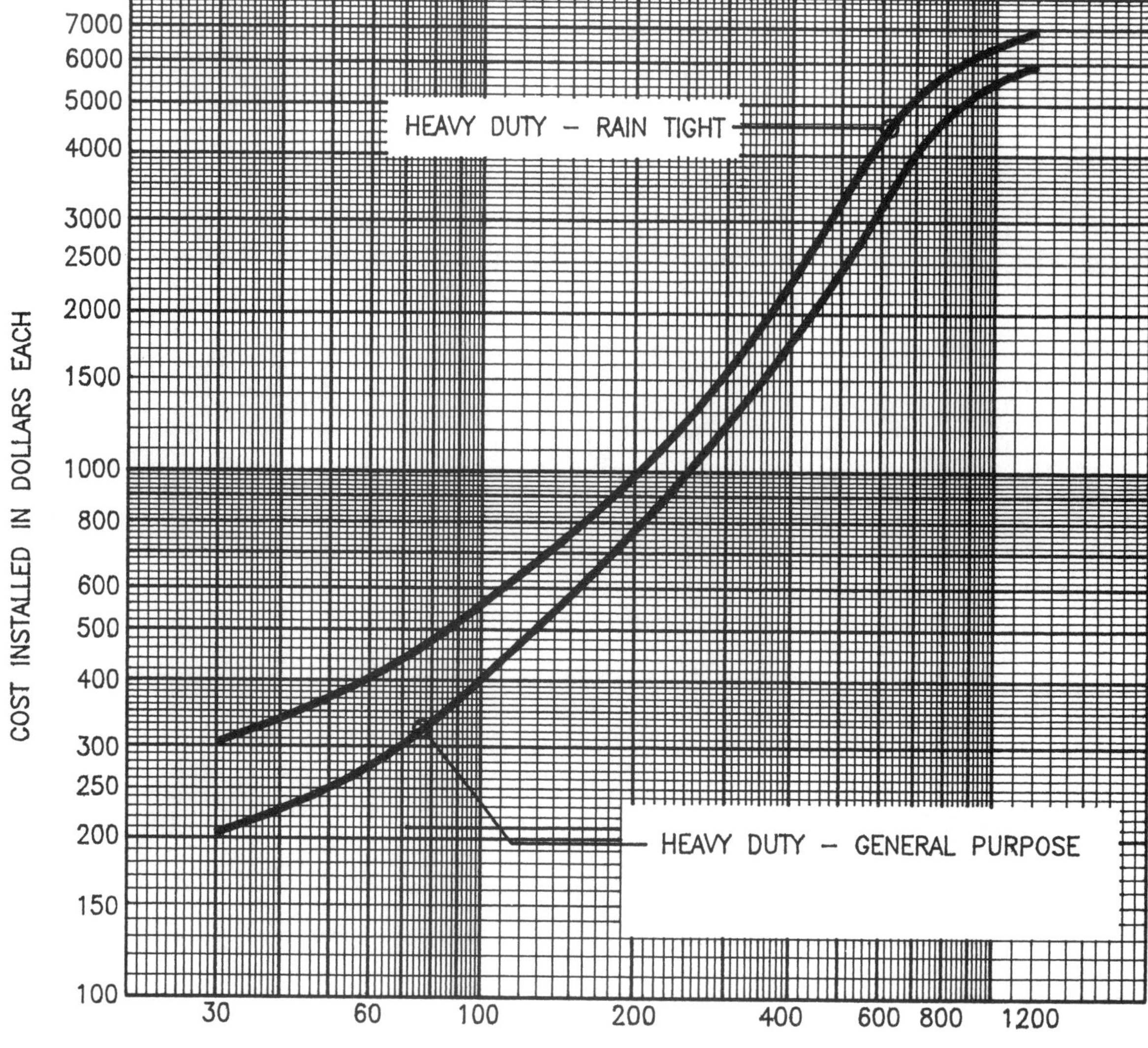

SWITCH SIZE IN AMPERES

The costs shown for the safety switches consist of the published contractors' book prices and further include the following:

1. *Fuses where required*
2. *Fastening devices for mounting to a masonry wall*
3. *A conduit terminal for the conduit size required*
4. *Wire required inside the enclosure.*
5. *Terminations*
6. *Labor for complete installation of switch, conduit terminal, wire, and fuses*

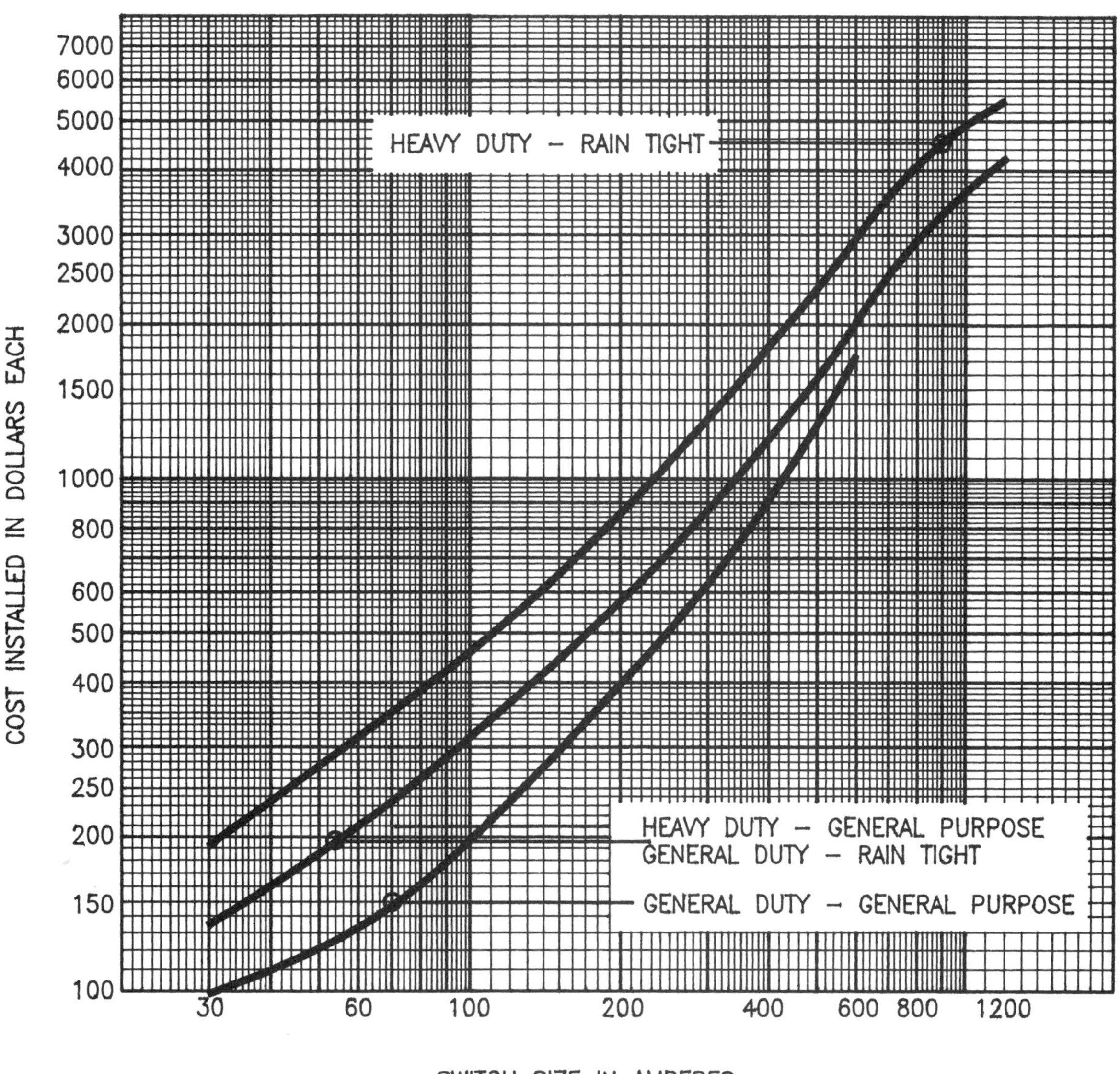

The costs shown for the safety switches consist of the published contractors' book prices and further include the following:

1. *Fuses where required*
2. *Fastening devices for mounting to a masonry wall*
3. *A conduit terminal for the conduit size required*
4. *Wire required inside the enclosure*
5. *Terminations*
6. *Labor for complete installation of switch, conduit terminal, wire, and fuses*

UL-LISTED AMPERE INTERRUPTING RATING OF SOME SQUARE D CIRCUIT BREAKERS				
TYPE OF BREAKER	120 VOLT	240 VOLT	480 VOLT	600 VOLT
QO	10,000	10,000		
QO–VH	22,000	22,000		
QH	65,000	65,000		
QE–VH	22,000	22,000		
EH	65.000	65,000	14,000	
FA–240	10,000	10,000		
FA–480	25,000	25,000	18,000	
FA–600	25,000	25,000	18,000	14,000
FH	65,000	65,000	25,000	18,000
FC		100,000	65,000	
KA		42,000	25,000	22,000
KH		65,000	35,000	25,000
KC		100,000	65,000	
LA		42,000	30,000	22,000
LH		65,000	35,000	25,000
MA		42,000	30,000	22,000
MH		65,000	65,000	25,000

COST OF INDIVIDUALLY ENCLOSED CIRCUIT BREAKERS

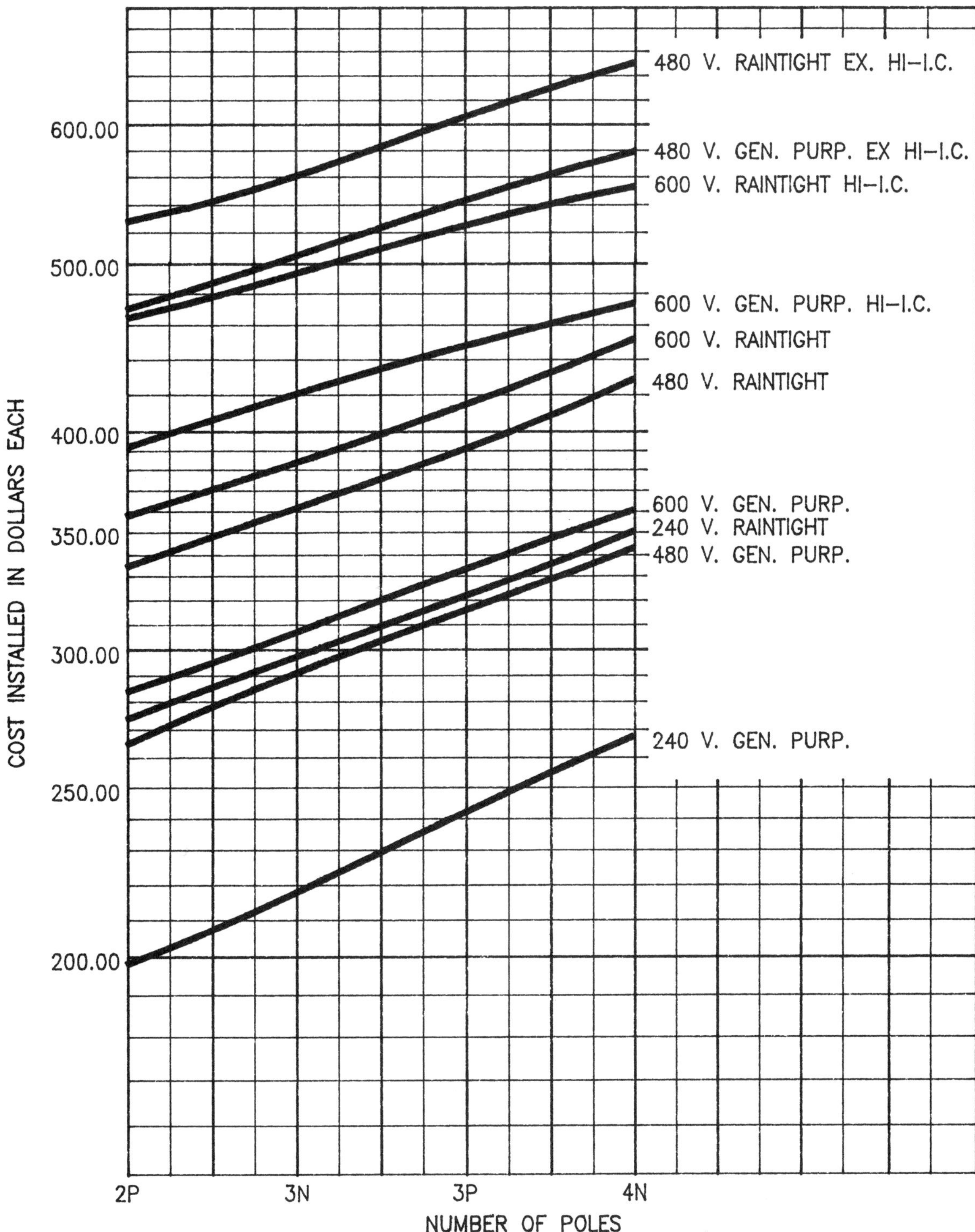

The costs shown for the enclosed circuit breakers in general-purpose and raintight enclosures consist of the published contractors' book prices, and also include materials for fastening to a masonry wall, a conduit terminal for the size required by the wire, and wire in the amount necessary for makeup. Raintight enclosures include a conduit hub of the proper size. Labor is provided for a complete installation.

2P = 2 wire—2 protected poles
3N = 3 wire—2 protected poles plus solid neutral
3P = 3 wire—3 protected poles
4N = 4 wire—3 protected poles plus solid neutral

COST OF INDIVIDUALLY ENCLOSED CIRCUIT BREAKERS

COST INSTALLED IN DOLLARS EACH

700.00
600.00
500.00
400.00
350.00
300.00

480 V. RAINTIGHT EX HI–I,C,
480 V. GEN. PURP. EX HI–I.C.
600 V. RAINTIGHT
600 V. GEN. PURP. HI–I.C.
600 V. RAINTIGHT
480 V. RAINTIGHT
600 V. GEN. PURP.
240 V. RAINTIGHT
480 V. GEN. PURP.
240 V. GEN. PURP.

2P 3N 3P 4N

NUMBER OF POLES

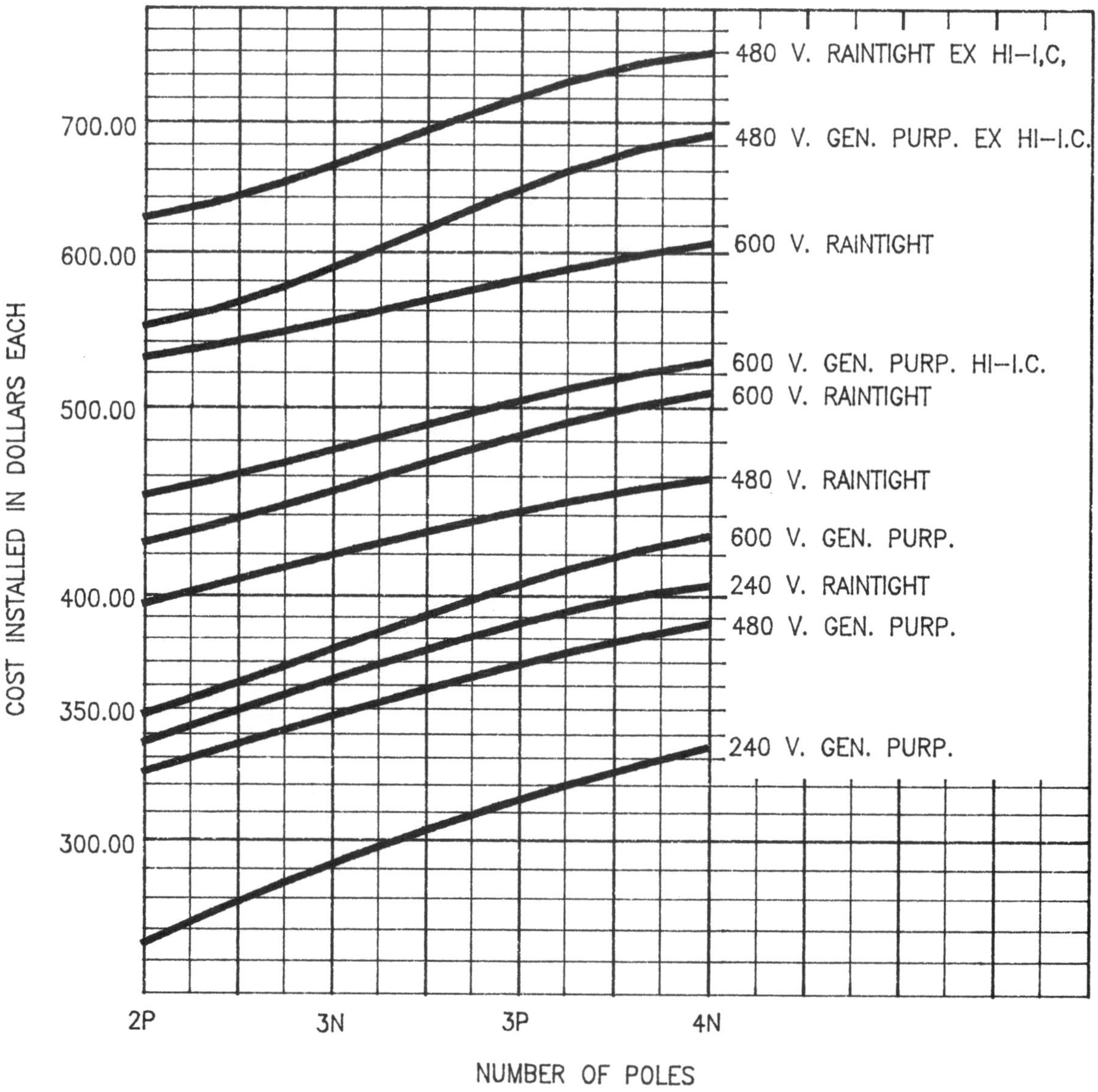

The costs shown for the enclosed circuit breakers in general-purpose and raintight enclosures consist of the published contractors' book prices, and also include materials for fastening to a masonry wall, a conduit terminal for the size required by the wire, and wire in the amount necessary for makeup. Raintight enclosures include a conduit hub of the proper size. Labor is provided for a complete installation.

2P = 2 wire—2 protected poles
3N = 3 wire—2 protected poles plus solid neutral
3P = 3 wire—3 protected poles
4N = 4 wire—3 protected poles plus solid neutral

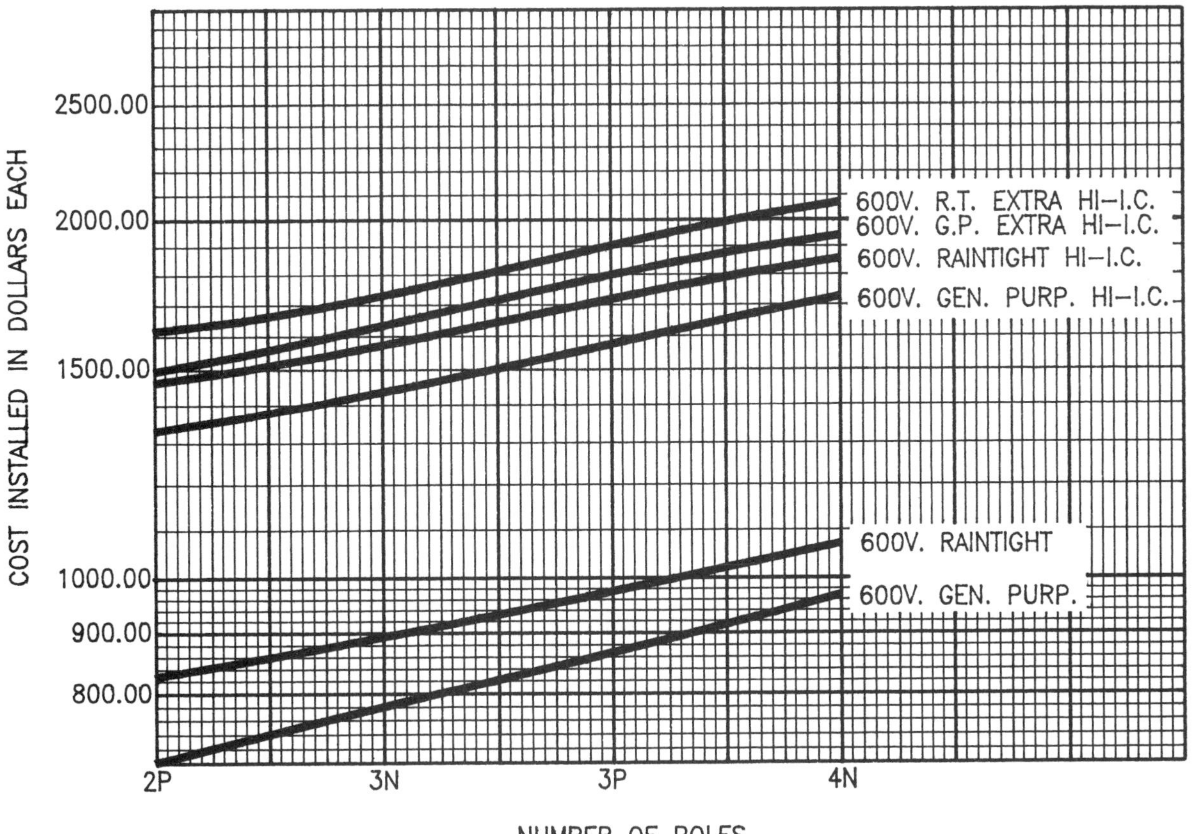

The costs shown for the enclosed circuit breakers in general-purpose and raintight enclosures consist of the published contractors' book prices, and also include materials for fastening to a masonry wall, a conduit terminal for the size required by the wire, and wire in the amount necessary for makeup. Raintight enclosures include a conduit hub of the proper size. Labor is provided for a complete installation.

2P = 2 wire—2 protected poles
3N = 3 wire—2 protected poles plus solid neutral
3P = 3 wire—3 protected poles
4N = 4 wire—3 protected poles plus solid neutral

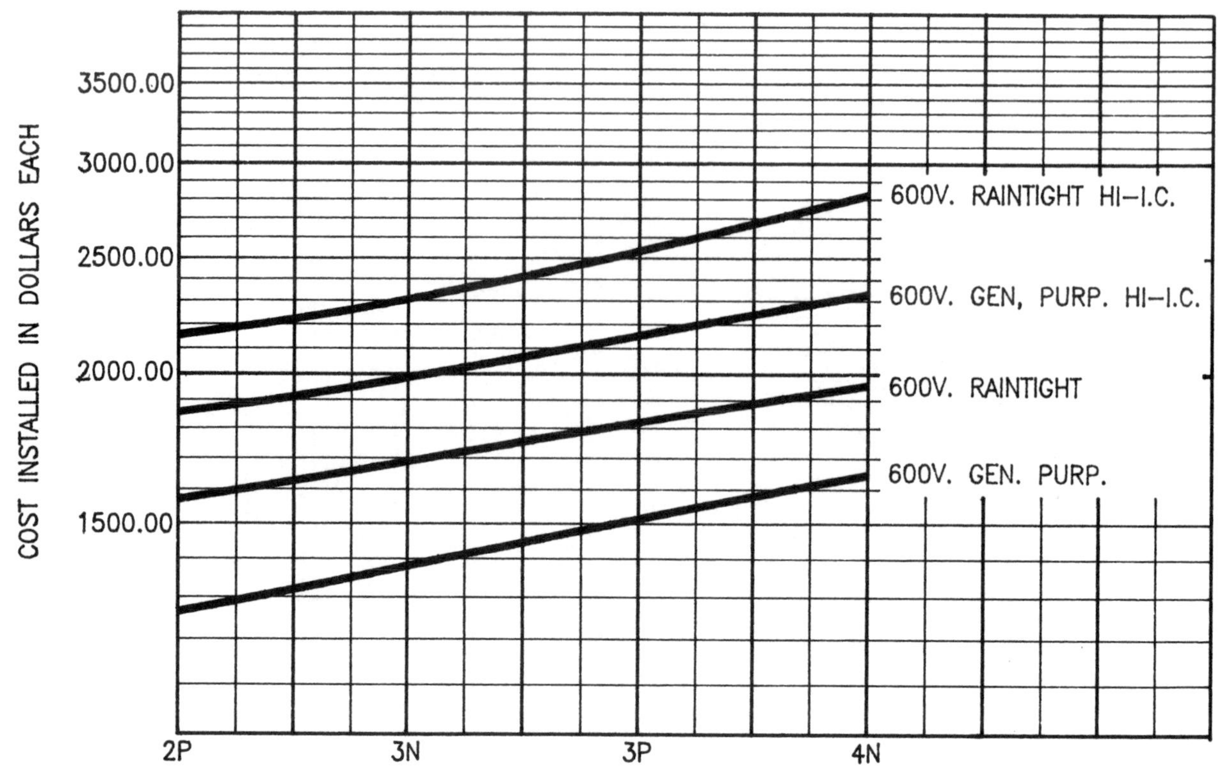

The costs shown for the enclosed circuit breakers in general-purpose and raintight enclosures consist of the published contractors' book prices, and also include materials for fastening to a masonry wall, a conduit terminal for the size required by the wire, and wire in the amount necessary for makeup. Raintight enclosures include a conduit hub of the proper size. Labor is provided for a complete installation.

2P = 2 wire—2 protected poles
3N = 3 wire—2 protected poles plus solid neutral
3P = 3 wire—3 protected poles
4N = 4 wire—3 protected poles plus solid neutral

COST OF SEPARATELY ENCLOSED CIRCUIT BREAKERS

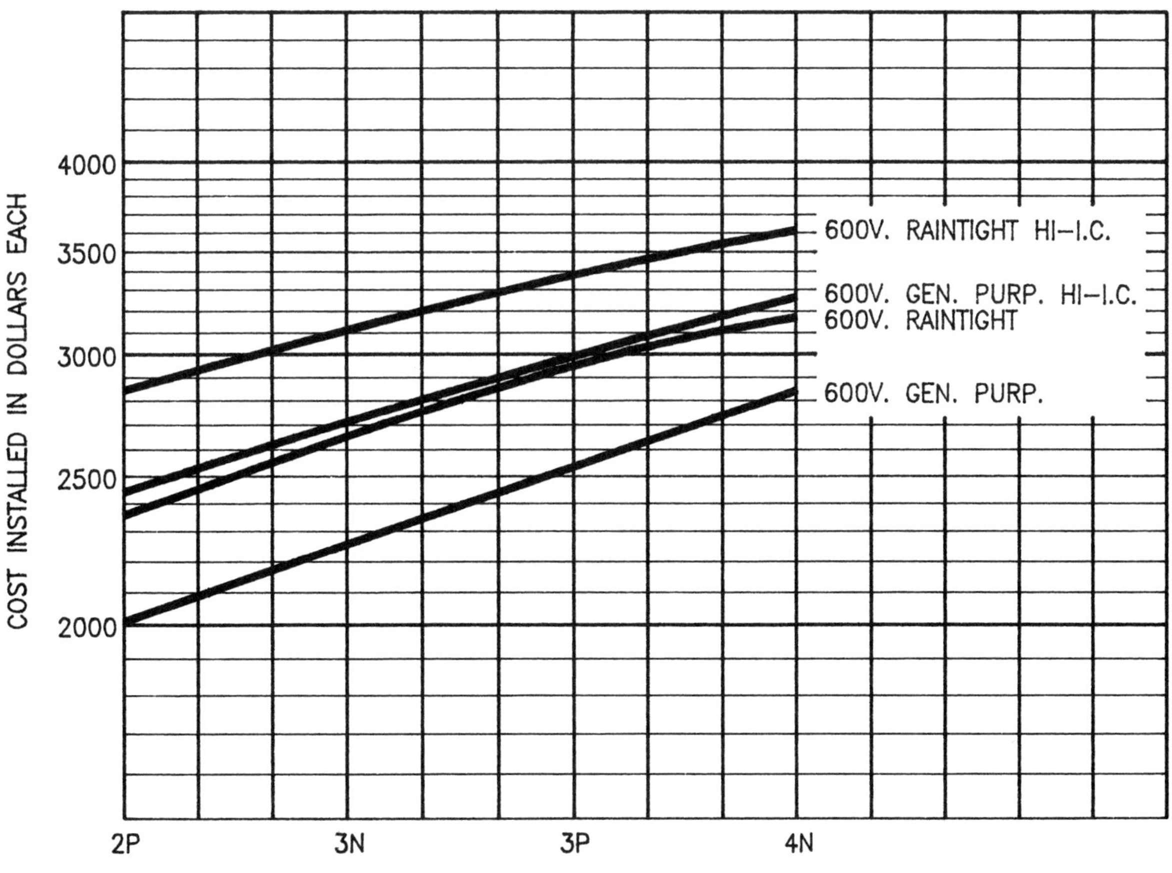

The costs shown for the enclosed circuit breakers in general-purpose and raintight enclosures consist of the published contractors' book prices, and also include materials for fastening to a masonry wall, a conduit terminal for the size required by the wire, and wire in the amount necessary for makeup. Raintight enclosures include a conduit hub of the proper size. Labor is provided for a complete installation.

2P = 2 wire—2 protected poles
3N = 3 wire—2 protected poles plus solid neutral
3P = 3 wire—3 protected poles
4N = 4 wire—3 protected poles plus solid neutral

COST OF INDIVIDUALLY ENCLOSED CIRCUIT BREAKERS

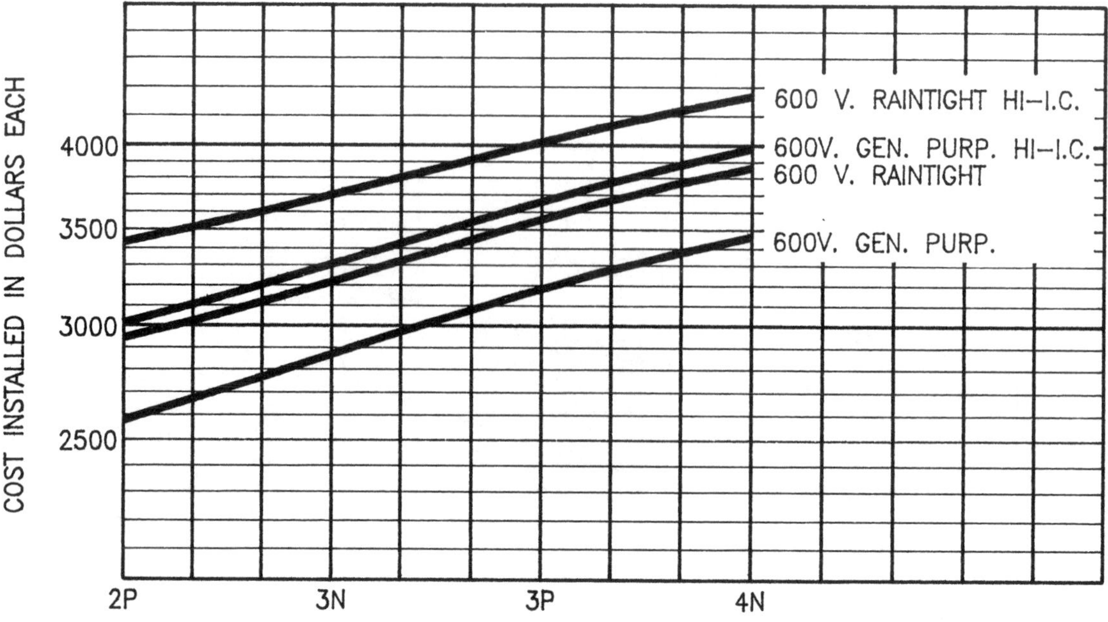

NUMBER OF POLES

The costs shown for the enclosed circuit breakers in general-purpose and raintight enclosures consist of the published contractors' book prices, and also include materials for fastening to a masonry wall, a conduit terminal for the size required by the wire, and wire in the amount necessary for makeup. Raintight enclosures include a conduit hub of the proper size. Labor is provided for a complete installation.

2P = 2 wire—2 protected poles
3N = 3 wire—2 protected poles plus solid neutral
3P = 3 wire—3 protected poles
4N = 4 wire—3 protected poles plus solid neutral

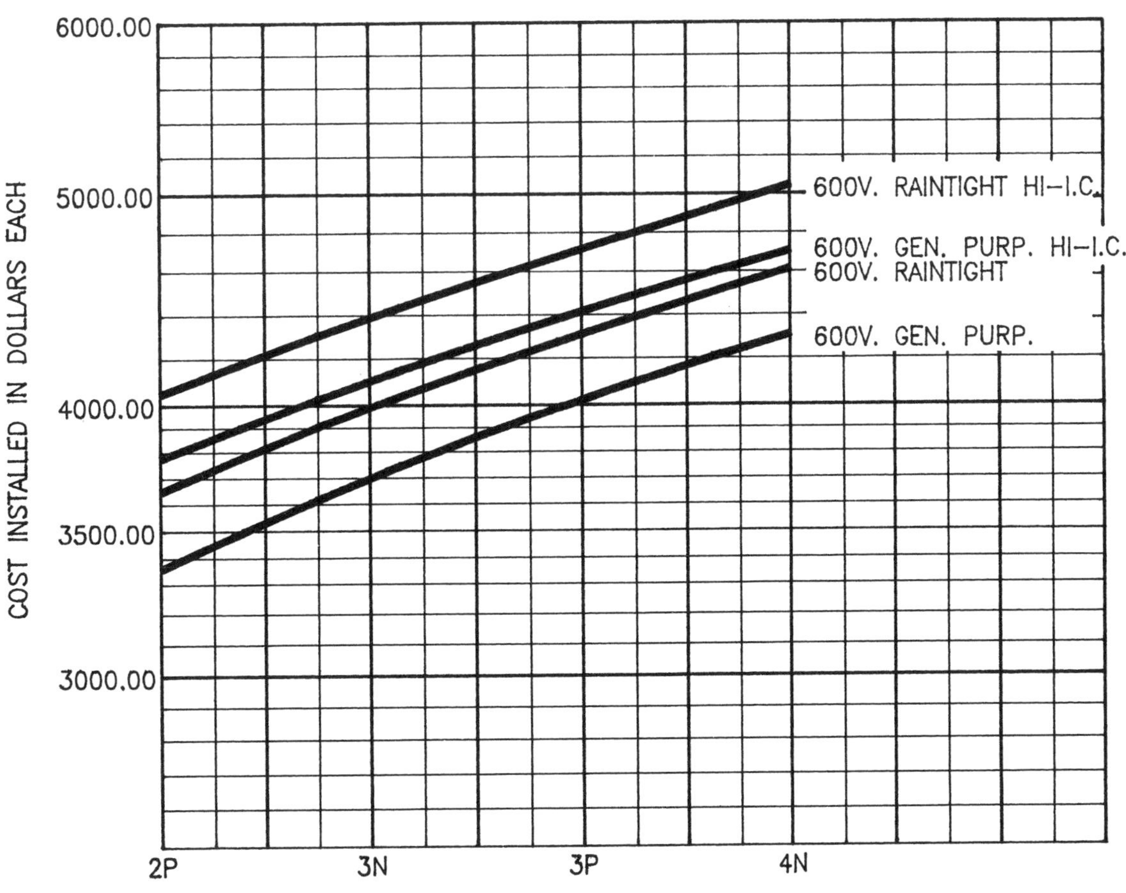

The costs shown for the enclosed circuit breakers in general-purpose and raintight enclosures consist of the published contractors' book prices, and also include materials for fastening to a masonry wall, a conduit terminal for the size required by the wire, and wire in the amount necessary for makeup. Raintight enclosures include a conduit hub of the proper size. Labor is provided for a complete installation.

2P = 2 wire—2 protected poles
3N = 3 wire—2 protected poles plus solid neutral
3P = 3 wire—3 protected poles
4N = 4 wire—3 protected poles plus solid neutral

B-28

COST OF INDIVIDUALLY ENCLOSED CIRCUIT BREAKERS

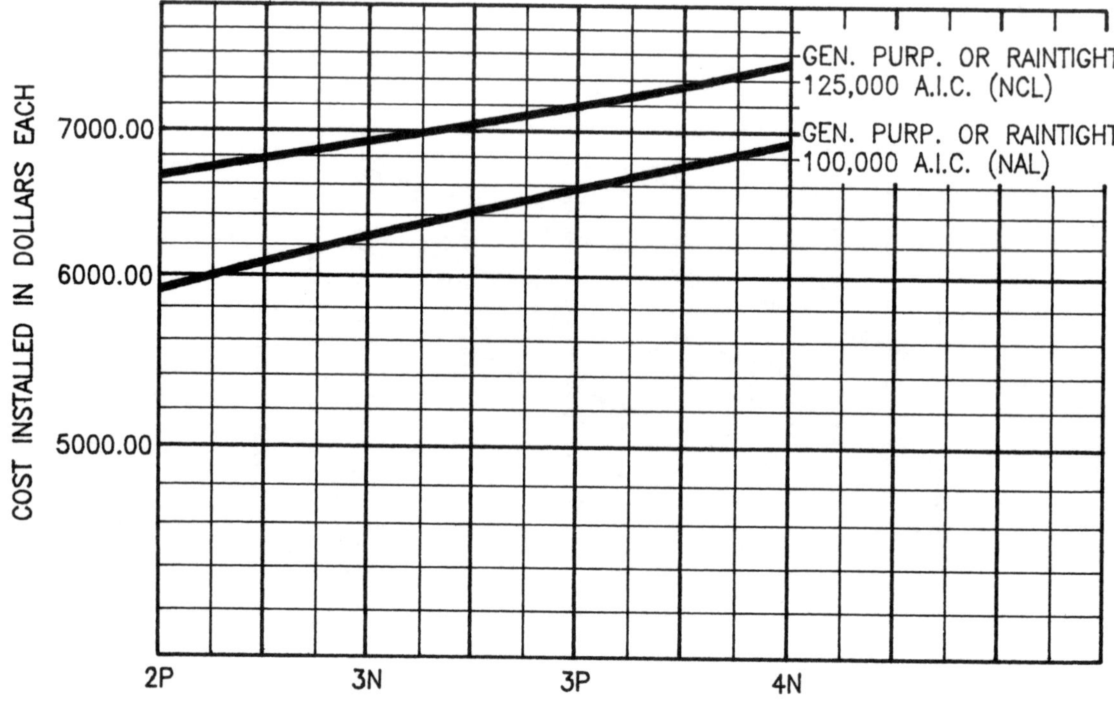

NUMBER OF POLES

The costs shown for the enclosed circuit breakers in general-purpose and raintight enclosures consist of the published contractors' book prices, and also include materials for fastening to a masonry wall, a conduit terminal for the size required by the wire, and wire in the amount necessary for makeup. Raintight enclosures include a conduit hub of the proper size. Labor is provided for a complete installation.

2P = 2 wire—2 protected poles
3N = 3 wire—2 protected poles plus solid neutral
3P = 3 wire—3 protected poles
4N = 4 wire—3 protected poles plus solid neutral

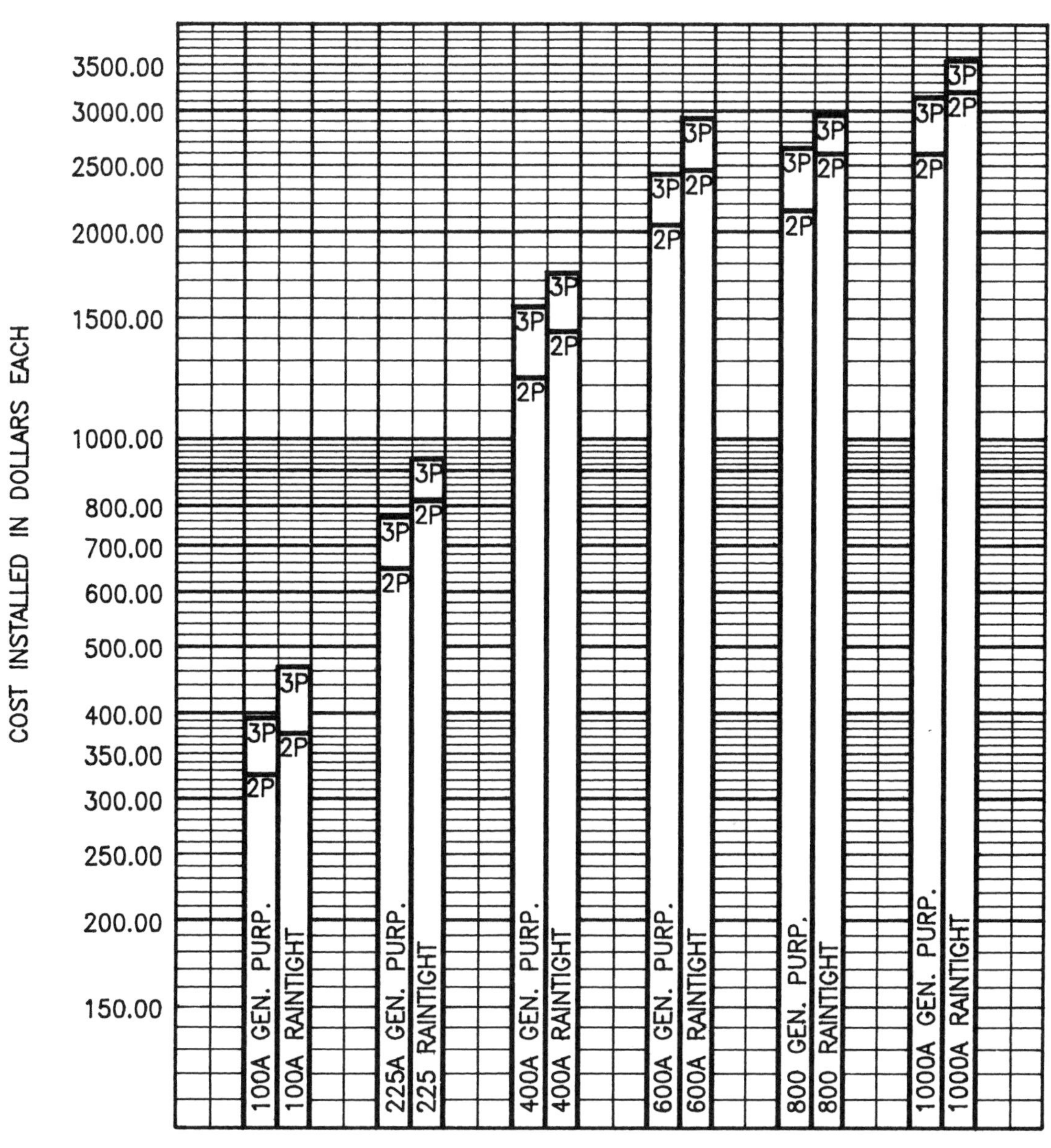

The costs shown for the enclosed molded-case switches in general-purpose and raintight enclosures consist of the published contractors' book prices, and also include material for fastening to a masonry wall, a conduit terminal of the size required by the wire, and wire in the amount necessary for makeup. Raintight enclosures include a conduit hub of the proper size. Labor is provided for a complete installation.

Services

C

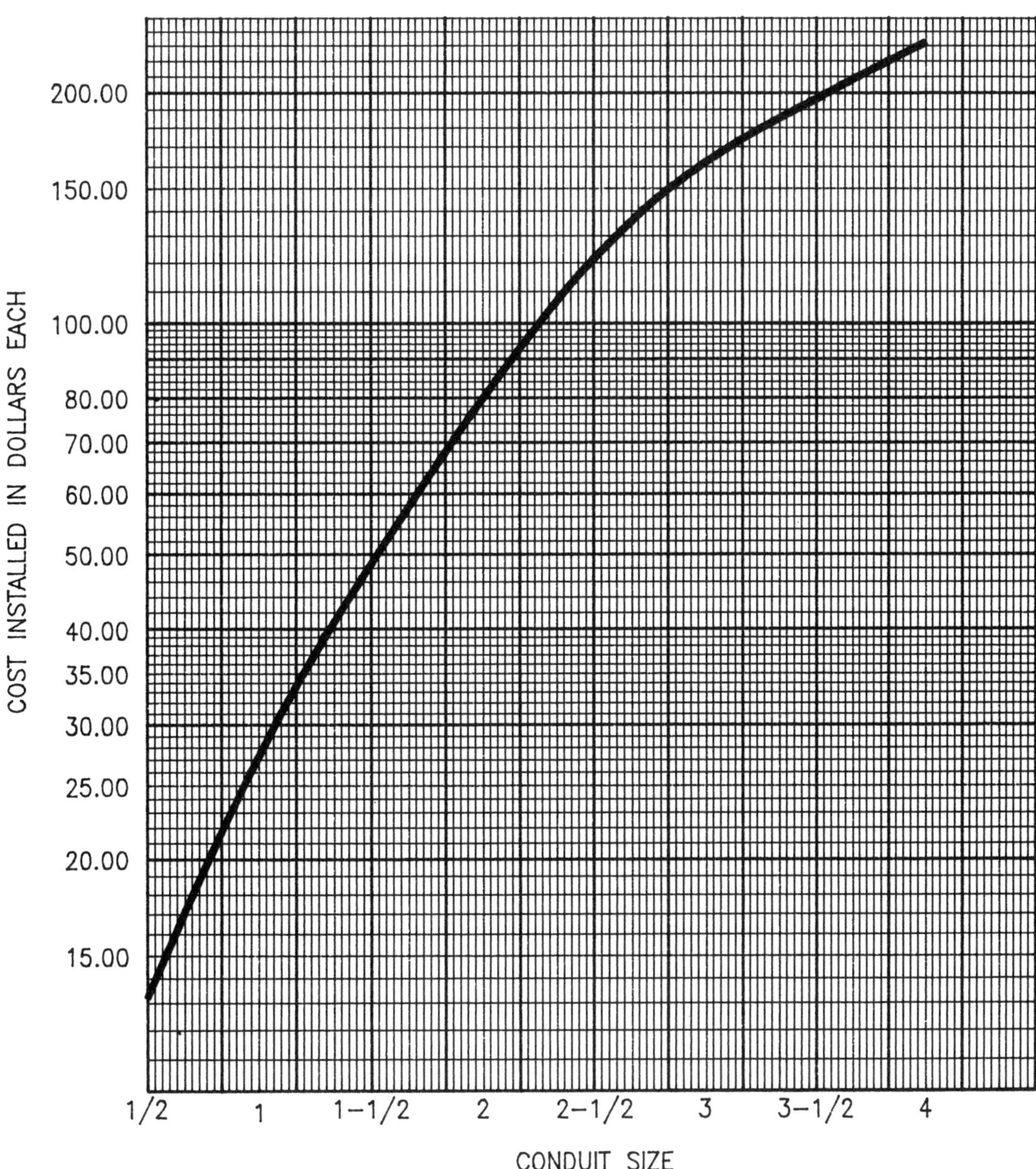

The costs shown for the service entrance weatherhead include the published contractors' book price and the labor for preparing the conduit for attaching. The overall installed cost for either EMT or GRC fittings is too insignificant to require separate curves.

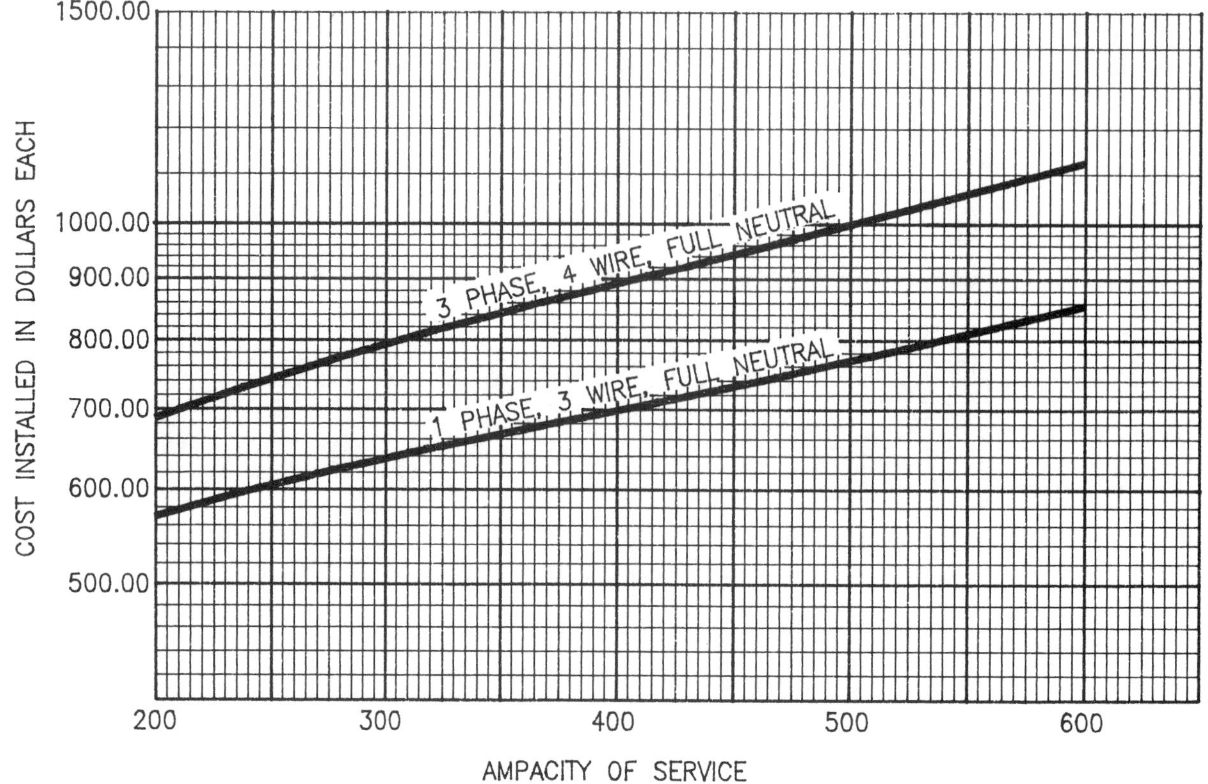

INDIVIDUAL METER SOCKETS	
TYPE OF SOCKET	INSTALLED COST
1 PH 100A SELF–CONT. RESIDENTIAL	$104.
1 PH 200A SELF–CONT. RESIDENTIAL	$114.
1 PH 200A SELF–CONT. COMMERCIAL	$187.
3 PH 200A SELF–CONT. COMMERCIAL	$216.
3 PH 20A INSTRUMENT RATED	$229.

The costs shown for the current transformer cabinets consist of the contractors' book price for a cabinet 30" x 24" x 9-1/2". Also included are a neutral bus, fastening devices for mounting to a masonry wall, and conductors of the number and size required. It is assumed that the transformers are furnished by the utility company and are installed by the contractor.

Labor is included for installing the cabinet and transformers, making up the conductor ends, connecting to the transformers, and cutting two holes in the cabinet for conduit terminals; however, the conduit terminals are not provided. See Section E for nipples and conduit terminals.

COST OF MULTI–METERING SERVICE DISCONNECT SWITCH

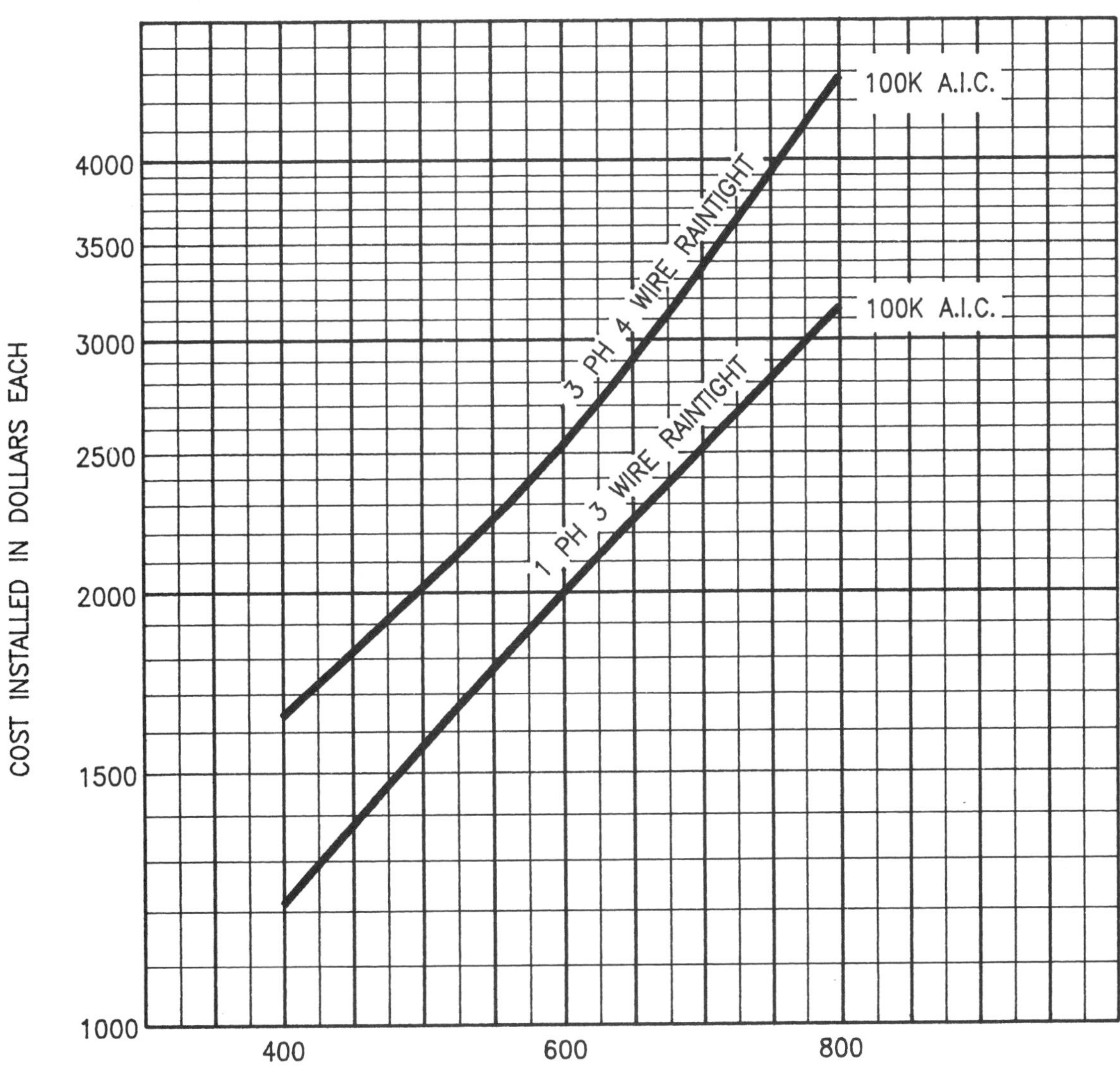

The costs shown for the main service disconnect for a multimetering center are based on the published contractors' book prices and are as manufactured by Square D Co. for outdoor installation. The main disconnect shown is a section containing a fused disconnect switch in single- or three-phase. The costs shown are representative of the total installed costs.

Included: (material and labor)

1. *Cabinet of the type required*
2. *Fuses*
3. *Fastening devices for surface mounting to a masonry wall*
4. *Conduit terminals of the size and proper number to suit the ampacity*
5. *Sufficient conductors of length and size to match ampacity and terminal makeup*

Excluded:

1. *Raintight hubs for service conduit, as an underground supply is assumed*

C-4

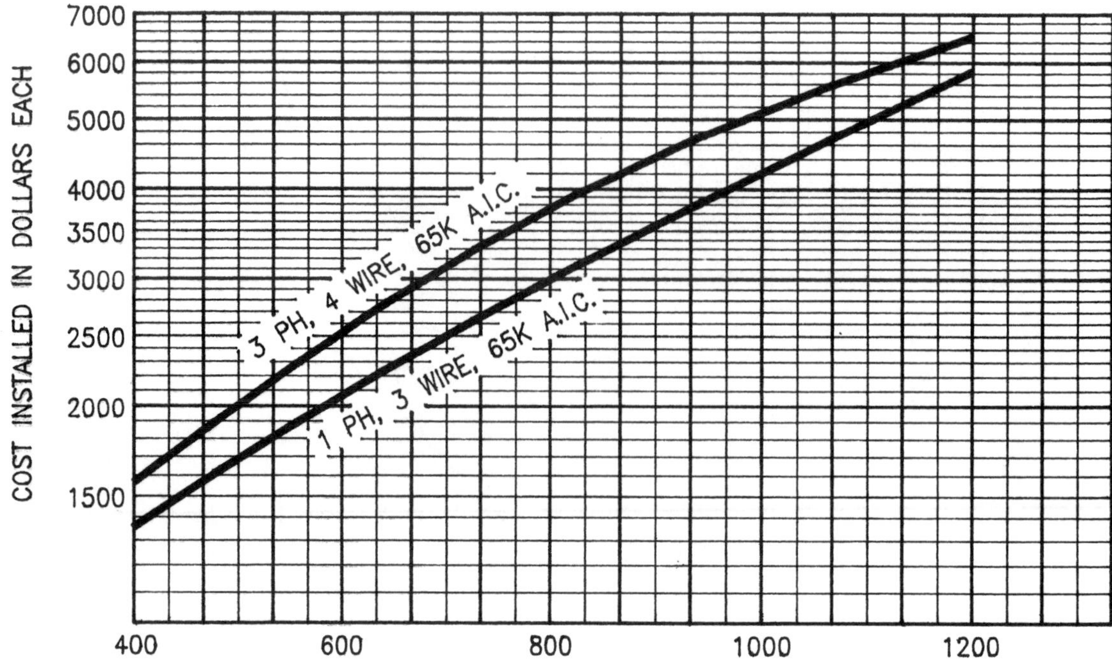

The costs shown for the main service disconnect for a multimetering center are based on the published contractors' book prices and are as manufactured by Square D Co. for outdoor installation. The main disconnect shown is a section containing a circuit breaker in single- or three-phase. The costs shown are representative of the total installed costs.

Included: (material and labor)

1. *Cabinet of the type required*
2. *Circuit breaker of the type required*
3. *Fastening devices for surface mounting to a masonry wall*
4. *Conduit terminals of the size and proper number to suit the ampacity*
5. *Sufficient conductors of length and size to match ampacity and terminal makeup*

Excluded:

1. *Raintight hubs for service conduit, as an underground supply is assumed*

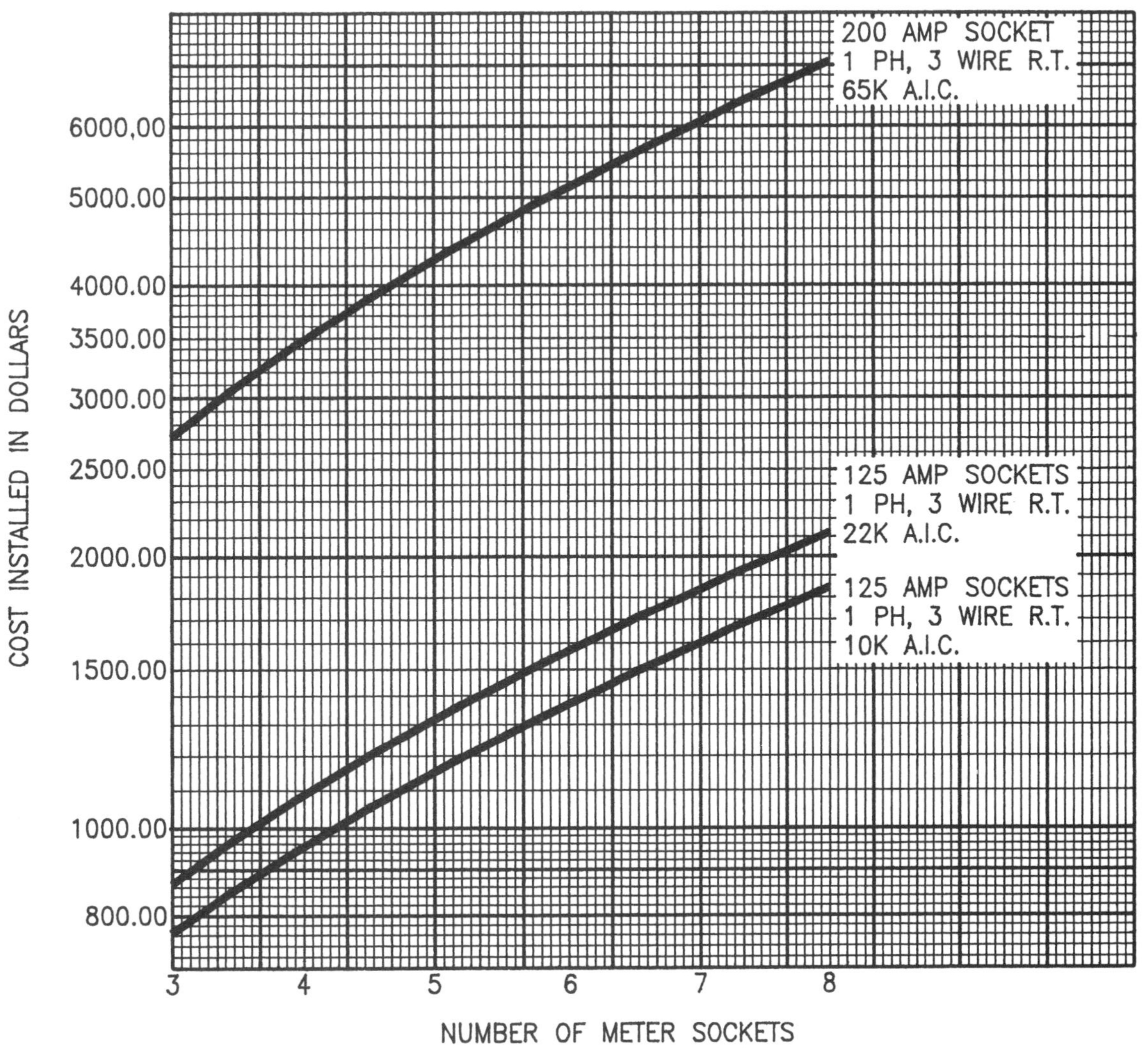

The costs shown for the wall-mounted meter center are based on the published contractors' book prices and are as manufactured by Square D Co. as an outdoor type of meter module.

These meter sockets are single-phase and shown in 125- and 200-ampere sizes, the larger usually used for electrically heated apartments. The total installed cost difference between indoor and raintight meter sockets is not significant enough to justify two curves.

Note: While the mains may be single- or three-phase, all services to individual occupancies are single-phase.

Included:

1. *Socket type of group and size required*
2. *Two-pole circuit breakers for each feeder*
3. *Fastening devices for securing to a masonry wall*
4. *GRC conduit terminals for each meter in the group*
5. *Sufficient conductors of length and size to match ampacity and terminal makeup for each feeder*

Excluded:

1. *Raintight hubs, as underground feeders are assumed*

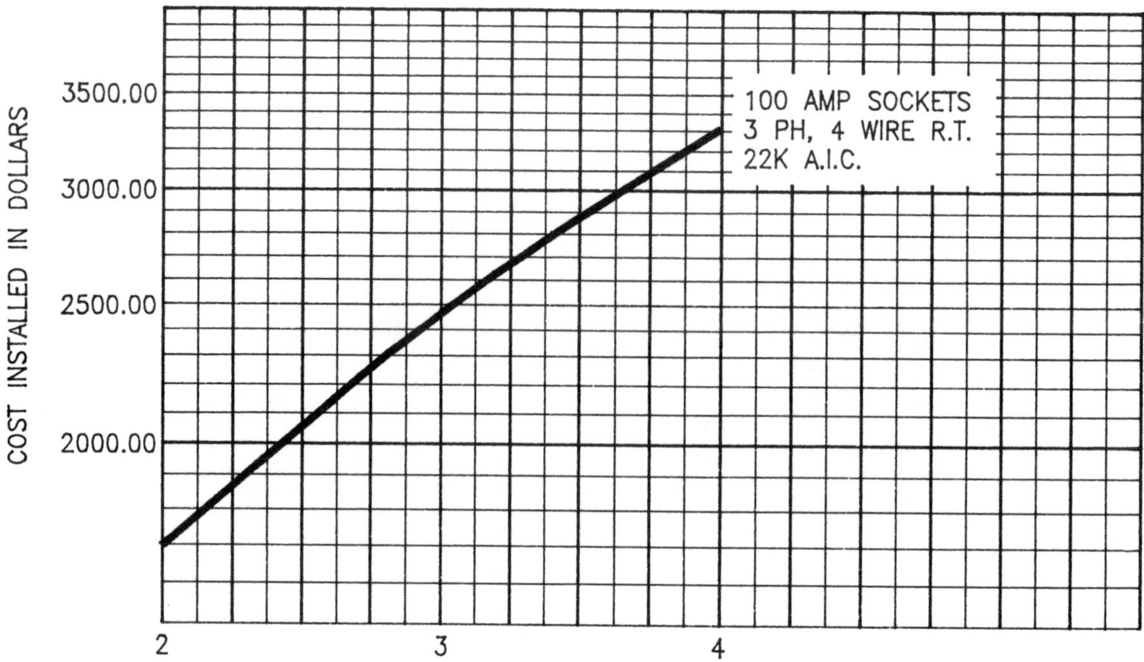

The costs shown for the wall-mounted meter center are based on the published contractors' book prices and are as manufactured by Square D Co. as an outdoor type of module.

These meter sockets are three-phase and shown in 100-ampere size. The difference in cost between indoor and outdoor meter sockets is insignificant.

Included: (material and labor)

1. *Three-pole circuit breaker for each feeder*
2. *Fastening devices for mounting to a masonry wall*
3. *GRC conduit terminals for each meter in the group*
4. *Sufficient conductors of length and size to match ampacity and terminal makeup for each feeder*

COST OF SCREW–COVERED WIREWAY

COST INSTALLED IN DOLLARS EACH

400.00
350.00
300.00
250.00
200.00
150.00
100.00
80.00
70.00
60.00
50.00
40.00
35.00

12" X 12"
8" X 8"
6" X 6"
4" X 4"
2–1/2" X 2–1/2"

1 2 3 4 5 6 7 8 9 10

LENGTH OF WIREWAY IN FEET

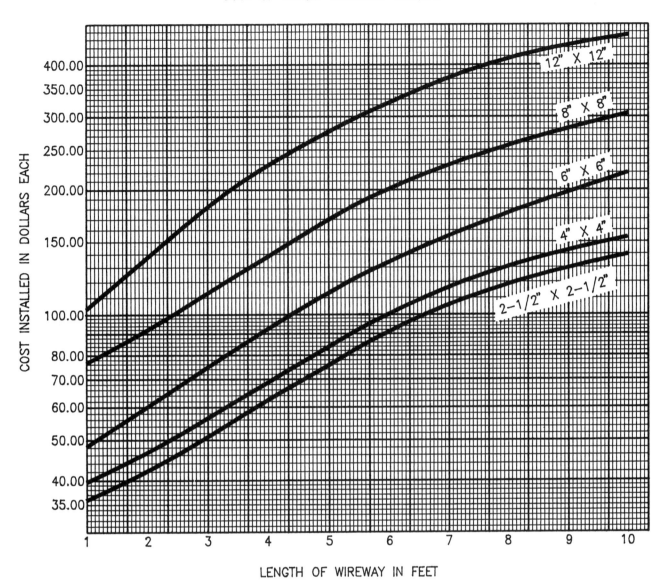

The costs shown for the screw- or hinged-cover wireways consist of the published contractors' book price, fastening devices for mounting on a masonry wall, and the labor required for such installation. The items shown on the graph are manufactured by Hoffman Engineering Co. and contain the necessary couplings and end fittings as required.

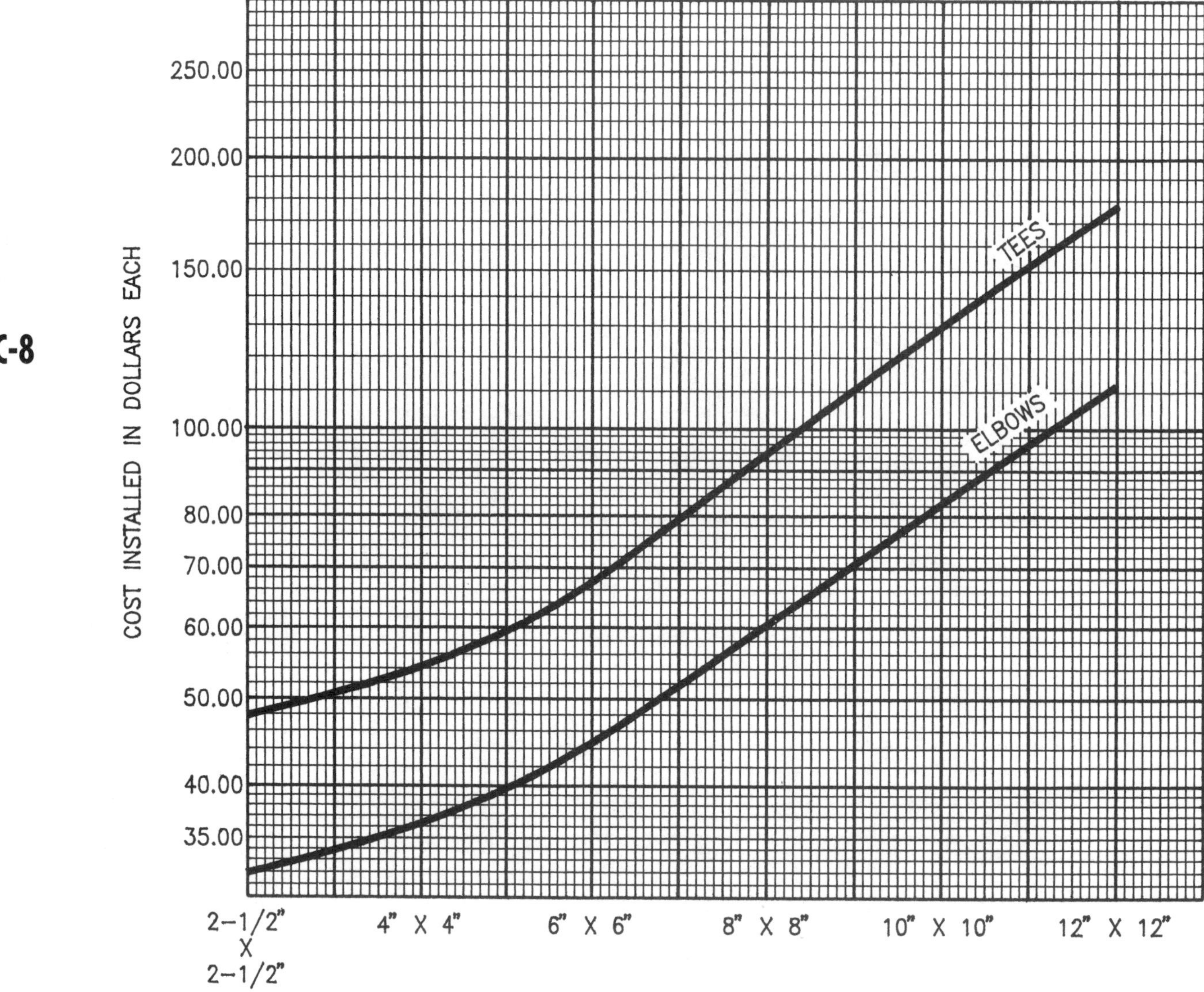

The costs shown for the tees and elbows for the wireway consist of the published contractors' book prices, fastening devices for mounting on a masonry wall, required couplings, and the labor for the installation. The items show are as manufactured by Hoffman Engineering Co.

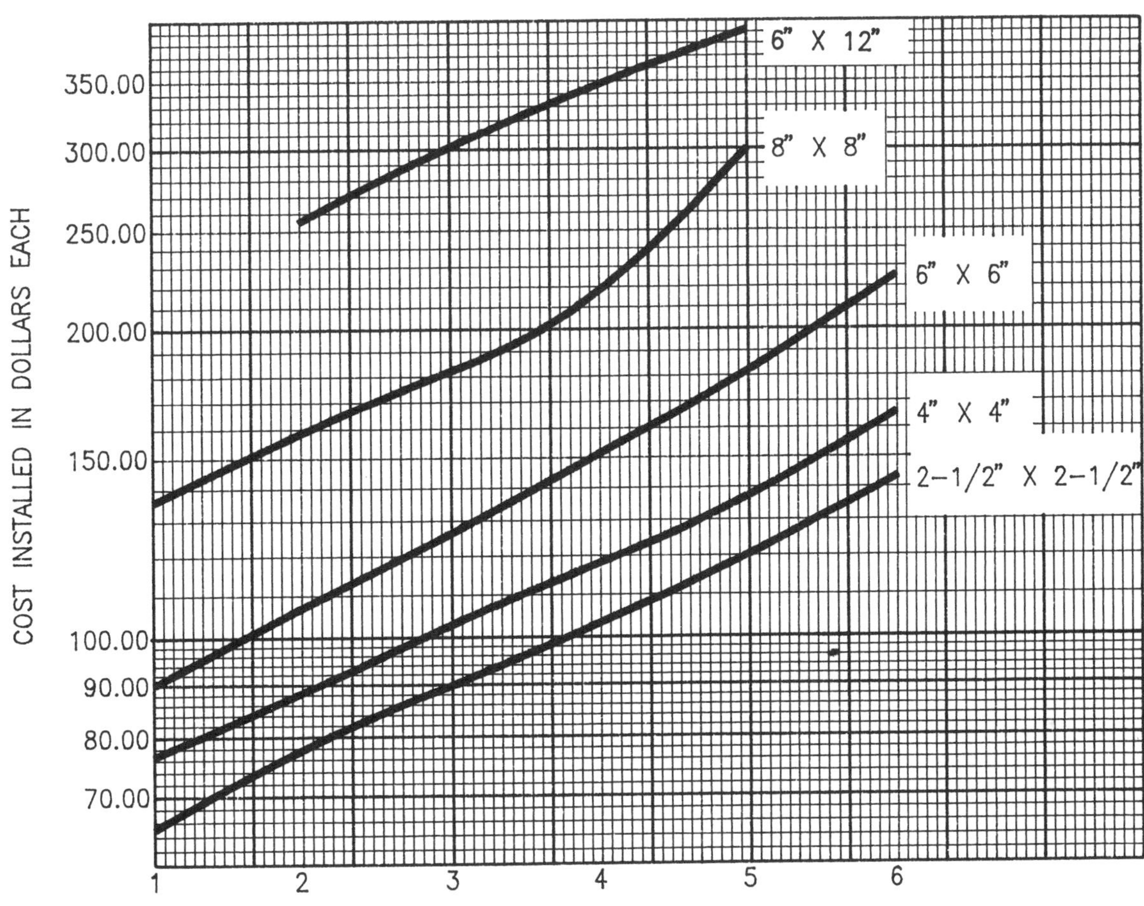

The costs shown for the raintight and oiltight wireway consist of the published contractors' book price, fastening devices for mounting on a masonry wall, and the labor required for such installation. The items shown are the standard sizes as manufactured by Hoffman Engineering Co. No fittings are available in this series. Covers are gasketed, and there are no conduit knockouts.

Grounding

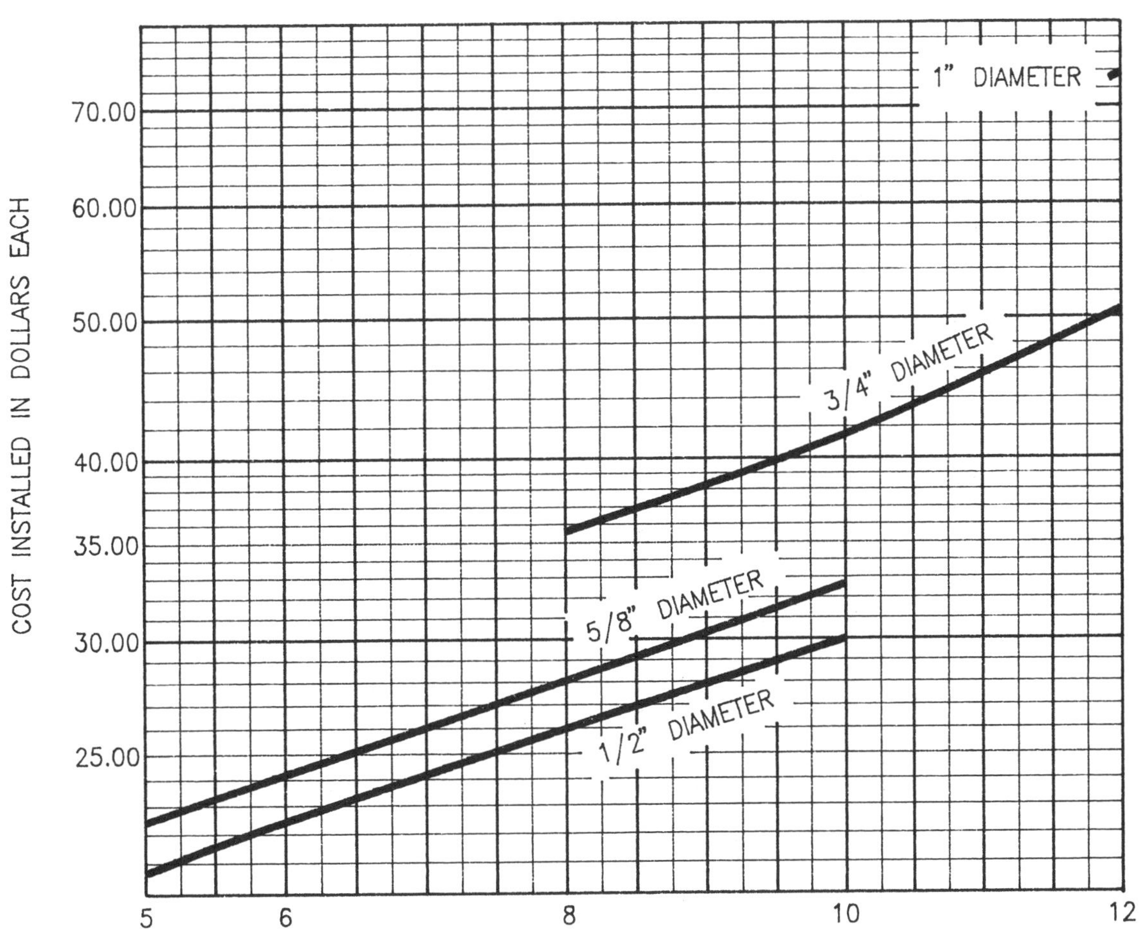

D

D-1

The costs shown for the copperclad ground rods are the contractors' published book prices for the rods as manufactured by Blackburn.

Included: (material and labor)

1. *Driving the rod to 6" below the surface in normal soils*
2. *Ground rod clamp for #8 to #1/0 wire*

D-2

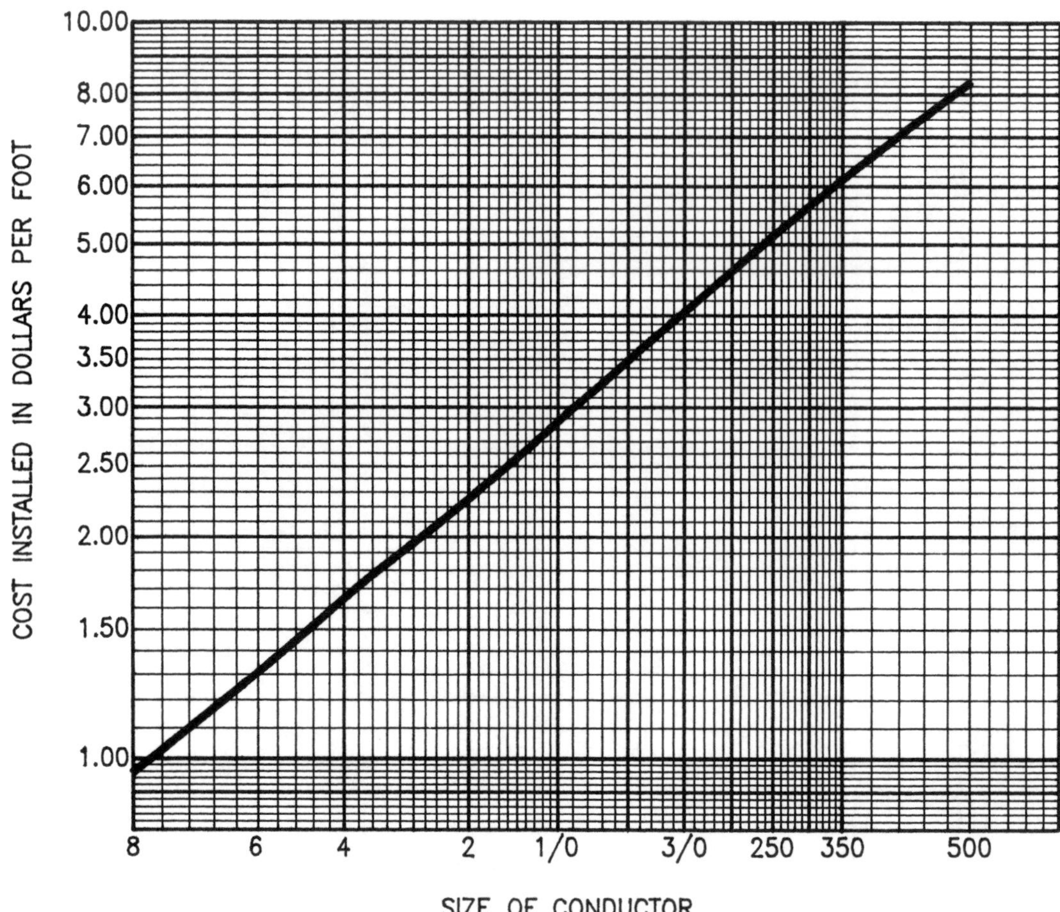

The costs shown for the bare copper wire consist of the published contractors' book prices for the sizes shown. The installation labor is based on a single conductor drawn in conduit; the figures will be close enough for most purposes.

COST OF GROUND CLAMPS	
SIZE OF WATER PIPE	COST INSTALLED
1/2", 3/4", AND 1"	$23.50
1–1/4", 1–1/2", AND 2"	31.25
2–1/2", 3", 3–1/2", AND 4"	47.75

The costs shown for the ground clamps are based upon T&B bronze clamps and the labor to attach to the pipe size shown and connect the ground wire.

GROUNDING CONDUCTOR – BARE SOFT DRAWN COPPER

FORM OF CONNECTION	INSTALLED COST EACH
SS Splice/Horizontal	$52.00
TA Tee/Horizontal	54.00
PT Parallel thru/Horizontal —Over and under	53.00
XA X/Horizontal— Same plane	54.00
GR Ell/Horizontal cable to vertical down rod— Right angle	44.00
GT Tee/Horizontal cable, Vertical rod	45.00

The cost of the welded connections shown includes the published contractors' book price for the weld metal required, one-fiftieth of the cost of the mold (a mold lasts for about 50 shots), and the labor of preparation. The prices shown are the average for copper wire sizes from #6 through #4/0.

D-4

FORM OF CONNECTION	INSTALLED COST EACH
① **HA** Tap/Horizontal — To steel, on surface ① **HB** Tap/Horizontal — To cast iron	$53.00
① **VF** Tap/Vertical — To steel, cable up and on surface ① **VK** Tap/Vertical — To cast iron, cable up	54.00
VS Tap/Vertical — Down at 45° to steel	$53.00
① **VN** Tap/Horizontal — To steel, on surface. Specify right or left hand. Right hand shown. ① **VR** Tap/Horizontal — To cast iron. Specify right or left hand. Right hand shown.	$53.00

The cost of the welded connections shown includes the published contractors' book price for the weld metal required, one-fiftieth of the cost of the mold (a mold lasts for about 50 shots), and the labor of preparation. The prices shown are the average for copper wire sizes from #6 through #4/0.

The installation of a lightning protection system which will provide the caliber of protection an owner rightfully expects involves knowledge not generally possessed by the usual electrical contractor. It is desirable, therefore, that both the designer and the contractor become acquainted with some of the system's installation peculiarities.

The referenced information can largely be found in the 1989 Edition of the Lightning Protection Code, ANSI/NFPA 78, which is procurable from the National Fire Protection Association at Batterymarch Park, Quincy, Mass. 02269.

D-5

CLASS I			CLASS II		
AN ORDINARY BUILDING IS ONE OF COMMON OR CONVENTIONAL DESIGN AND CONSTRUCTION USED FOR ORDINARY PURPOSES, WHETHER COMMERCIAL, FARM, INSTITUTIONAL, INDUSTRIAL. A CLASS I ORDINARY BUILDING IS ONE WHICH IS LESS THAN 75 FEET IN HEIGHT.			A CLASS II ORDINARY BUILDING IS ONE MORE THAN 75 FEET IN HEIGHT. THE DISTINCTION IN TERMS OF LIGHTNING PROTECTION IS THAT AIR TERMINALS, CONDUCTORS, AND GROUND RODS OF CLASS II STRUCTURES ARE OF LARGER DIMENSIONS AND HIGHER CONDUCTANCE THAN MINIMUM ALLOWANCES FOR CLASS I BUILDINGS.		
DESCRIPTION	COST INSTALLED IN DOLLARS PER FOOT		DESCRIPTION	COST INSTALLED IN DOLLARS PER FOOT	
	COPPER	ALUMINUM		COPPER	ALUMINUM
MAIN CONDUCTOR EXPOSED ON WOOD Cu: 65,600 Cm min Al: 115,000 Cm min.	3.00	2.43	MAIN CONDUCTOR EXPOSED ON WOOD Cu: 122,000 Cm min Al: 211,600 Cm min	4.40	3.55
MAIN CONDUCTOR Exposed on masonry	4.20	3.65	MAIN CONDUCTOR Exposed on masonry	4.75	4.40
MAIN CONDUCTOR Adhesive cable holder	3.20	1.40	MAIN CONDUCTOR Adhesive cable holder	4.55	3.70
MAIN CONDUCTOR In free air	2.05	1.50	MAIN CONDUCTOR In free air	3.15	2.35
SECONDARY CONDUCTOR Cu: 28,500 Cm min Al: 43,000 Cm min with 6' cbl, clamp and terminal	2.90	2.05	SECONDARY CONDUCTOR Cu: 28,500 Cm min Al: 43,000 Cm min with 6' cbl, clamp and terminal	3.40	2.45

CLASS I		
AN ORDINARY BUILDING IS ONE OF COMMON OR CONVENTIONAL DESIGN AND CONSTRUCTION USED FOR ORDINARY PURPOSES, WHETHER COMMERCIAL, FARM, INSTITUTIONAL, INDUSTRIAL. A CLASS I ORDINARY BUILDING IS ONE WHICH IS LESS THAN 75 FEET IN HEIGHT.		
DESCRIPTION	COST INSTALLED IN DOLLARS PER FOOT	
	COPPER	ALUMINUM
AIR TERMINAL Surface Mtd 	$54.50	$52.25
AIR TERMINAL Concealed base 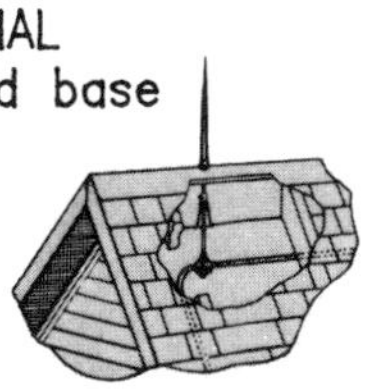	$80.50	$81.00
AIR TERMINAL Adhesive base 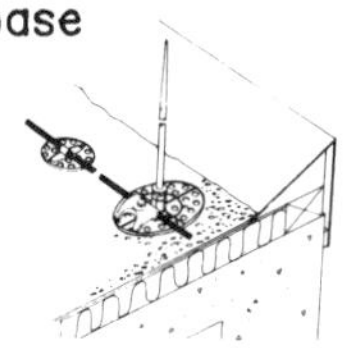	$58.50	$53.25
AIR TERMINAL Parapet base 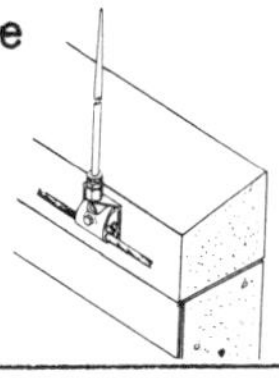	$55.50	$58.00
AIR TERMINAL Chimney type 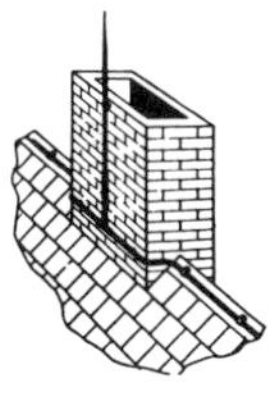	$75.00	$78.50

CLASS II		
A CLASS II ORDINARY BUILDING IS ONE MORE THAN 75 FEET IN HEIGHT. THE DISTINCTION IN TERMS OF LIGHTNING PROTECTION IS THAT AIR TERMINALS, CONDUCTORS, AND GROUND RODS OF CLASS II STRUCTURES ARE OF LARGER DIMENSIONS AND HIGHER CONDUCTANCE THAN MINIMUM ALLOWANCES FOR CLASS I BUILDINGS.		
DESCRIPTION	COST INSTALLED IN DOLLARS PER FOOT	
	COPPER	ALUMINUM
AIR TERMINAL Surface Mtd 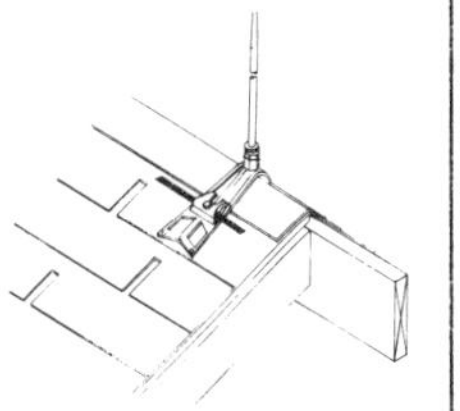	$86.79	$76.50
AIR TERMINAL Concealed base 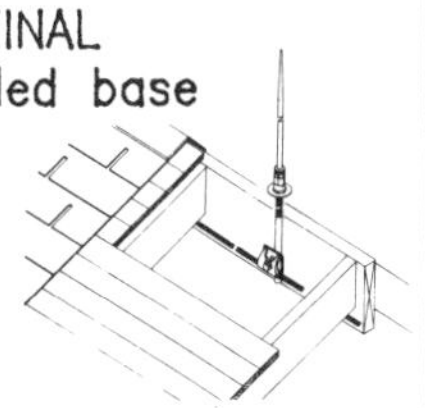	$98.19	$94.00
AIR TERMINAL Adhesive base 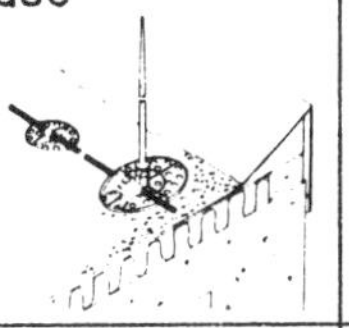	$89.50	$60.75
AIR TERMINAL Parapet base 	$109.50	$73.00
AIR TERMINAL Chimney type 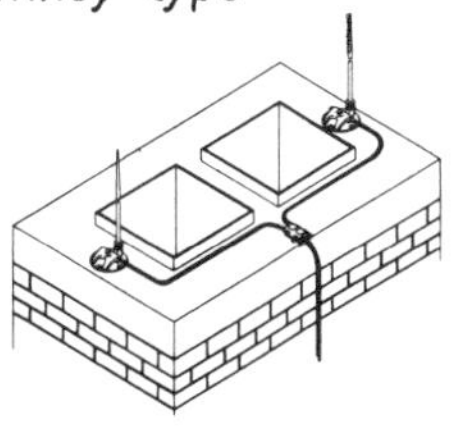	$105.50	$77.50

D-7

CLASS I		
AN ORDINARY BUILDING IS ONE OF COMMON OR CONVENTIONAL DESIGN AND CONSTRUCTION USED FOR ORDINARY PURPOSES, WHETHER COMMERCIAL, FARM, INSTITUTIONAL, INDUSTRIAL. A CLASS I ORDINARY BUILDING IS ONE WHICH IS LESS THAN 75 FEET IN HEIGHT.		
DESCRIPTION	COST INSTALLED IN DOLLARS EACH	
	COPPER	ALUMINUM
BUS TERMINAL	25.40	25.00
METAL BONDING PLATE	24.00	22.45
SILL COCK	29.80	29.20
THRU ROOF OR WALL	71.40	69.20
EAVE TROUGH	26.25	26.00

CLASS II		
A CLASS II ORDINARY BUILDING IS ONE MORE THAN 75 FEET IN HEIGHT. THE DISTINCTION IN TERMS OF LIGHTNING PROTECTION IS THAT AIR TERMINALS, CONDUCTORS, AND GROUND RODS OF CLASS II STRUCTURES ARE OF LARGER DIMENSIONS AND HIGHER CONDUCTANCE THAN MINIMUM ALLOWANCES FOR CLASS I BUILDINGS.		
DESCRIPTION	COST INSTALLED IN DOLLARS EACH	
	COPPER	ALUMINUM
BUS TERMINAL	30.80	27.65
METAL BONDING PLATE	37.65	35.05
BONDING PLATE TO STRUCTURAL STEEL	48.60	44.10
THRU ROOF OR WALL	74.70	71.20
N.A.		

CLASS I		
AN ORDINARY BUILDING IS ONE OF COMMON OR CONVENTIONAL DESIGN AND CONSTRUCTION USED FOR ORDINARY PURPOSES, WHETHER COMMERCIAL, FARM, INSTITUTIONAL, INDUSTRIAL. A CLASS I ORDINARY BUILDING IS ONE WHICH IS LESS THAN 75 FEET IN HEIGHT.		
DESCRIPTION	COST INSTALLED IN DOLLARS EACH	
	COPPER	ALUMINUM
CABLE TO I BEAM 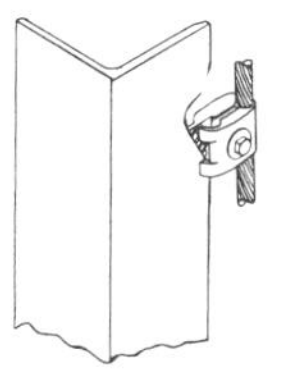	25.75	23.70
PIPE STRAP 	34.20	33.00
COPPER TO ALUMINUM CABLE 	26.75	26.75

CLASS II		
A CLASS II ORDINARY BUILDING IS ONE MORE THAN 75 FEET IN HEIGHT. THE DISTINCTION IN TERMS OF LIGHTNING PROTECTION IS THAT AIR TERMINALS, CONDUCTORS, AND GROUND RODS OF CLASS II STRUCTURES ARE OF LARGER DIMENSIONS AND HIGHER CONDUCTANCE THAN MINIMUM ALLOWANCES FOR CLASS I BUILDINGS.		
DESCRIPTION	COST INSTALLED IN DOLLARS EACH	
	COPPER	ALUMINUM
CABLE TO I BEAM 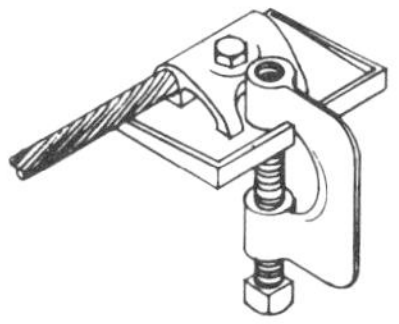	25.75	23.75
PIPE STRAP 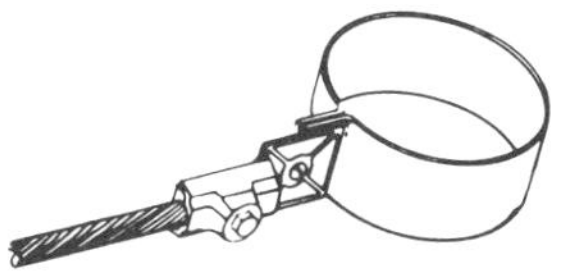	27.65	26.45
COPPER TO ALUMINUM CABLE 	37.90	37.90
GROUNDING DISCONNECT 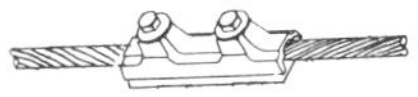	44.30	40.90

D-9

COST OF LIGHTNING PROTECTION SPLICES AND GROUNDING CONNECTIONS

CLASS I

AN ORDINARY BUILDING IS ONE OF COMMON OR CONVENTIONAL DESIGN AND CONSTRUCTION USED FOR ORDINARY PURPOSES, WHETHER COMMERCIAL, FARM, INSTITUTIONAL, INDUSTRIAL. A CLASS I ORDINARY BUILDING IS ONE WHICH IS LESS THAN 75 FEET IN HEIGHT.

DESCRIPTION	COST INSTALLED IN DOLLARS EACH	
	COPPER	ALUMINUM
STRAIGHT SPLICER	5.60	4.75
PARALLEL SPLICER	21.45	7.80
TEE SPLICER	7.50	6.70
GROUND ROD & CLAMP 1/2" X 10'	61.85	----
WATER PIPE CLAMP	30.50	28.00

CLASS II

A CLASS II ORDINARY BUILDING IS ONE MORE THAN 75 FEET IN HEIGHT. THE DISTINCTION IN TERMS OF LIGHTNING PROTECTION IS THAT AIR TERMINALS, CONDUCTORS, AND GROUND RODS OF CLASS II STRUCTURES ARE OF LARGER DIMENSIONS AND HIGHER CONDUCTANCE THAN MINIMUM ALLOWANCES FOR CLASS I BUILDINGS.

DESCRIPTION	COST INSTALLED IN DOLLARS EACH	
	COPPER	ALUMINUM
STRAIGHT SPLICER	17.52	16.75
PARALLEL SPLICER	12.70	10.95
TEE SPLICER	20.10	17.85
GROUND ROD & CLAMP 5/8" X 10'	64.90	----
WATER PIPE CLAMP	39.20	37.35

COST OF LIGHTNING PROTECTION GROUND PLATES AND ARRESTERS

DESCRIPTION	COST INSTALLED IN DOLLARS EACH
GROUND PLATES For areas where rods are impossible to drive due to rocky conditions FLAT PLATES	115.00
ELECTRIC SERVICE LIGHTNING ARRESTERS Single phase, 3 wire 120/240 volt	84.00
Three phase, 4 wire 120/208 volt	137.25
TELEVISION ANTENNA ARRESTER TV ANTENNA PROTECTION 1: APPROVED CLAMP WITH 1½" CONTINUOUS CONTACT WITH MAST AND FULL SIZE CABLE. 2: LEAD IN ARRESTER.	42.00

Feeders

E

CONDUITS

CONDUIT FITTINGS

CONDUCTORS

CONDUCTOR TERMINALS AND TAPS

FEEDER BUSWAY

PLUG-IN BUSWAY

DUCT BANKS

CABLE TRAYS—LADDER TYPE—4" DEEP

COST OF FEEDER CONDUIT

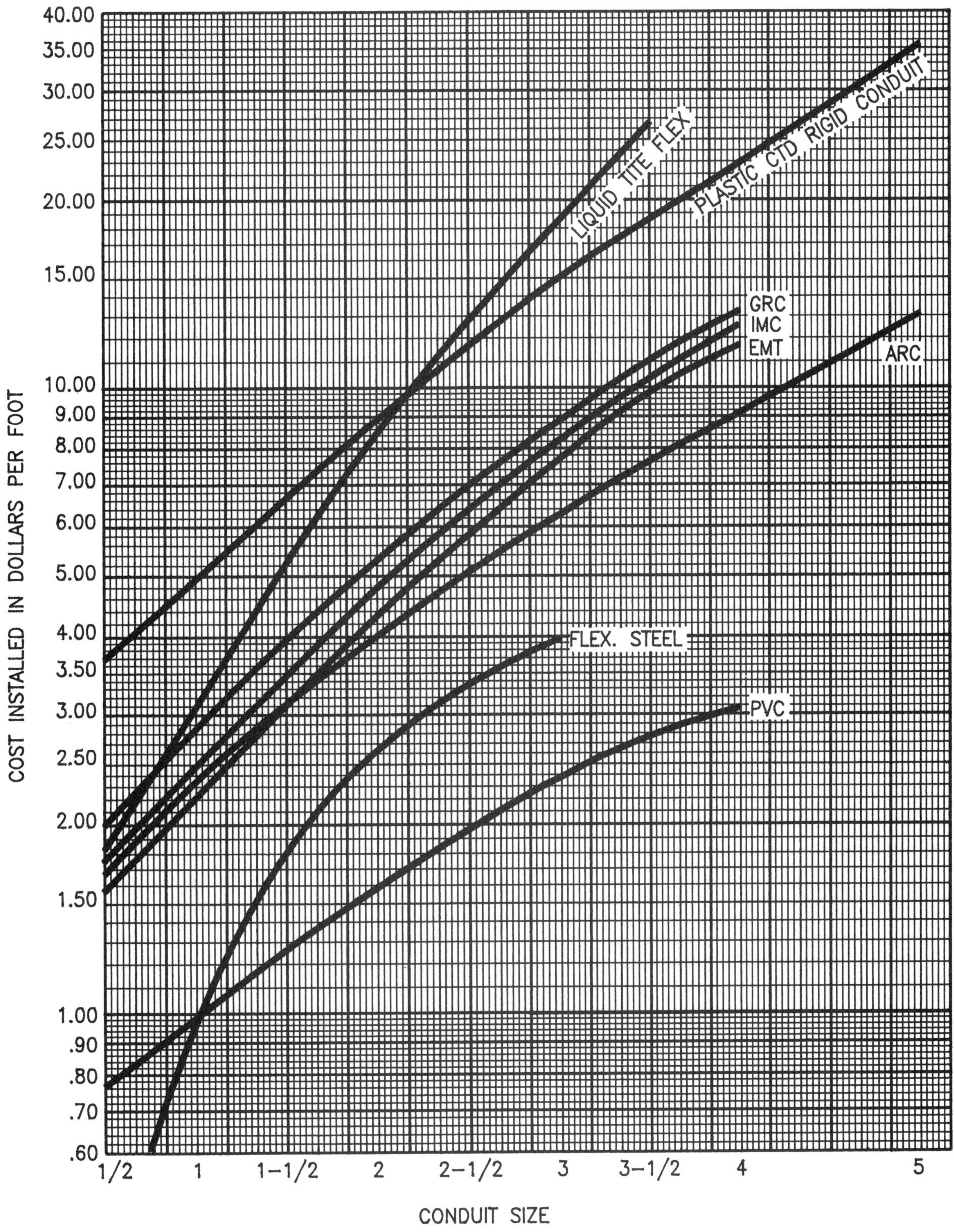

The costs shown for these conduits consist of the published contractors' book price and the necessary labor for installation exposed on wood at a height not exceeding 12 feet. No ground wire is included in PCV conduit.

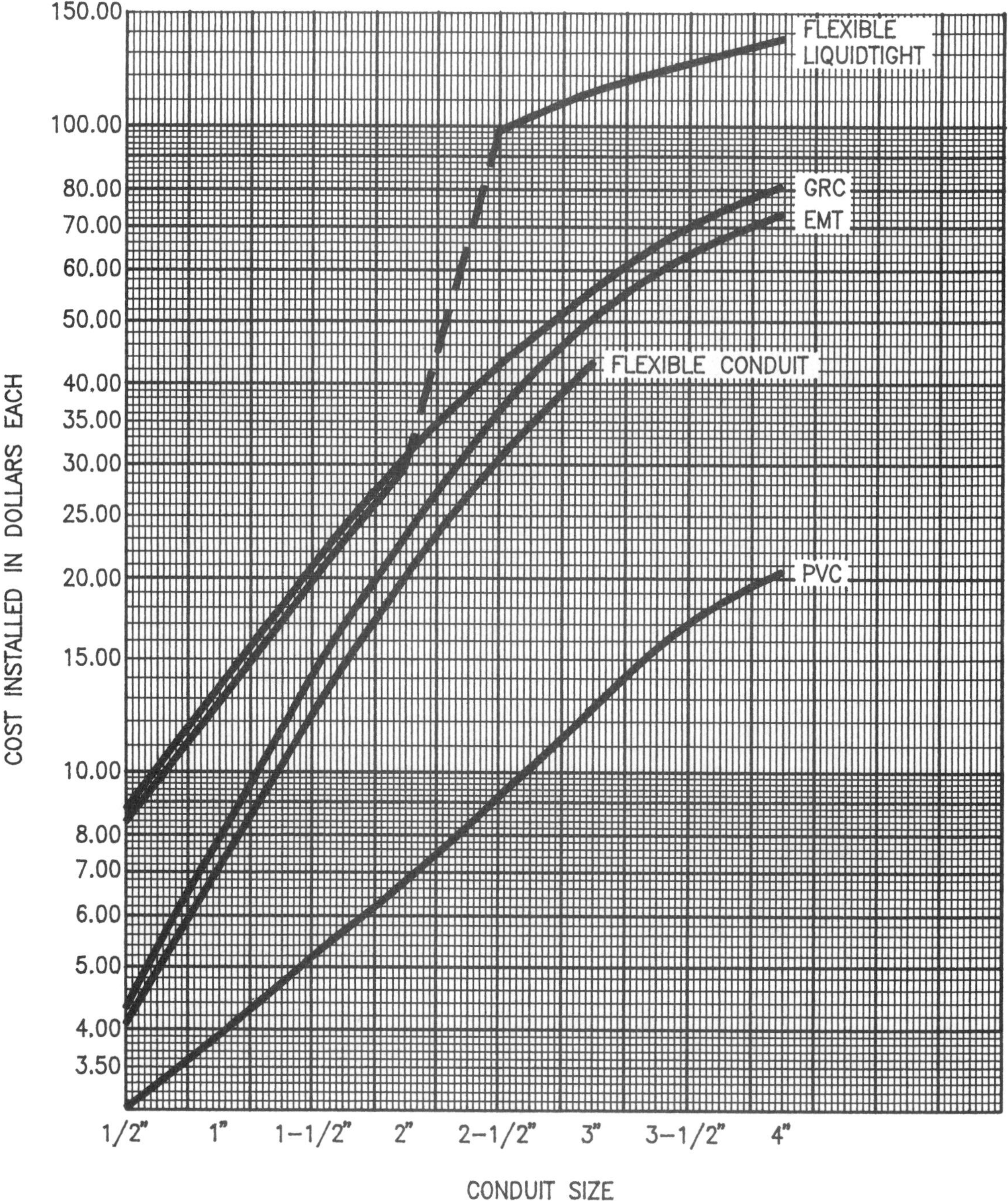

The costs shown for the conduit terminals include the published contractors' book price for the terminals shown. They also include the labor to cut and thread the conduit to the required length and installation of the terminal to the box.

E-2

COST OF CONDUIT FITTINGS

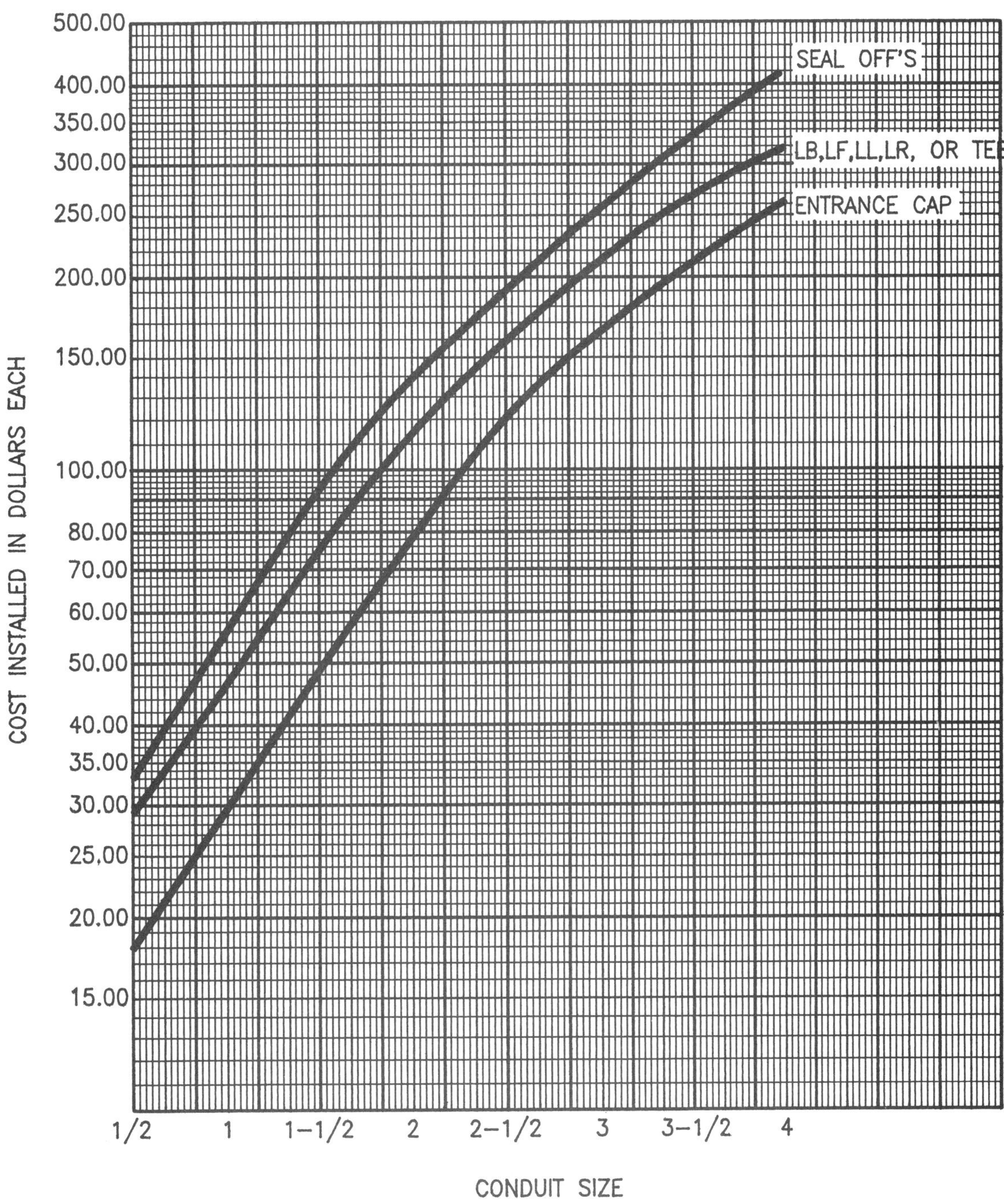

The costs shown for the conduit fittings include the published contractors' book price for the various fittings shown of the gasketed type to suit the kind of conduit required. They also include the labor for preparing the end of the conduit and installing the fitting. Seal-offs are considered to be used with GRC in hazardous applications, and include the installation of the sealing compound as required.

COST OF CONDUIT COUPLINGS

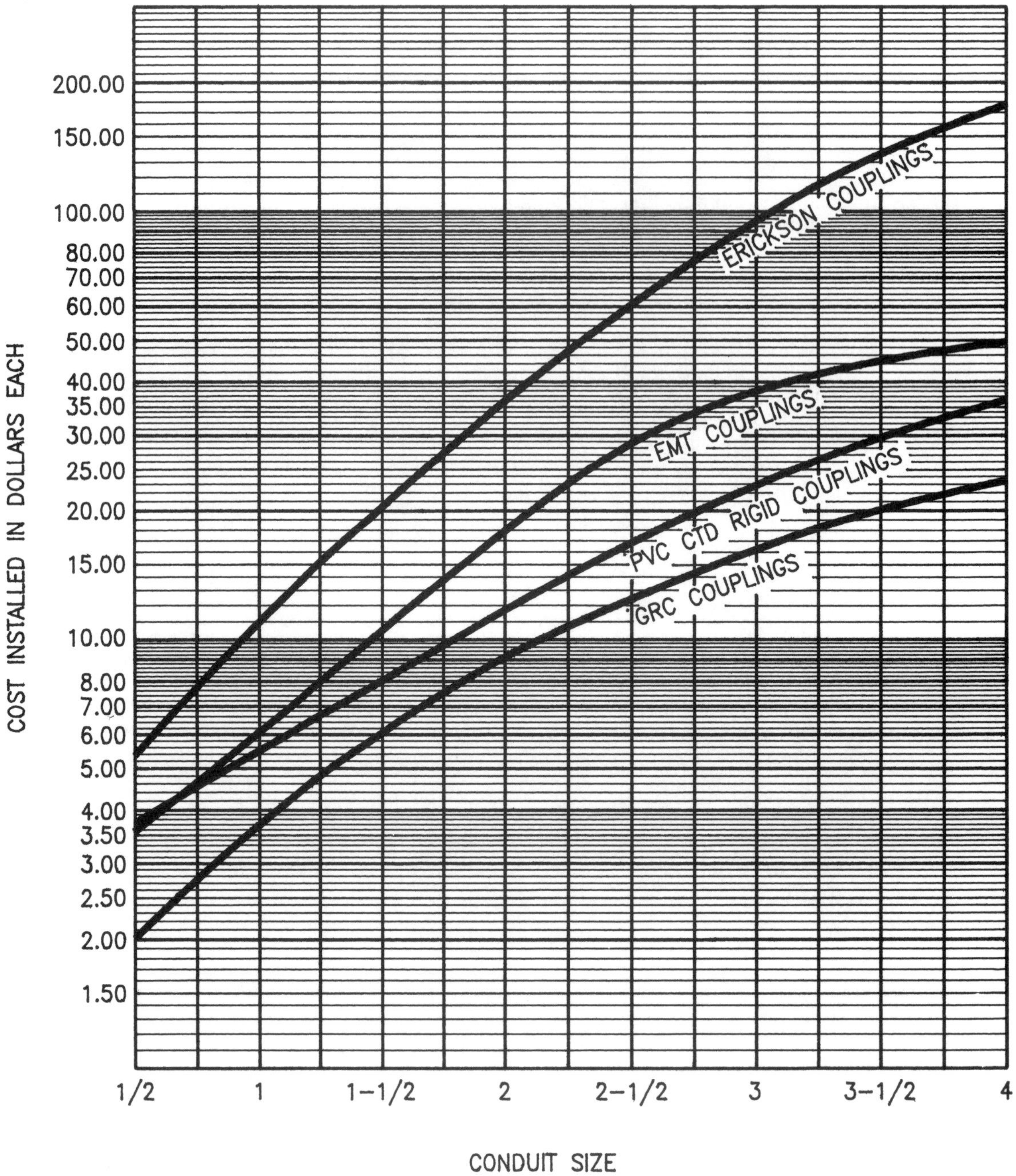

COST INSTALLED IN DOLLARS EACH

200.00
150.00
100.00
80.00
70.00
60.00
50.00
40.00
35.00
30.00
25.00
20.00
15.00
10.00
8.00
7.00
6.00
5.00
4.00
3.50
3.00
2.50
2.00
1.50

ERICKSON COUPLINGS

EMT COUPLINGS

PVC CTD RIGID COUPLINGS

GRC COUPLINGS

1/2 1 1-1/2 2 2-1/2 3 3-1/2 4

CONDUIT SIZE

The costs shown for the Erickson coupling include the published contractors' book price for the sizes included and sufficient labor for cutting and threading GRC conduit to accept the coupling.

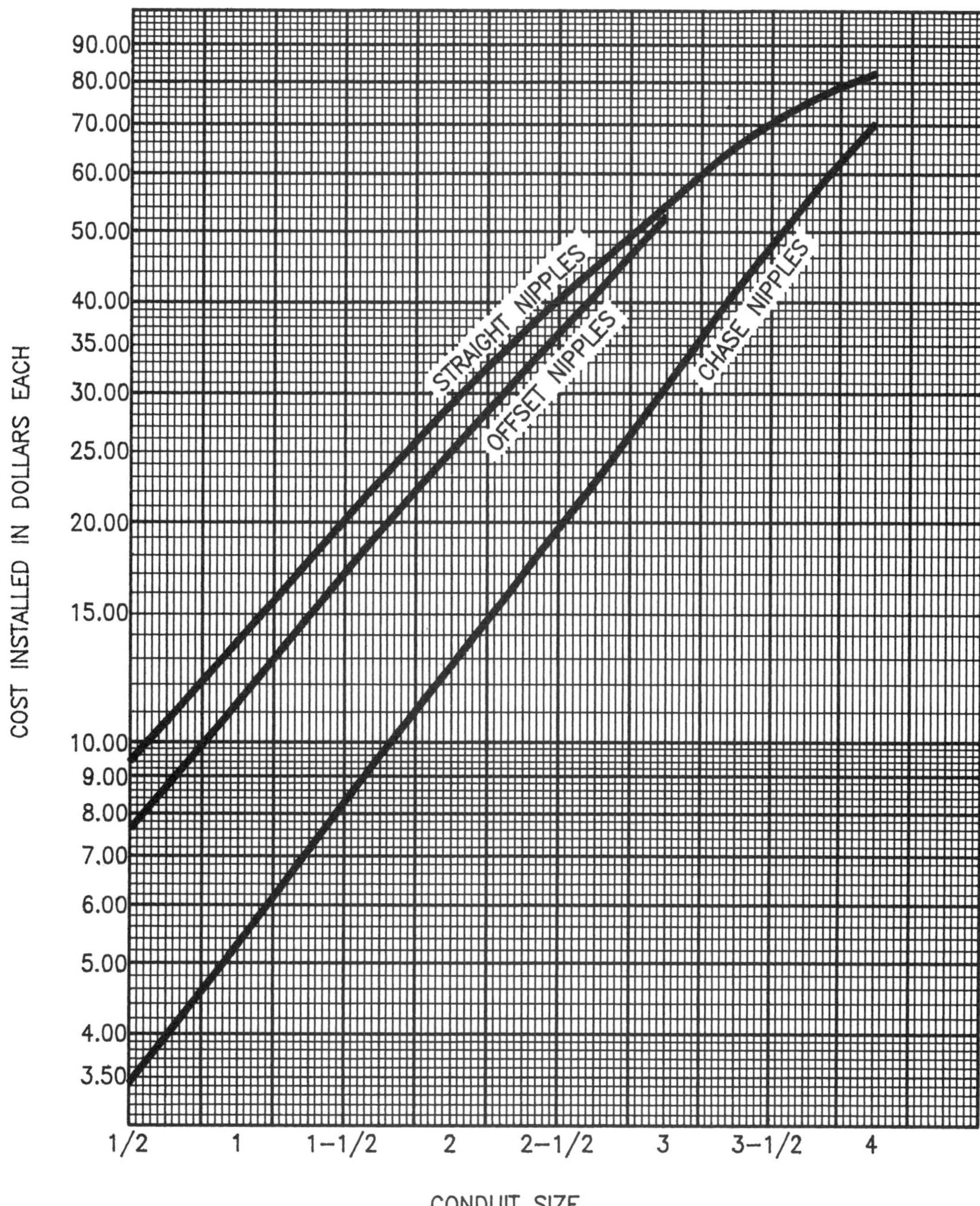

The costs shown for conduit nipples consist of the cost of a 4-inch-long GRC nipple with two locknuts and a metal-insulated bushing at each end of the nipple. The labor includes the installation of the nipple, but not cutting the holes in the steel panel. See Section L for cutting holes in a steel panel.

COST OF FIELD BENDS

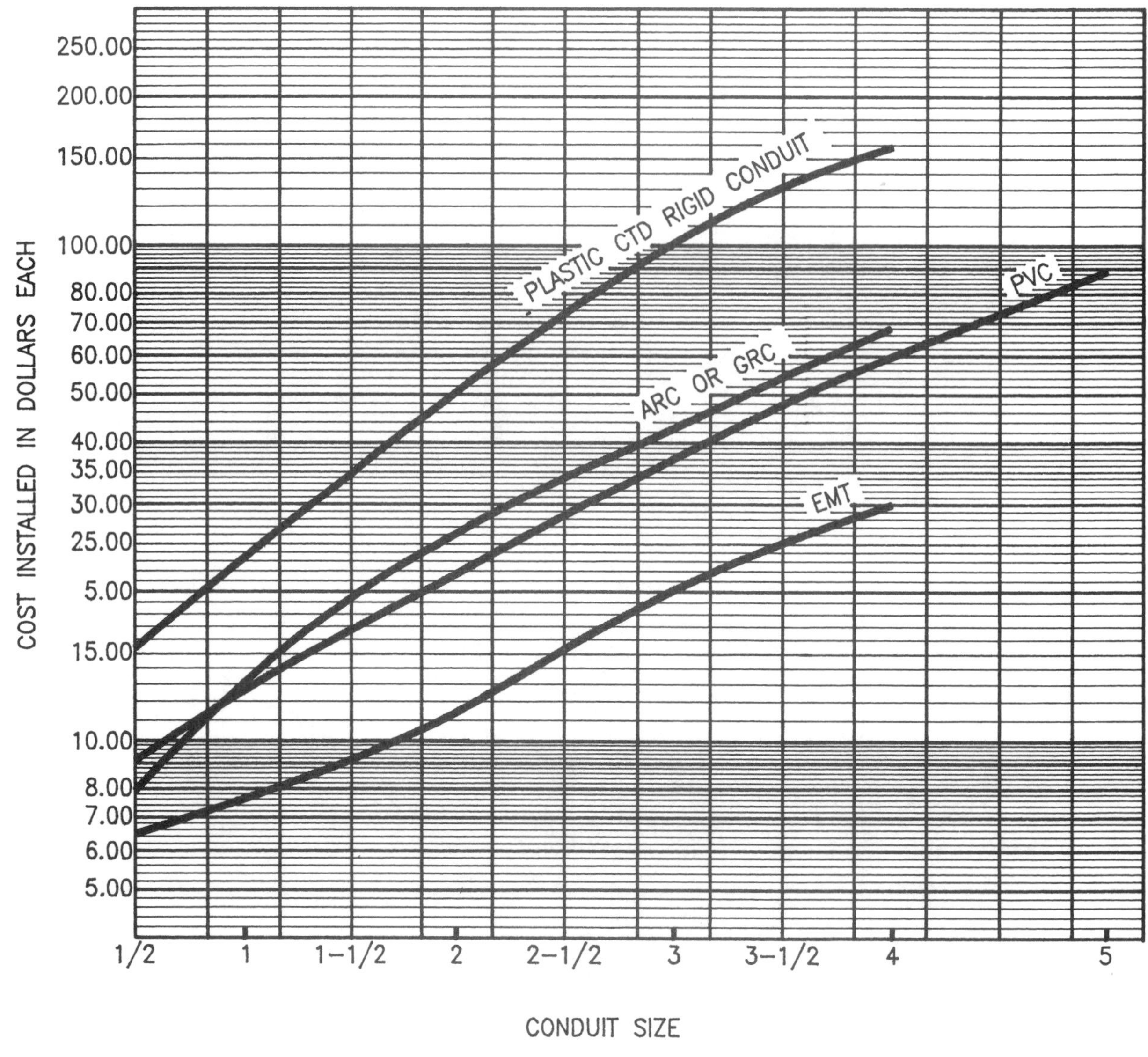

The costs shown for the field bends have no material associated with them; however, they do include the labor for making bends with a hydraulic bender or a heat type of bender for the PVC.

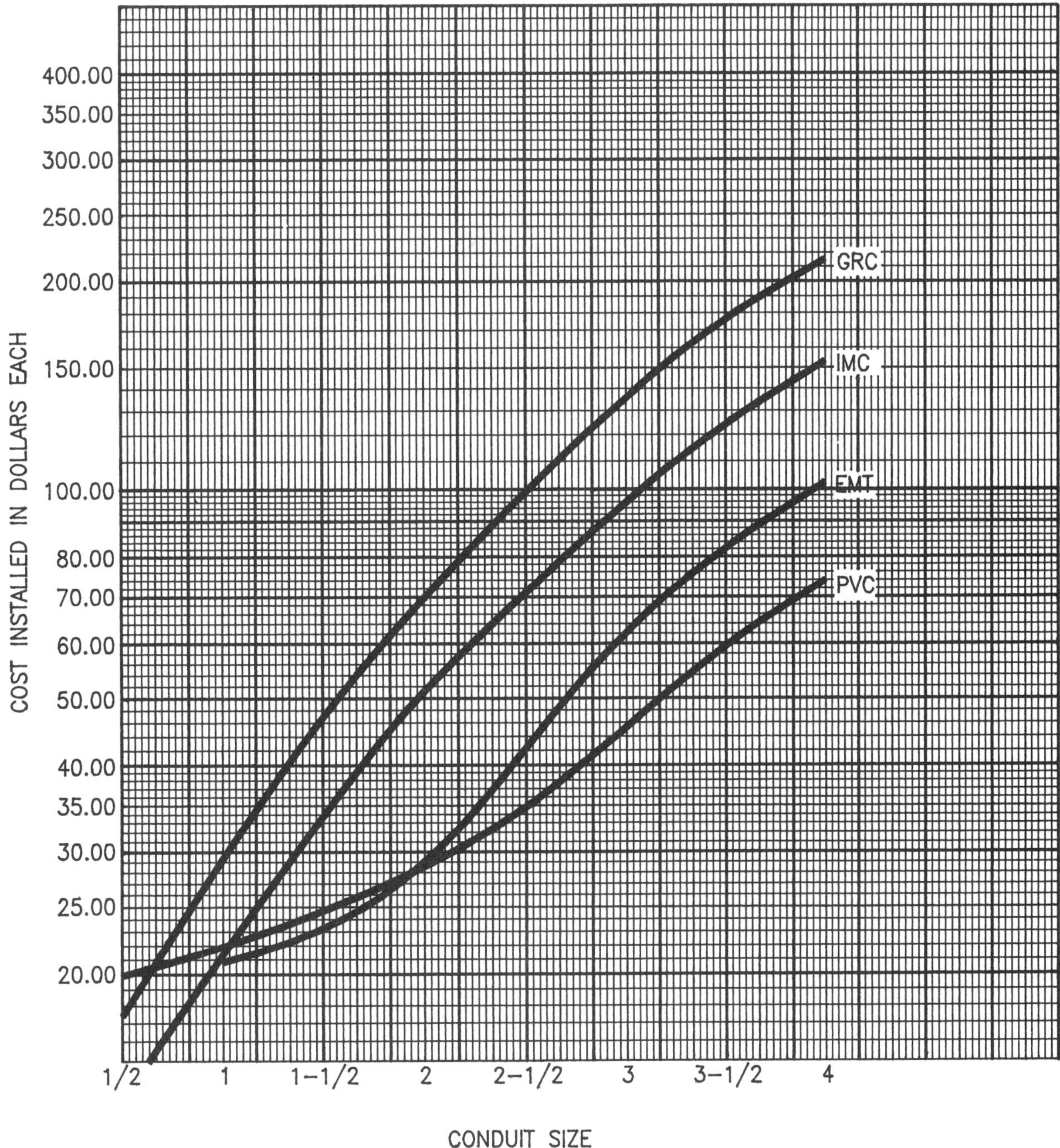

The costs shown on this graph for conduit elbows include the published contractors' book price for factory-made elbows. They also include one coupling and the labor for cutting and threading one end of the conduit to fit the elbow as required.

COST OF COPPER FEEDER CONDUCTORS

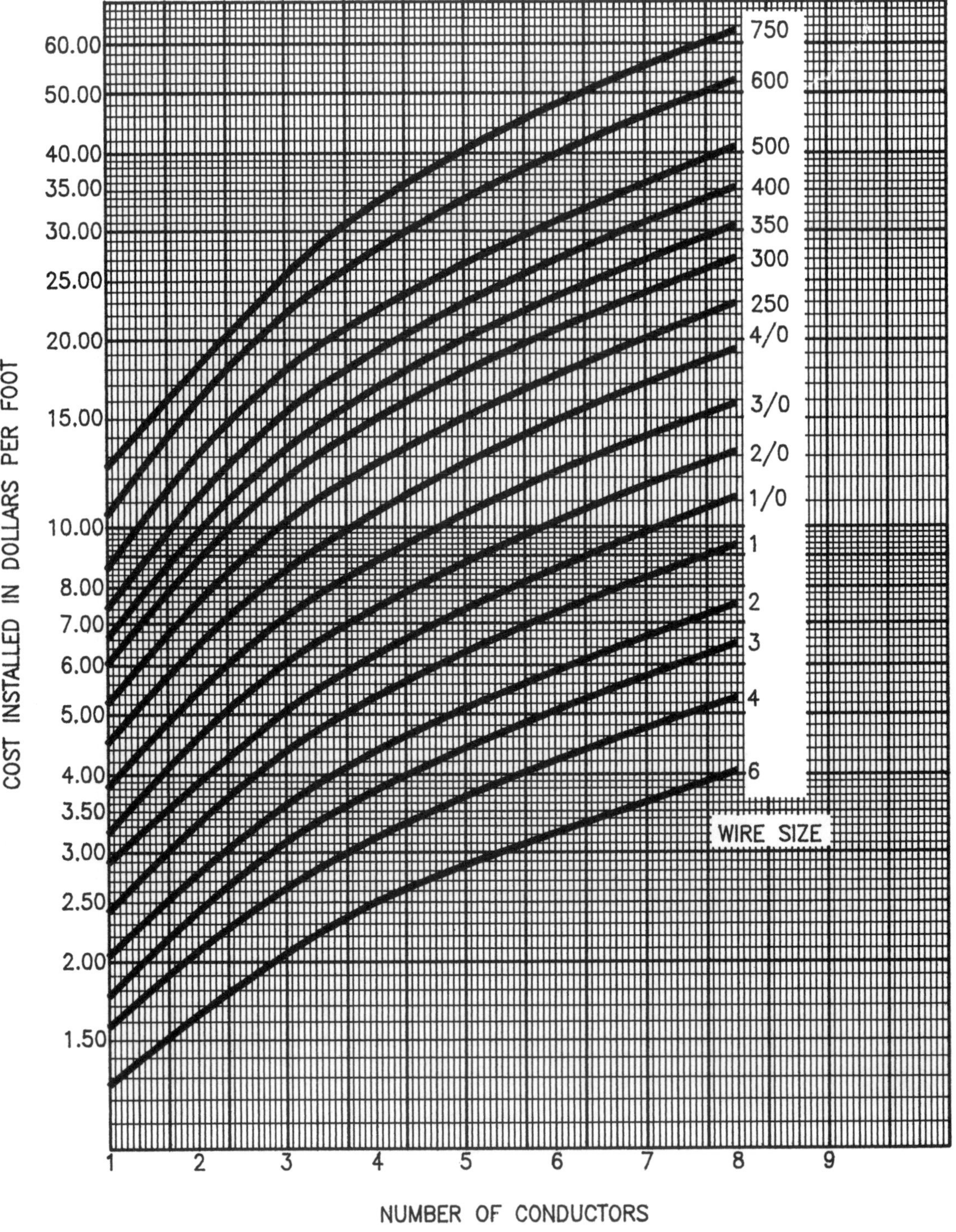

The costs shown for copper feeder conductors include the published contractors' book price for the copper wire and insulation indicated on the graph. The installation labor is predicated on an average pull of 100 feet in conduit.

COST OF COPPER FEEDER CONDUCTORS

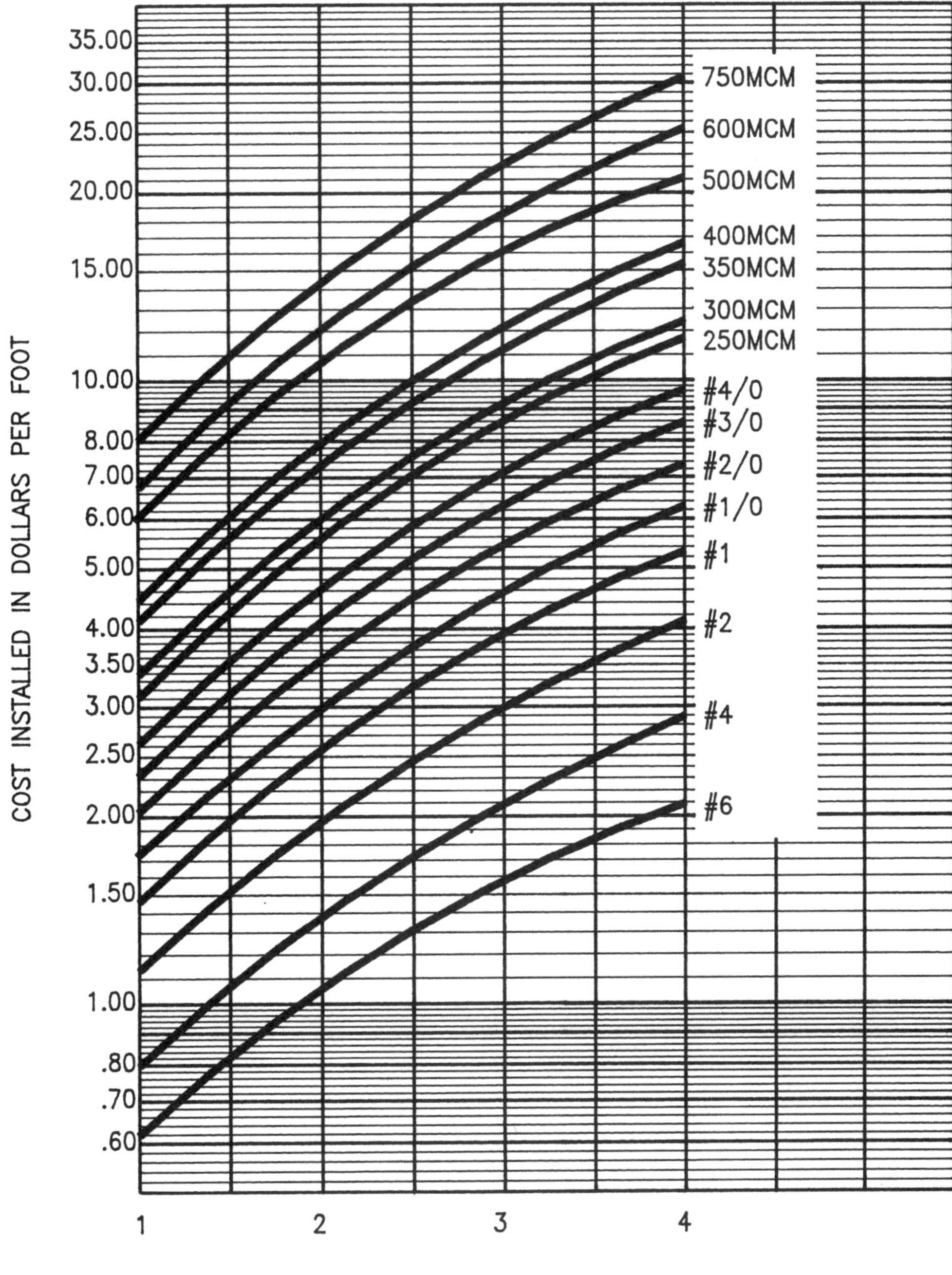

The costs shown for copper USE/XLPE conductors include the published contractors' book price for the copper wire and the insulation indicated. The installation labor is predicated upon laying conductors in a open trench. Trenching costs are not included; for these, see Miscellaneous Section L.

COST OF INSULATED GROUNDING CONDUCTORS

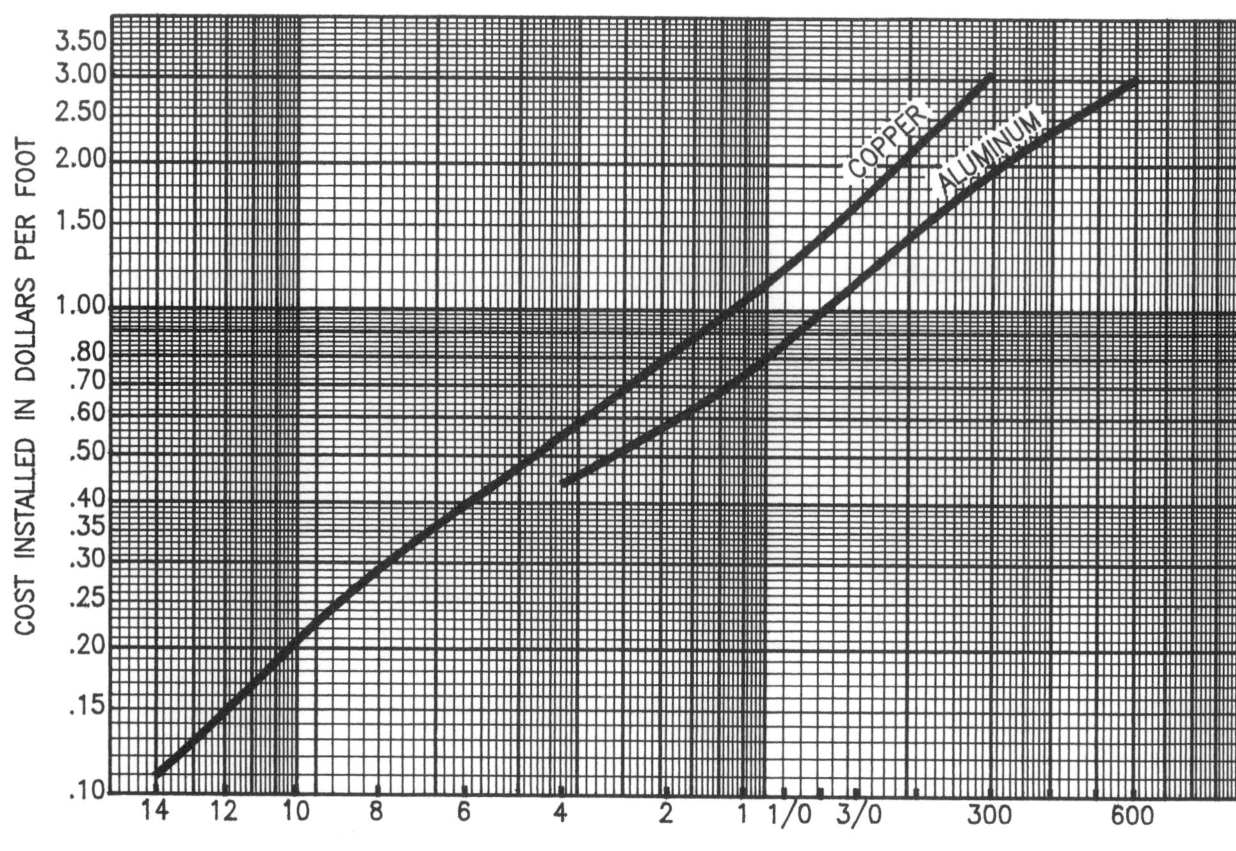

CONDUCTOR SIZE

E-10

The costs shown for insulated grounding conductors include the published contractors' book price for type of wire indicated. The installation labor is predicated upon pulling a single conductor along with four phase conductors of the size normally used for the size of grounding conductors required.

COST OF ALUMINUM FEEDER CONDUCTORS

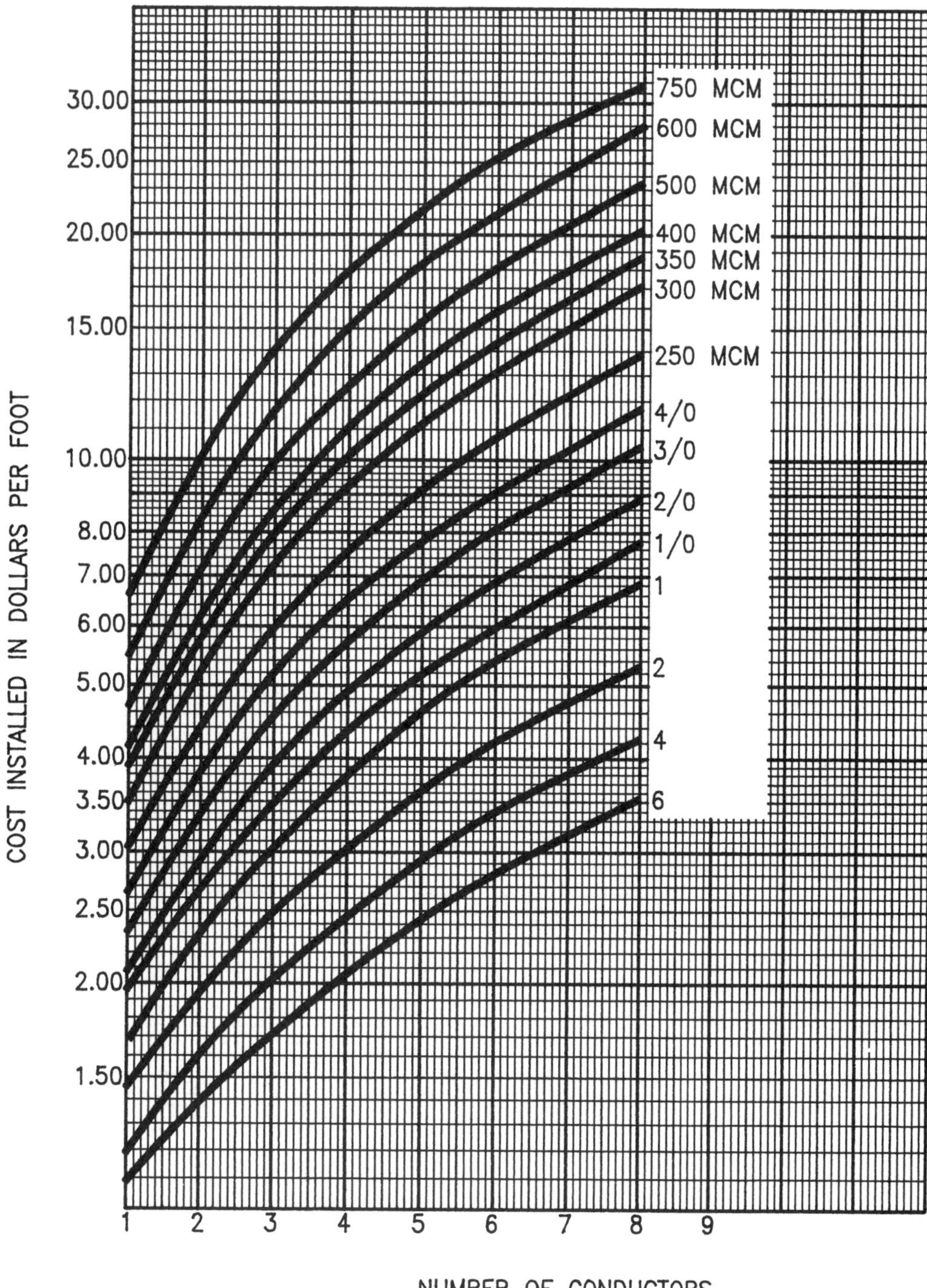

The costs shown for aluminum feeder conductors include the published contractors' book price for the aluminum wire with insulation as indicated. The installation labor is predicated on an average pull of 100 feet in conduit.

COST OF ALUMINUM FEEDER CONDUCTORS

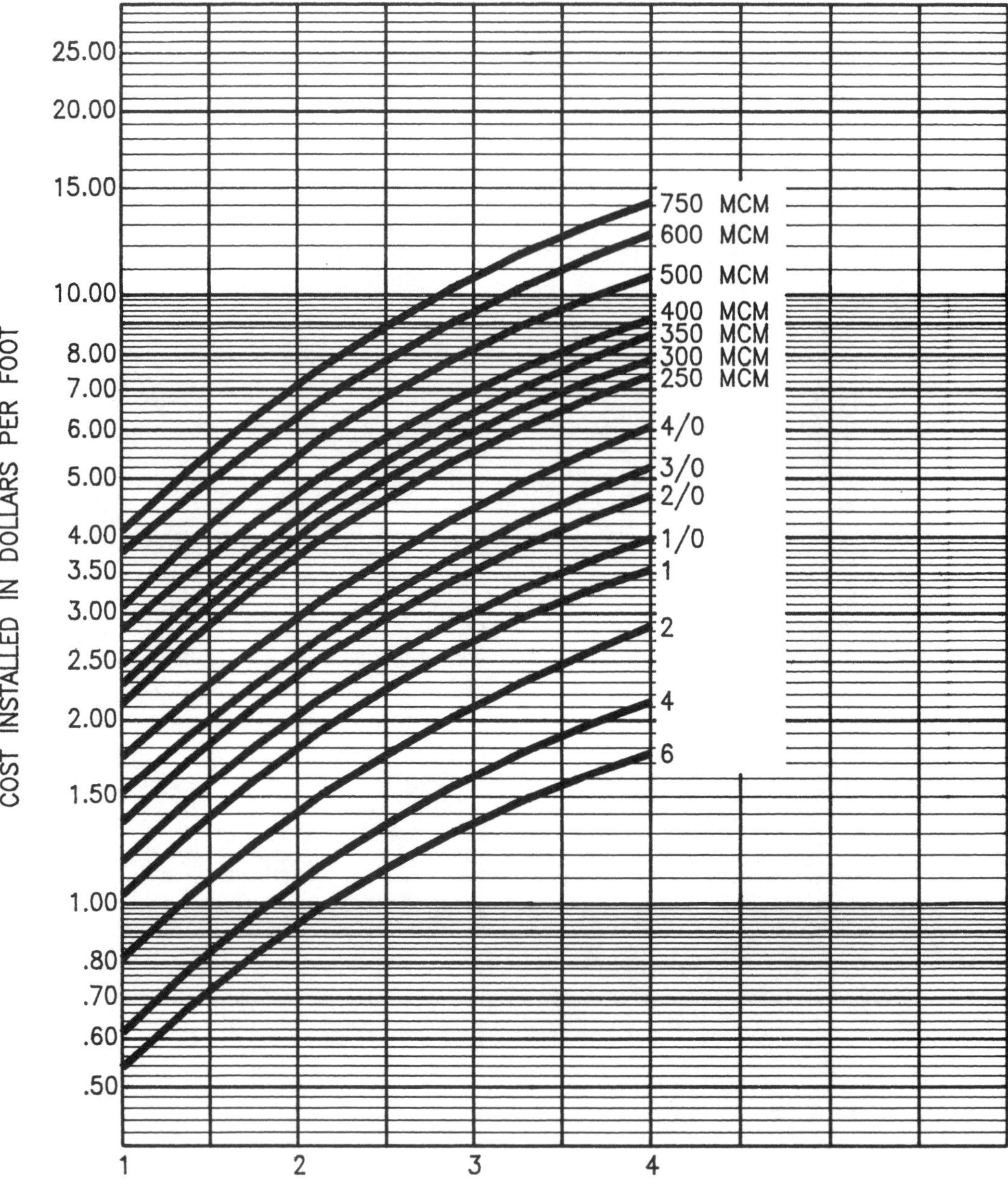

E-12

The costs shown for aluminum feeder conductors include the published contractors' book price for the aluminum wire with insulation as indicated. The installation labor is predicated upon laying conductors in an open trench. The cost of digging the trench is not included. See Miscellaneous Section L for trenching costs.

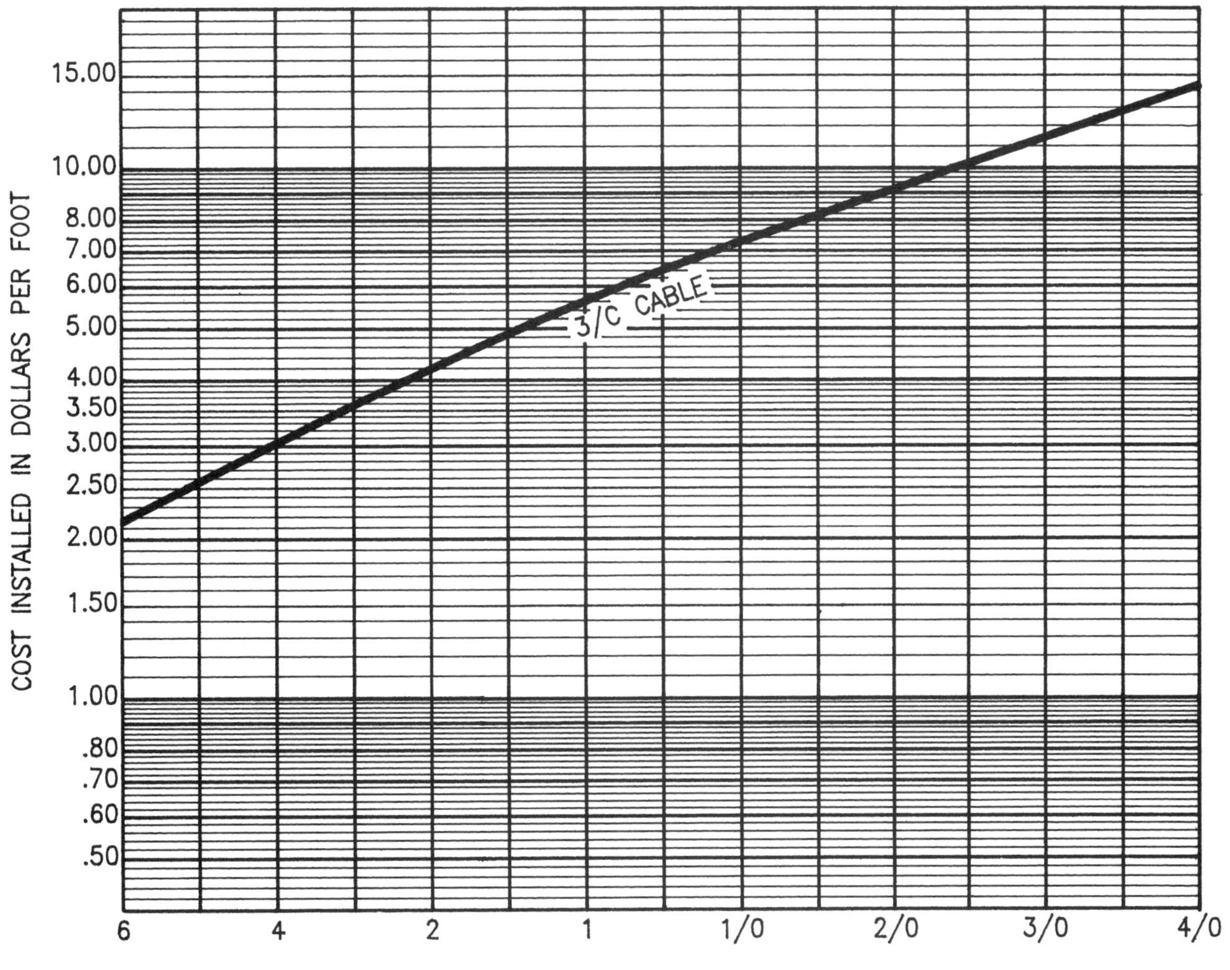

The costs shown for service entrance cable, type SE, include the published contractors' book price for the cable shown and straps for supporting it on 4-foot centers. Also included is the labor for installation on exposed wood surfaces.

COST OF SERVICE DROP CABLE

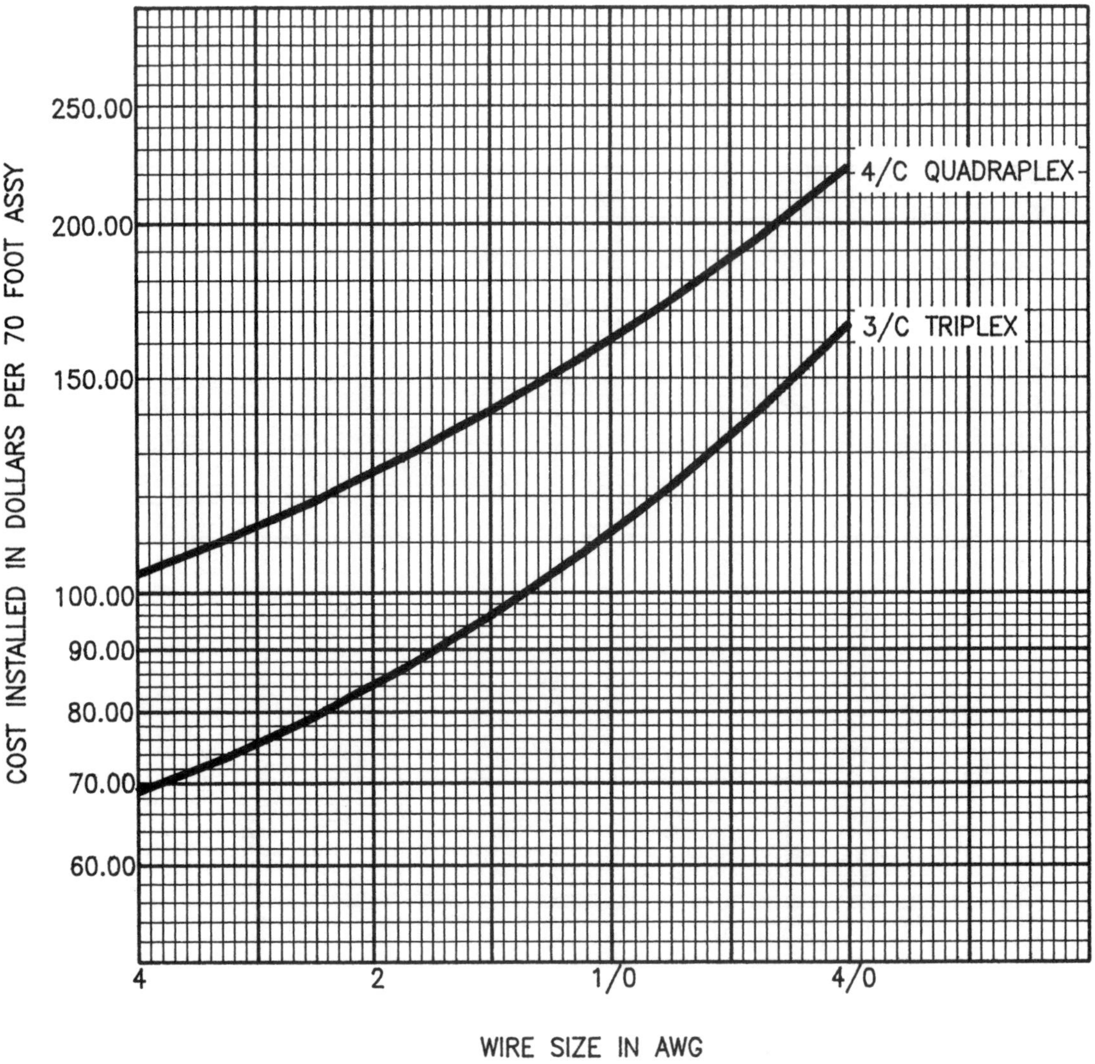

The costs shown for self-supporting service drop cable include the published contractors' book price for the aluminum wire with a steel messenger for support and the labor for installing 70 feet of wire and the anchors required on the pole and building at each end. A 70-foot length is used as an average.

COST OF FEEDER CONDUCTOR TERMINALS

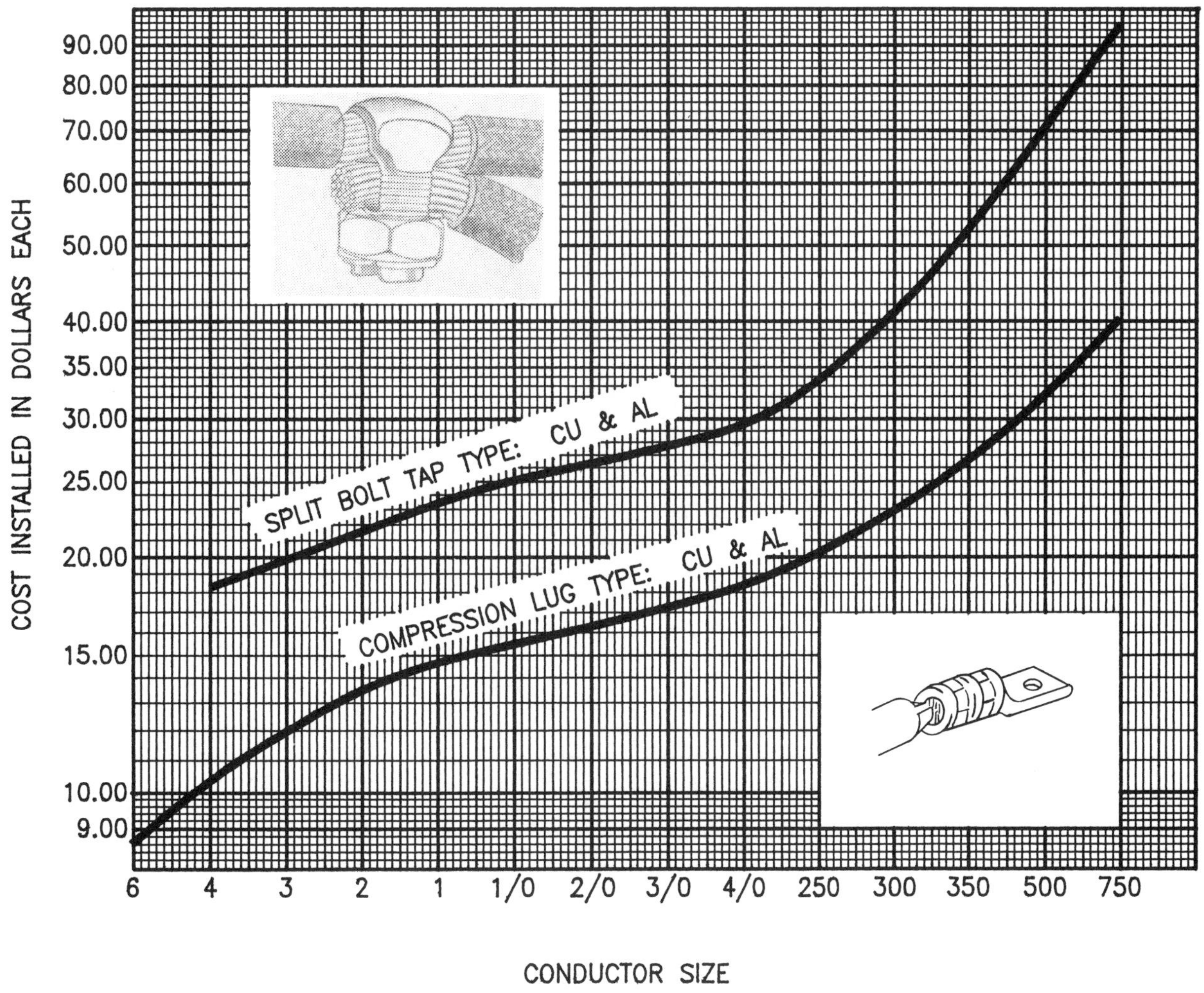

COST INSTALLED IN DOLLARS EACH

90.00
80.00
70.00
60.00
50.00
40.00
35.00
30.00
25.00
20.00
15.00
10.00
9.00

SPLIT BOLT TAP TYPE: CU & AL

COMPRESSION LUG TYPE: CU & AL

6 4 3 2 1 1/0 2/0 3/0 4/0 250 300 350 500 750

CONDUCTOR SIZE

The costs shown for the aluminum compression type of terminal include the published contractors' book price for the Thomas & Betts wrought-aluminum tin-plated terminal prefilled with oxide-inhibiting compound. The labor includes cutting and stripping the cable and installing the terminal with the proper manual-type compression tools.

The costs shown for the copper split bolt tap connector include the published contractors' book price for the Burndy split bolt solderless connector and electrical tape. Labor is provided for cable preparation and taping.

COST OF FEEDER BUSWAY

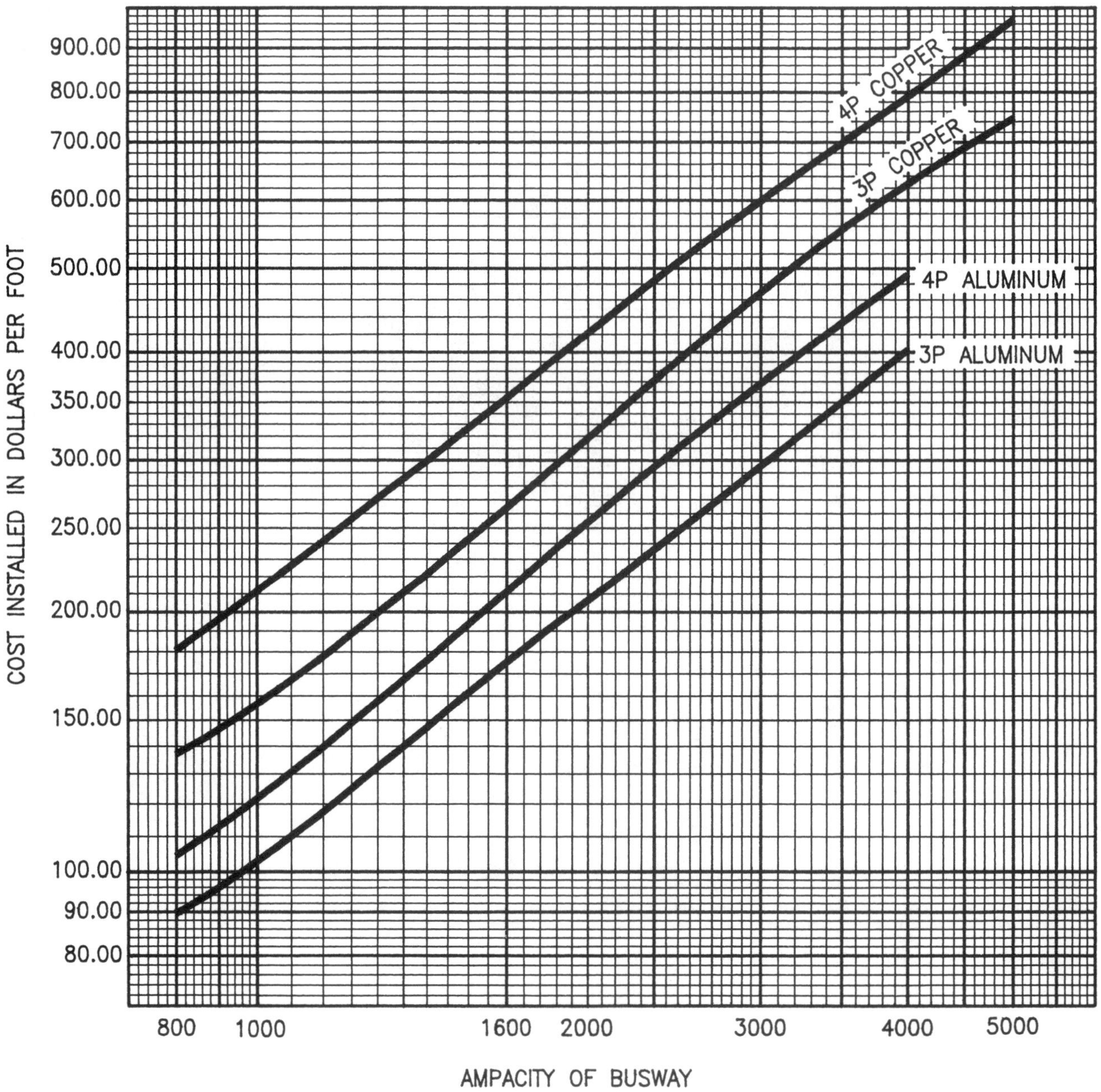

The costs shown for copper and aluminum feeder busway consist of the published contractors' book prices and two 36-inch hangers for every 10 feet of busway. Labor is included to mount the hangers and install the busway. Four-wire busway has a full neutral.

COST OF FEEDER BUSWAY TRANSFORMER TAPS

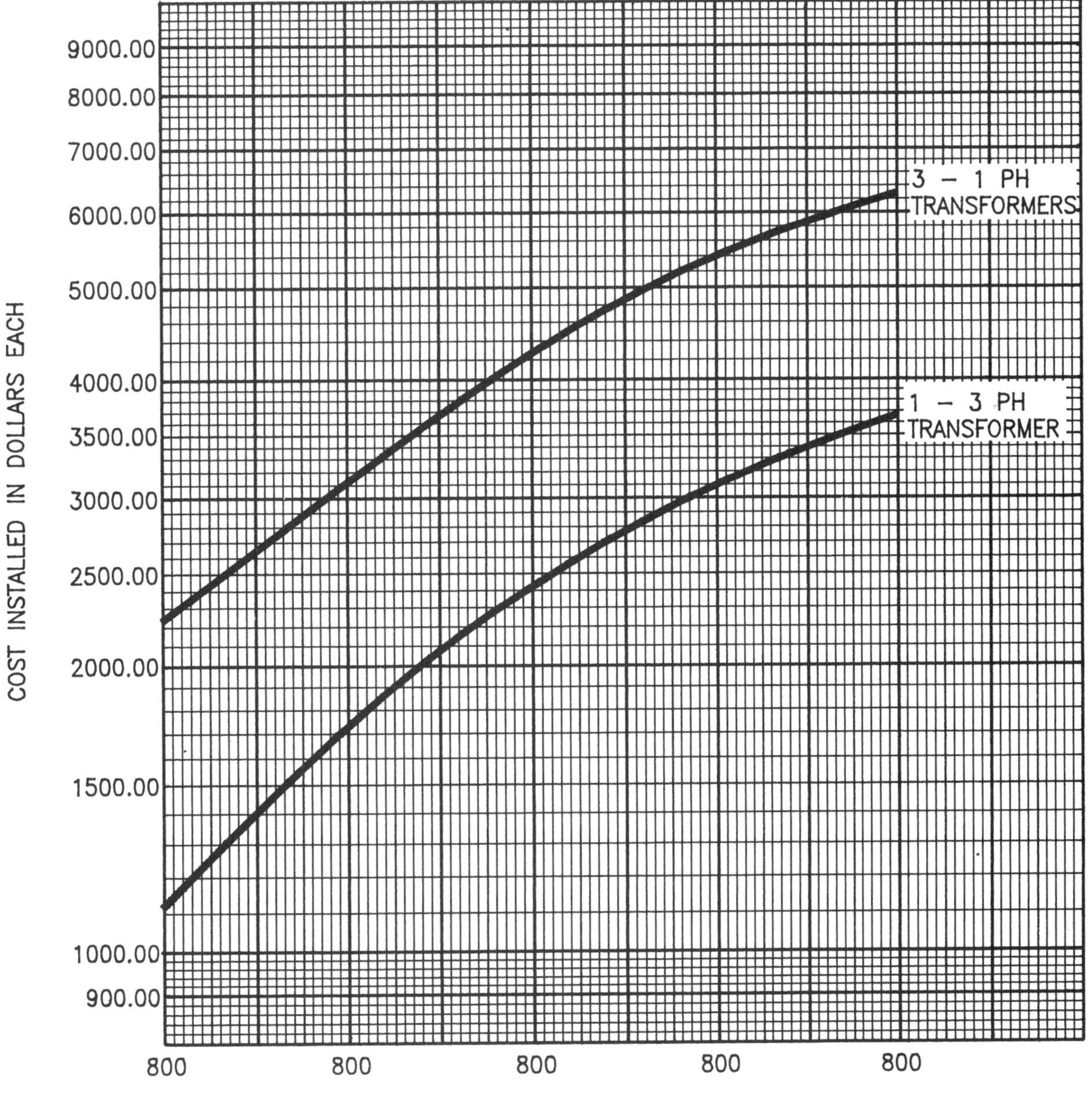

The costs shown for the feeder busway transformer taps consist of the contractors' published book price for the taps indicated. The cost of the busway length must be added to these. The three-phase tap from a single transformer has four busway connections—three hot legs and a neutral. For three single-phase transformers, there are six busway connections—two for each transformer. Included in the costs shown are 5-foot drops of copper, in the ampacity of the busway, and copper terminals at each end of the drop, with labor to make up the terminations and install the busway tap and wire.

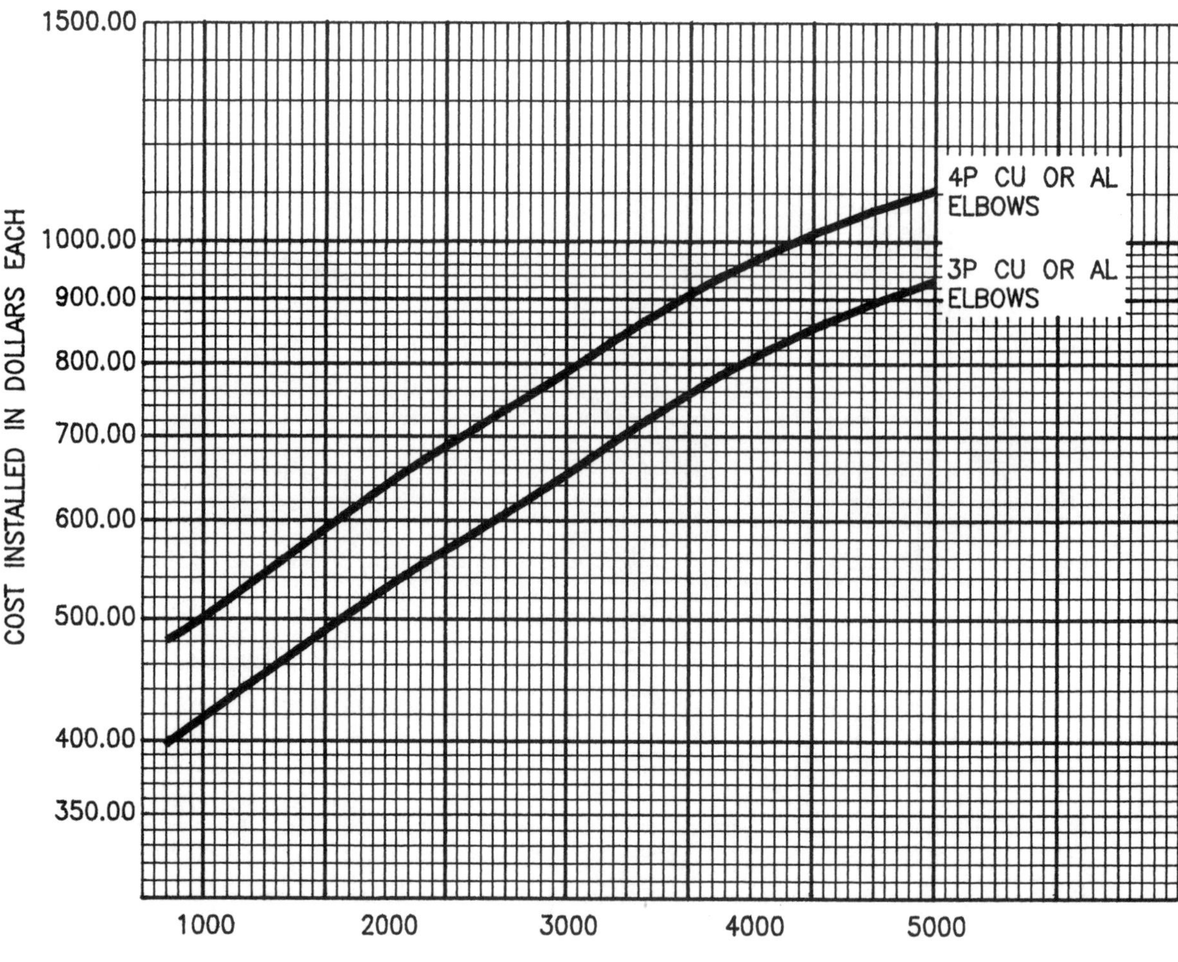

The costs shown for feeder busway elbows consist of the published contractors' book price for a "labor only" charge by the manufacturer. The length of the busway duct through the fitting must be added to these elbow charges. The cost of the labor required by the contractor for assembling and hanging the duct is included in the prices shown on the graph.

COST OF FEEDER BUSWAY TEES

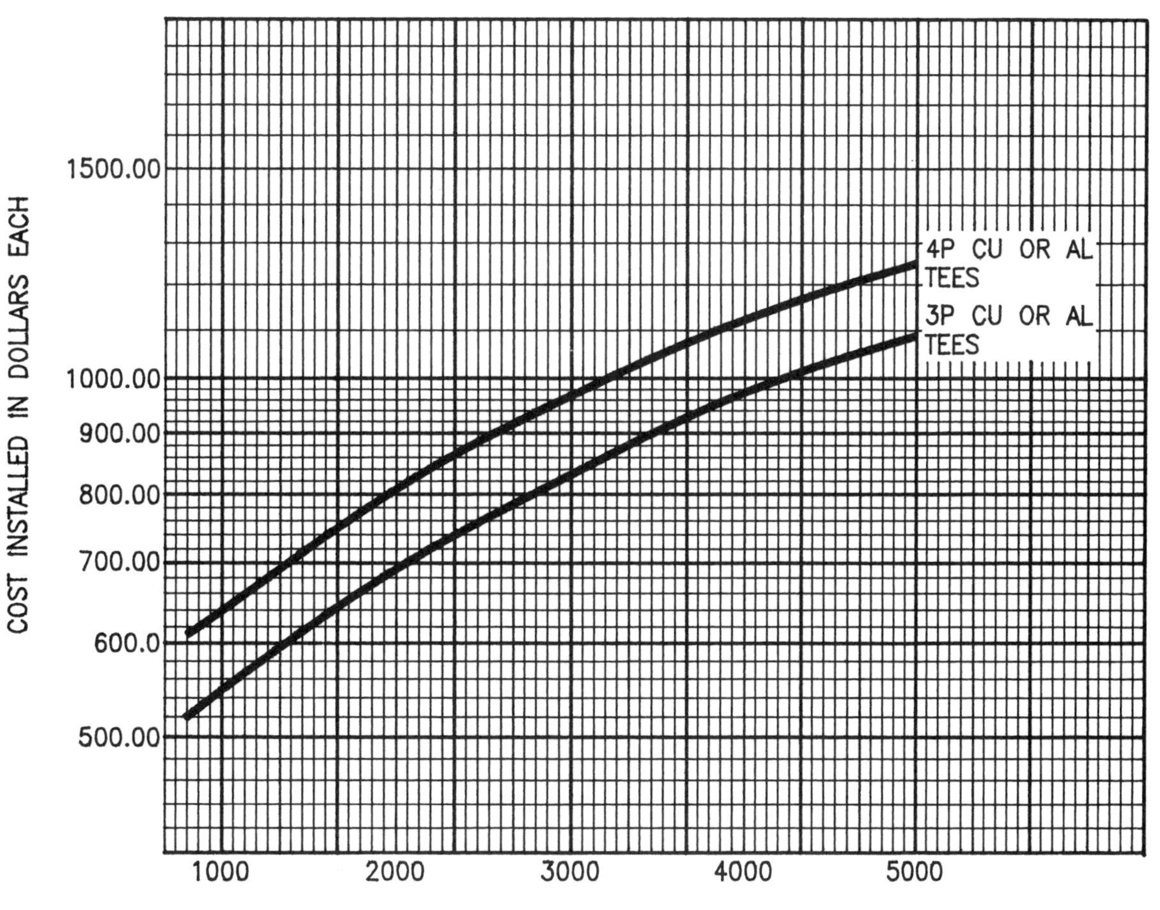

AMPACITY OF BUS

The costs shown for feeder busway tees consist of the published contractors' book price for the "labor only" charge by the manufacturer. The length of the busway duct through the fitting must be added to these tee charges. The cost of the labor required by the contractor for assembling and hanging the duct is included in the prices shown on the graph.

COST OF FEEDER BUSWAY TERMINALS

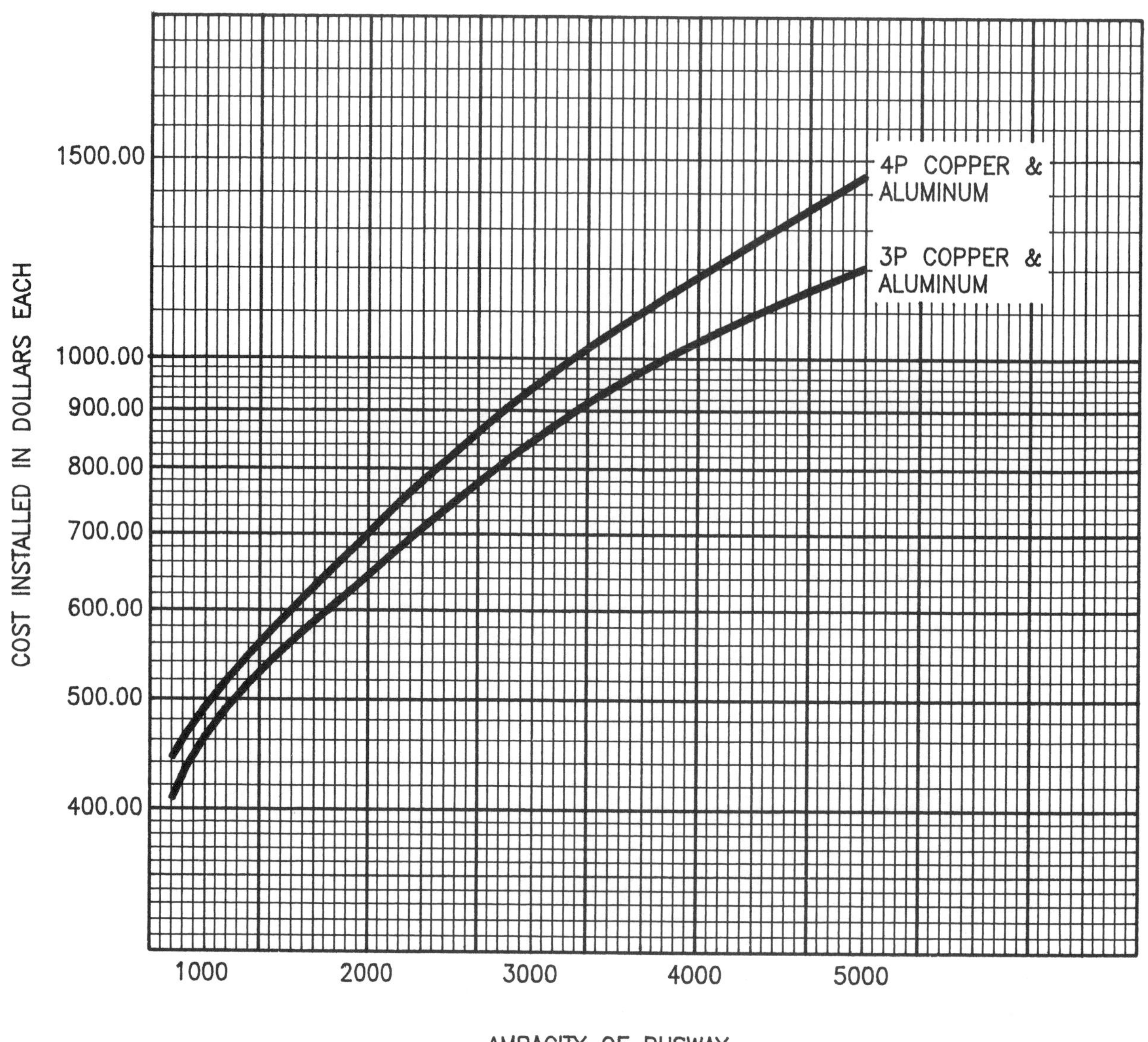

E-20

The costs shown for feeder busway terminals consist of the published contractors' book price for a "labor only" charge by the manufacturer. The footage of the busway duct through the fitting must be added to these terminal charges. The cost of the labor required by the contractor for assembling and hanging the duct is included in the prices shown on the graph.

COST OF PLUG-IN BUSWAY

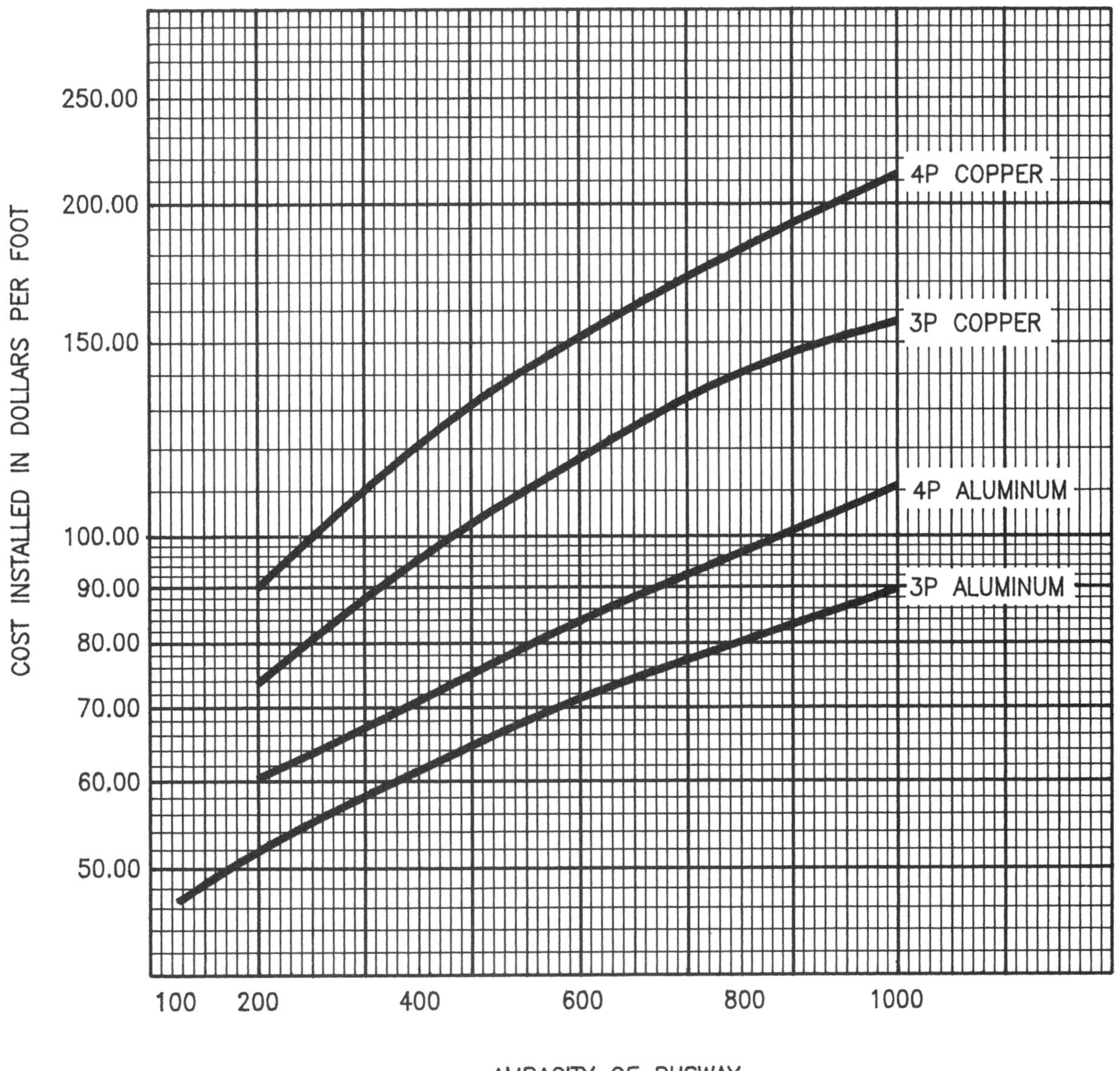

The costs shown for the plug-in busway consist of the published contractors' book price and include one 36-inch hanger rod every 5 feet with a fitting for fastening to a steel bar joist. The duct is full neutral for the types shown, and labor for installing the busduct is included.

COST OF PLUG–IN BUSWAY ELBOWS

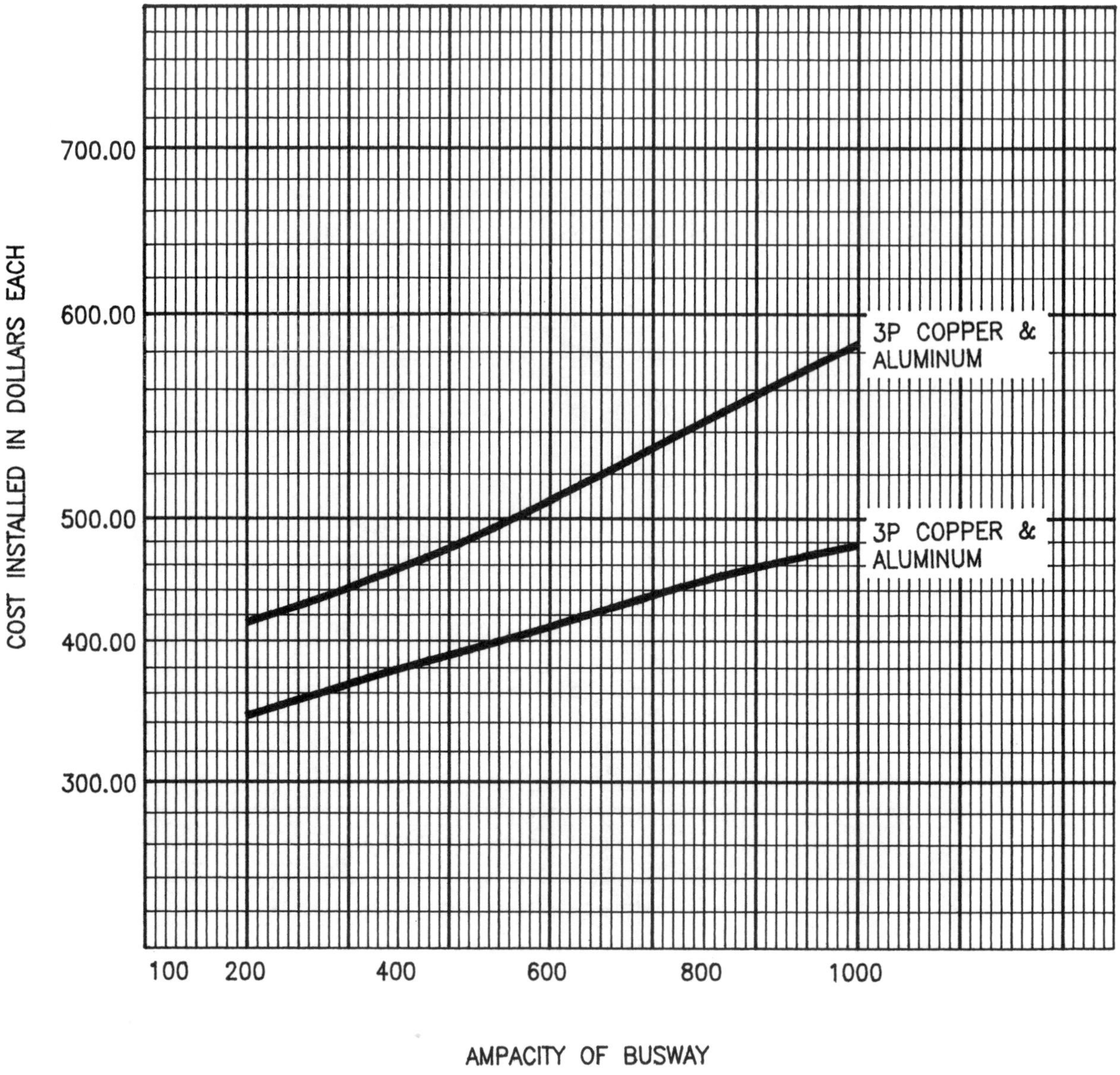

The costs shown for the busway elbows consist of the published contractors' book price and are the manufacturer's labor charges for making the elbows. The busway cost must be included with the busway footage by measuring through these elbows. The costs shown here include the contractor's charge for installing the busduct elbows as well as the contractor's cost for the elbows.

COST OF PLUG–IN BUSWAY TEES

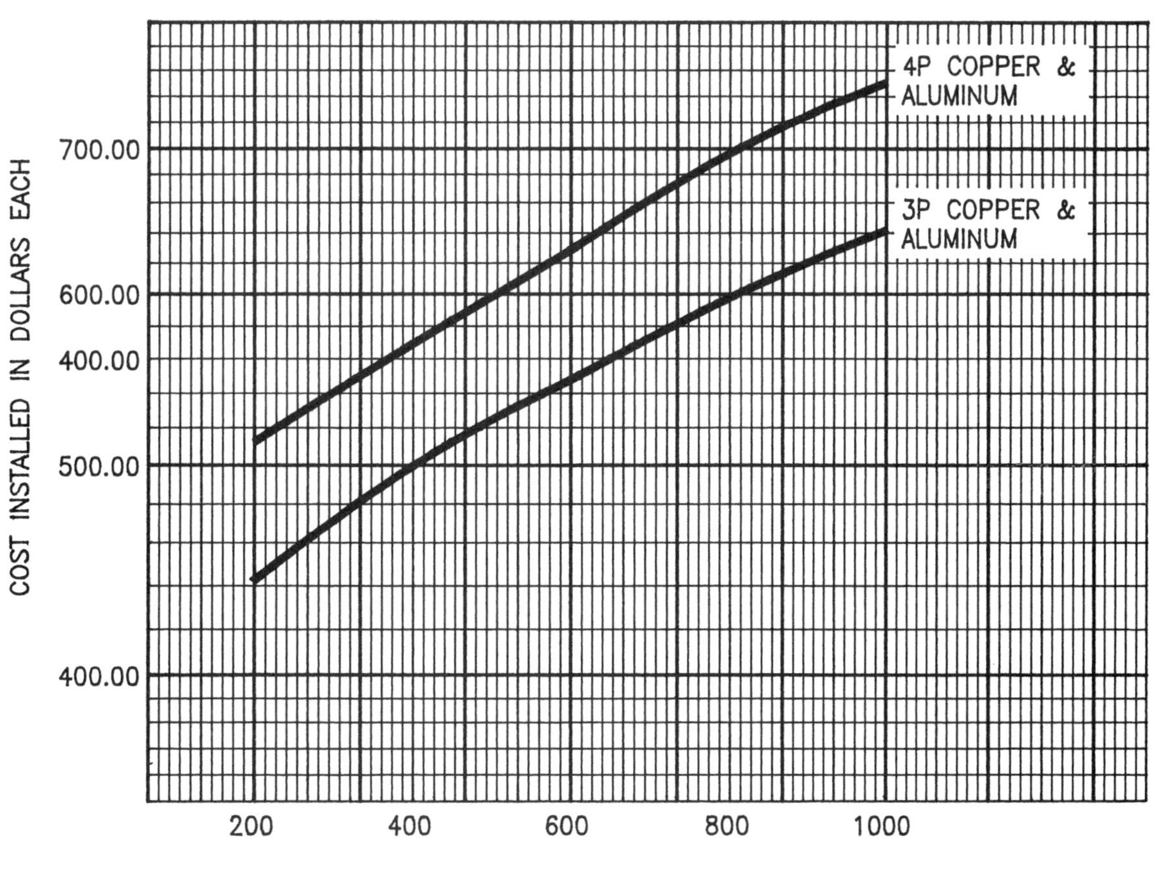

The costs shown for the busway tees consist of the published contractors' book price and are the manufacturer's labor charges for making the tees. The busway cost must be included with the busway footage by measuring through the tees. The costs shown here include the contractor's charge for installing the busduct tees as well as the contractor's cost for the tees.

COST OF PLUG–IN BUSWAY CABLE TAP BOX

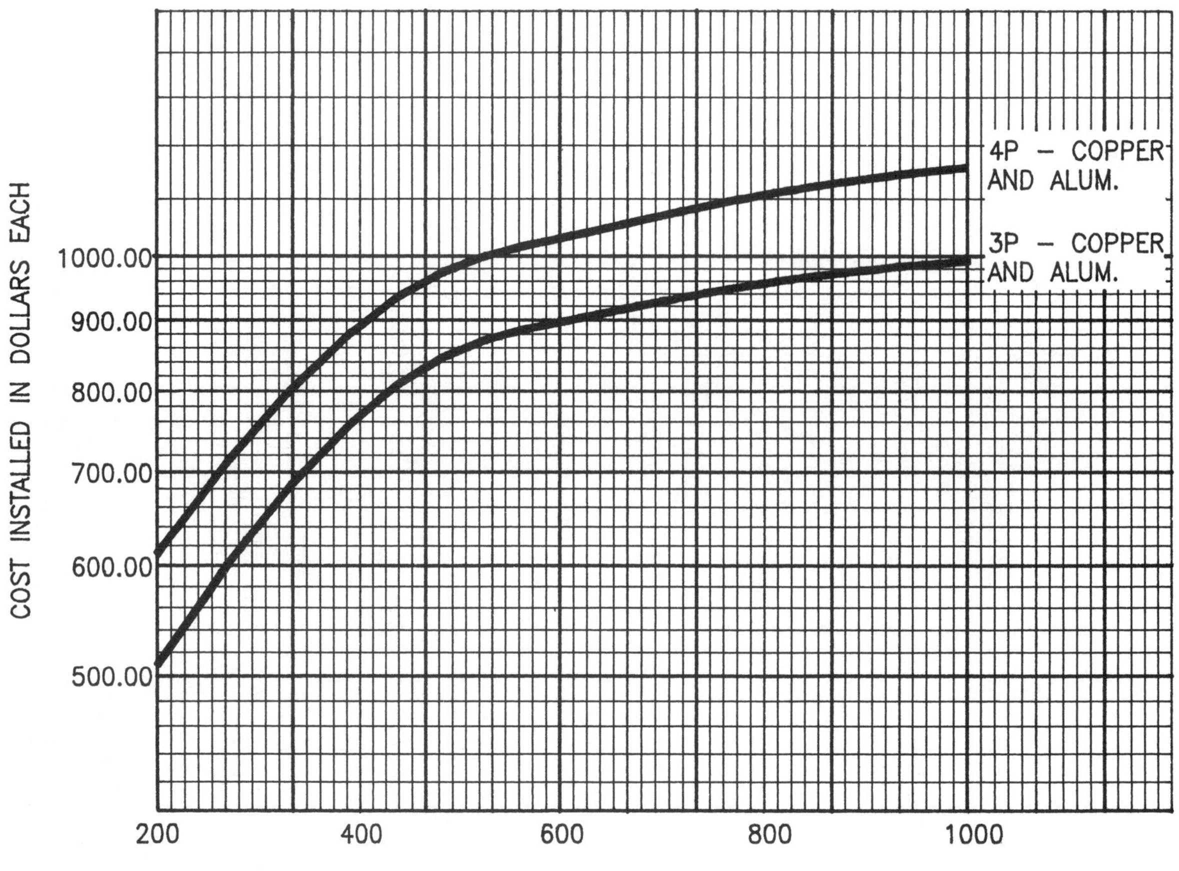

The costs shown for the busway cable tap box consist of the published contractors' book price and are the manufacturer's labor charges for making the fitting. The busway cost must be included with the busway footage by measuring through these fittings. The cost of the labor by the contractor for assembling and hanging the busway fitting is included in the prices shown on the graph.

COST OF PLUG–IN BUSWAY SWITCHES

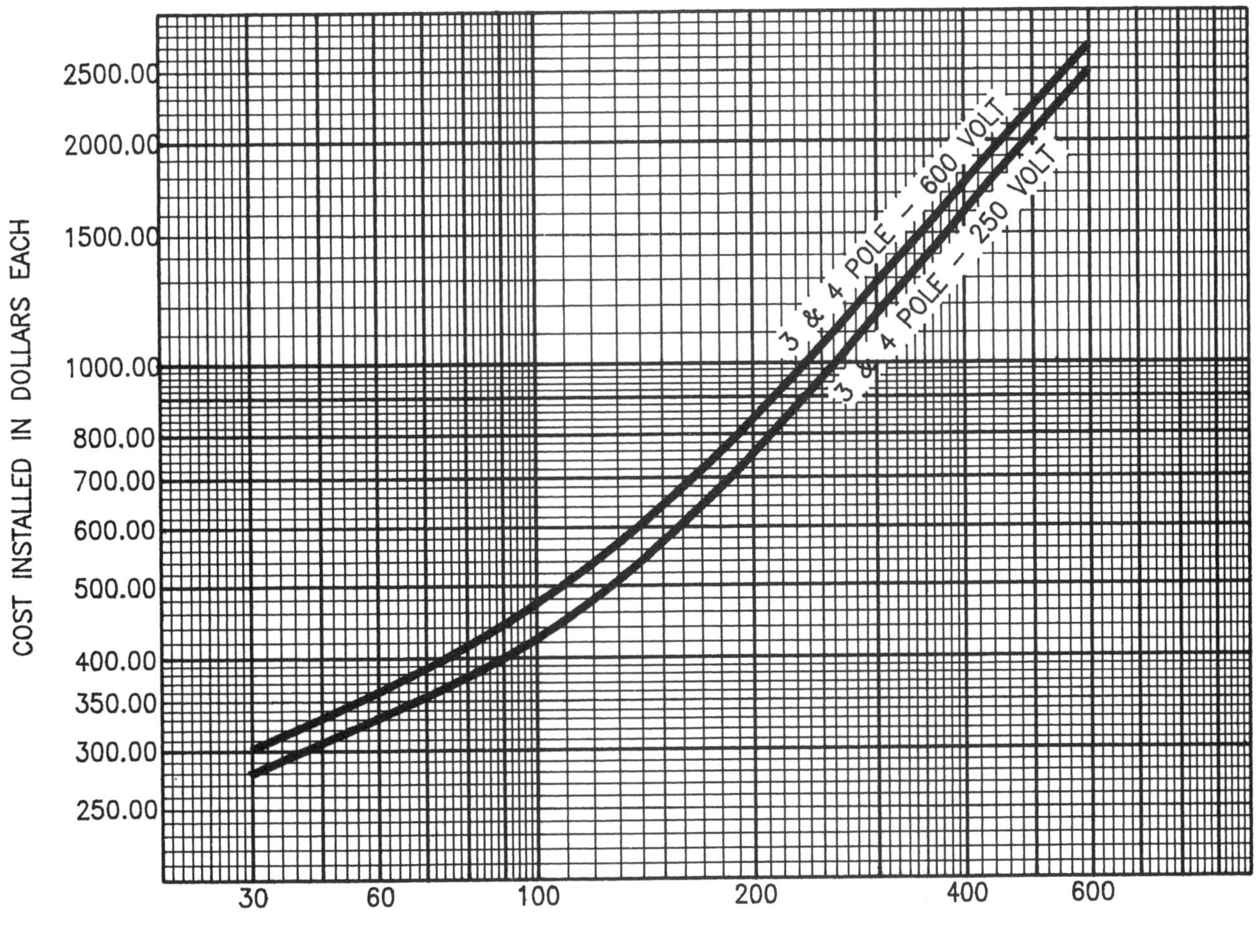

The costs shown for the plug-in busway switches in the 250- and 600-volt classes consist of the published contractors' book prices with the necessary one-time fuses and installation on the busway. The costs shown do not include conduit terminals or the conductor length required within the switch.

COST OF NONMETALLIC DUCT BANK

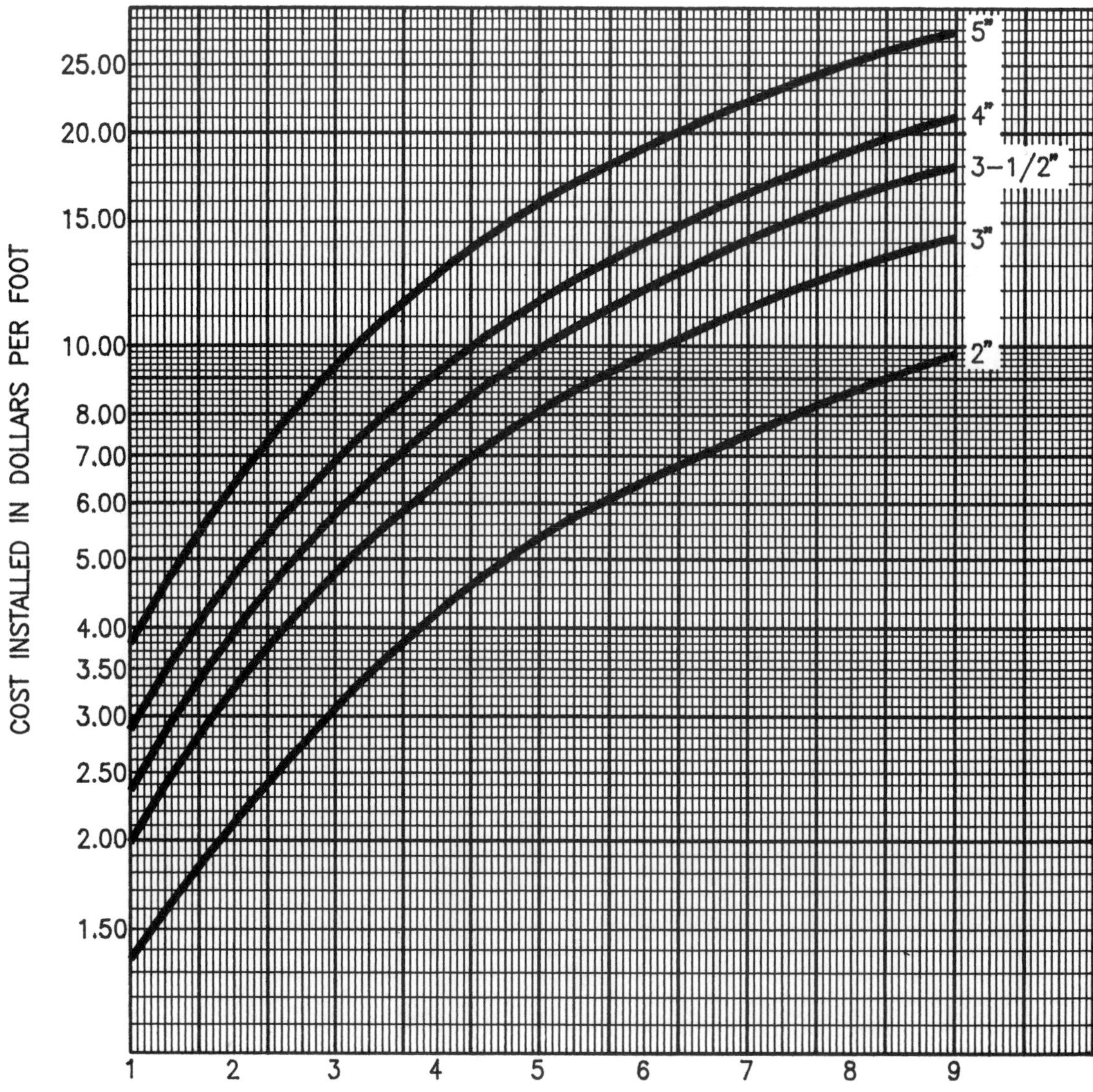

NUMBER OF PLASTIC DUCTS IN BANK

The costs shown for nonmetallic duct, earth cover, include the published contractors' book price for plastic duct of the sizes shown. Included are the spacers, cement, and #10 iron fish wire for each duct. Labor is included for installation of the above; however, no trenching or backfilling is provided in the costs shown. See Section L for trenching and backfilling.

COST OF NONMETALLIC DUCT BANK

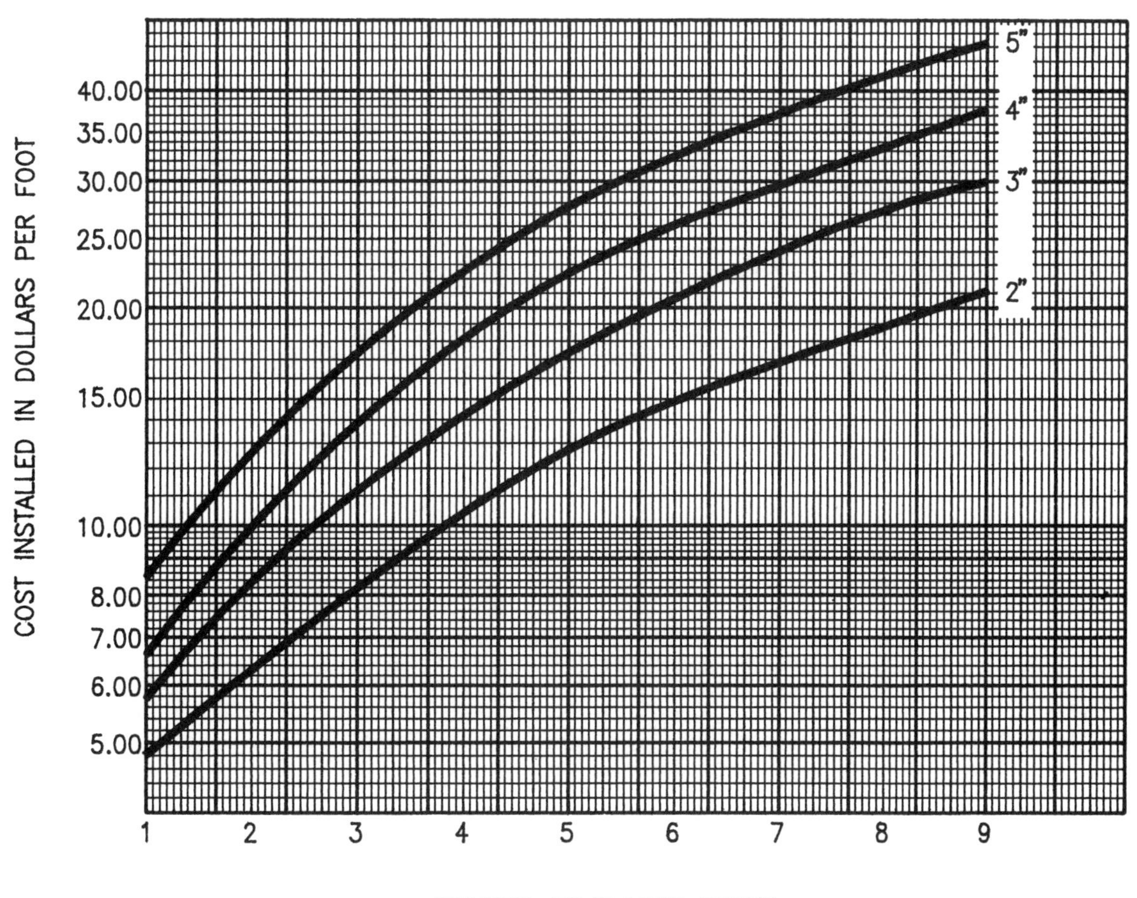

The costs shown for nonmetallic duct bank, concrete encased, include the published contractors' book price for plastic duct of the sizes shown. Included are the couplings, cement, plastic spacers on 5-foot centers for 2-inch separation in both directions, #10 iron fish wire for each duct, and concrete to provide a 3-inch envelope around the duct bank. Labor is included for the installation of the above; however, no trenching or backfilling is provided in the costs shown. See Miscellaneous Section L for trenching and backfilling.

The costs shown for the nonmetallic duct bank, reinforced-concrete-encased, include the published contractors' book price for plastic duct of the sizes shown. Included are the cement, plastic spacers on 5-foot centers for 2-inch separation in both directions, #10 iron fish wire for each duct, rebar, and concrete to provide a 3-inch envelope around the duct bank. Labor is included for the installation of the above; however, no trenching or backfilling is provided in the costs shown. See Miscellaneous Section L for trenching and backfilling.

COST OF NONMETALLIC DUCT BANK

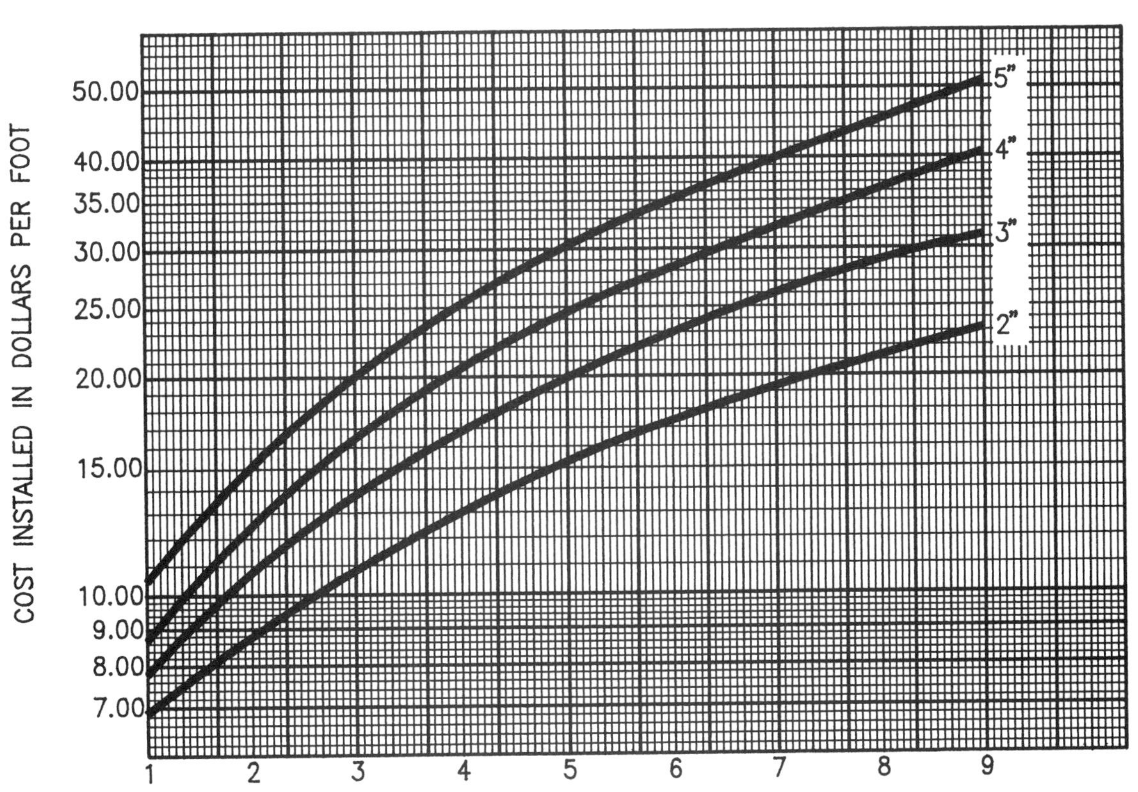

NUMBER OF PLASTIC DUCTS IN BANK

E

E-28

The costs shown for cable tray (ladder type) and fitting consist of the published contractors' book prices for the tray and fittings shown. All tray and fittings shown here are 4 inches deep and have rung spacing of 9 inches on centers and are as manufactured by Square D Co.

Included: (material and labor)

1. *Splice plates and bolts*
2. *Two 36-inch hanger rods on 5-foot centers*
3. *Rod-suspension assemblies appropriate to the tray*

Excluded:

1. *Freight and cartage from factory*
2. *Covers*

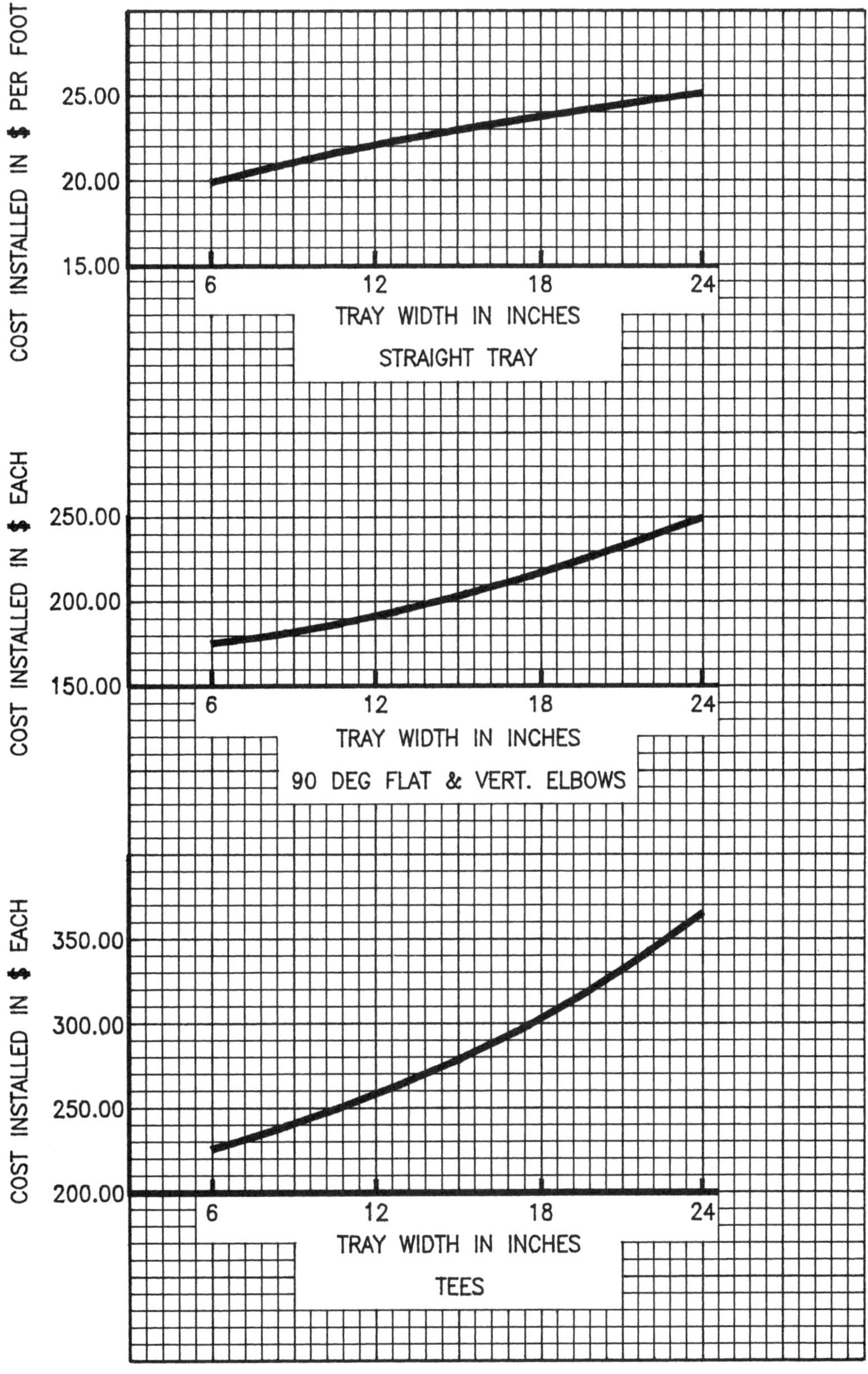
COST INSTALLED IN $ PER FOOT
25.00
20.00
15.00
6
12
18
24
TRAY WIDTH IN INCHES
STRAIGHT TRAY
COST INSTALLED IN $ EACH
250.00
200.00
150.00
6
12
18
24
TRAY WIDTH IN INCHES
90 DEG FLAT & VERT. ELBOWS
COST INSTALLED IN $ EACH
350.00
300.00
250.00
200.00
6
12
18
24
TRAY WIDTH IN INCHES
TEES

Branch Circuits

COST OF EMT WITH WIRE

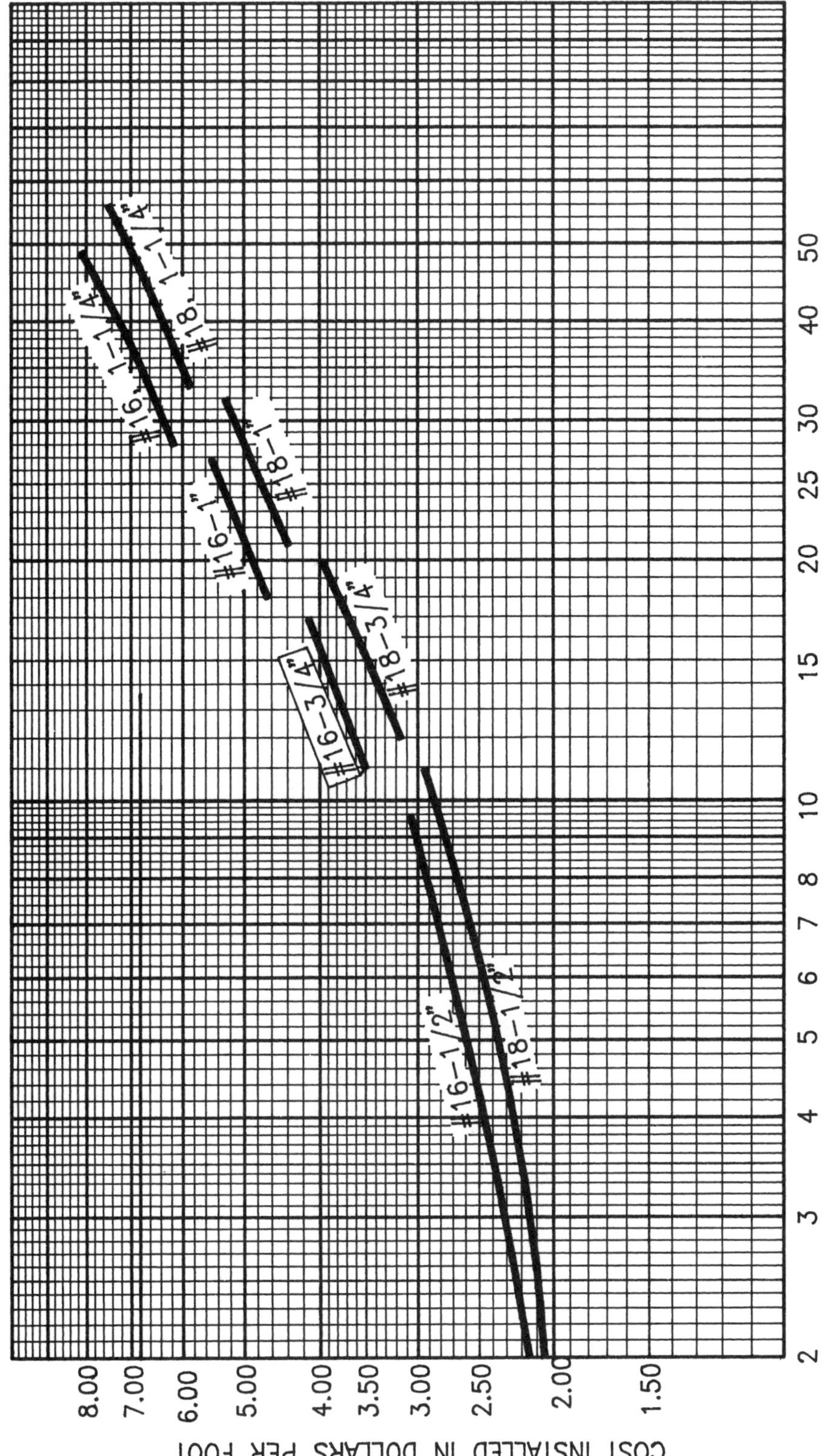

The costs shown for EMT conduit and TFF wire include the published contractors' book price and labor for installation of both conduit and wire. The graph complies with the 1990 National Electrical Code, Chapter 9, Table 2.

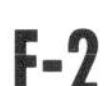

COST OF EMT WITH WIRE

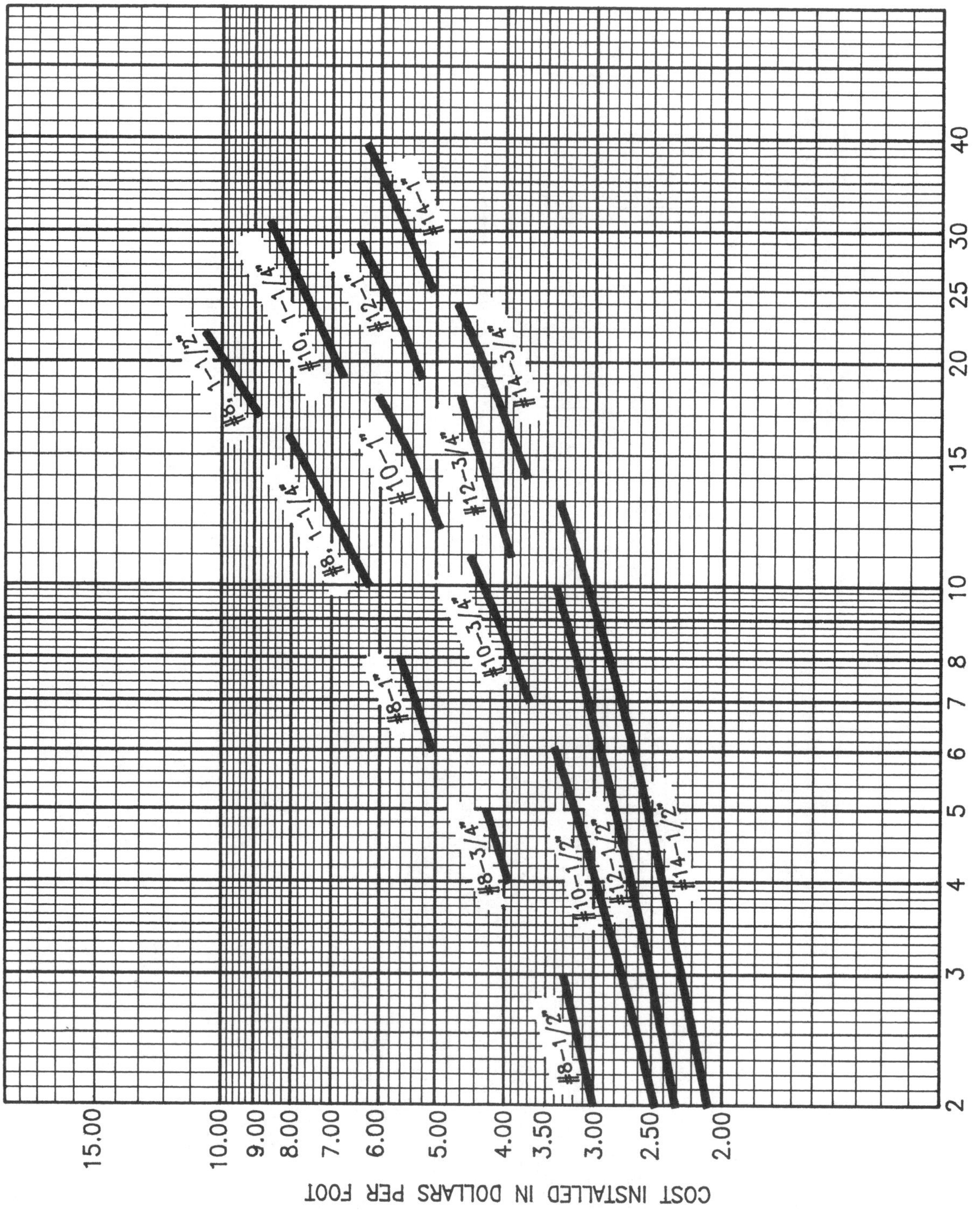

NUMBER OF CONDUCTORS AND CONDUIT
2
3
4
5
6
7
8
10
15
20
25
30
40
COST INSTALLED IN DOLLARS PER FOOT
15.00
10.00
9.00
8.00
7.00
6.00
5.00
4.00
3.50
3.00
2.50
2.00
#8. 1-1/2"
#10. 1-1/4"
#12-1"
#14-1"
#8. 1-1/4"
#10-1"
#12-3/4"
#14-3/4"
#10-3/4"
#8-1"
#8-3/4"
#10-1/2"
#12-1/2"
#14-1/2"
#8-1/2"

F-2

The costs shown for EMT conduit and THWN/THHN wire include the published contractors' book price and labor for installation of both conduit and wire. The graph complies with the 1990 National Electrical Code, Chapter 9, Table 3B.

COST OF IMC OR GRC CONDUIT WITH WIRE

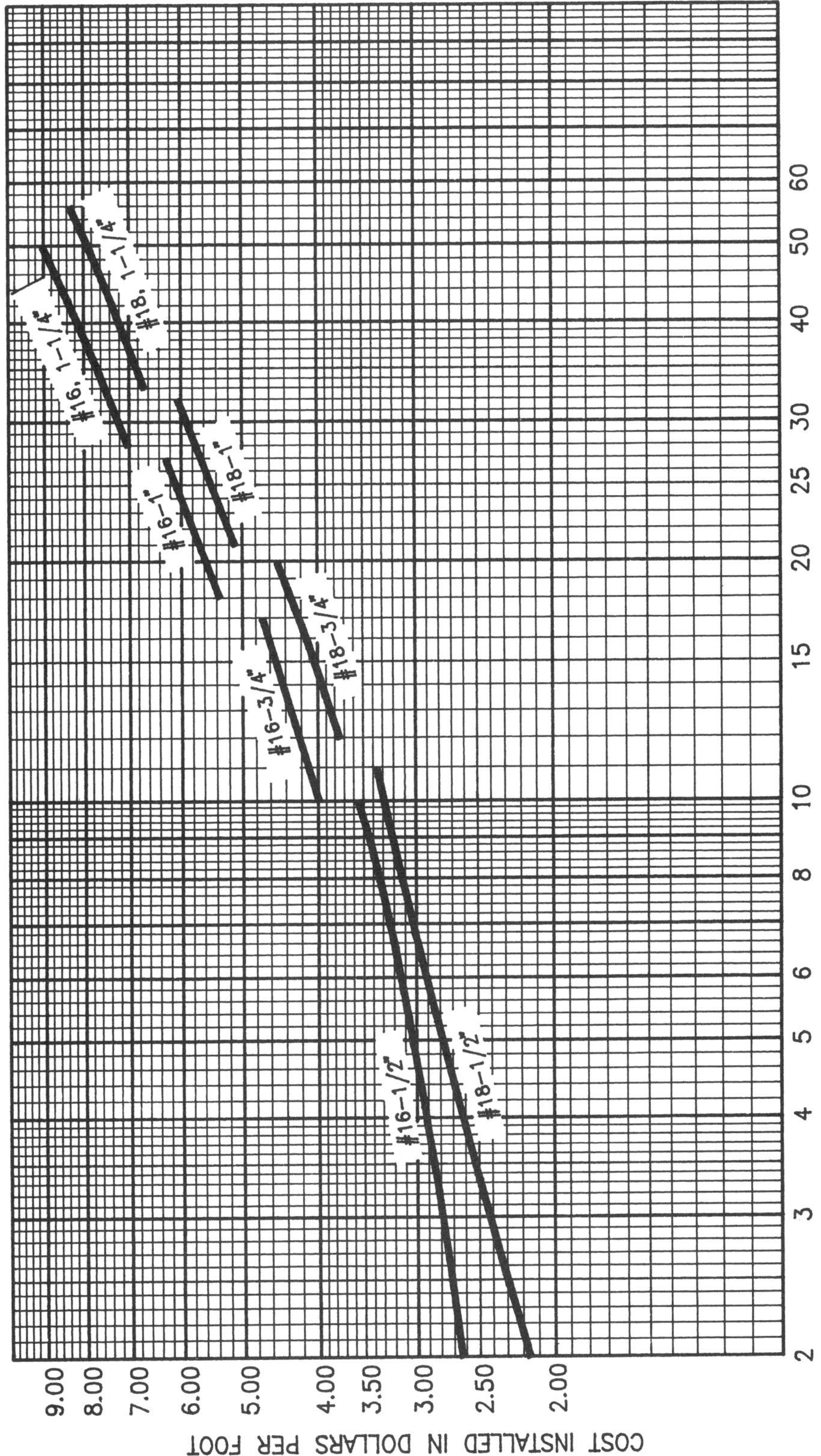

The costs shown for the IMC and GRC conduit with TFF wire include the published contractors' book price and labor for installation of both conduit and wire. The graph complies with the 1990 National Electrical Code, Chapter 9, Table 2.

COST OF IMC OR GRC WITH WIRE

F-4

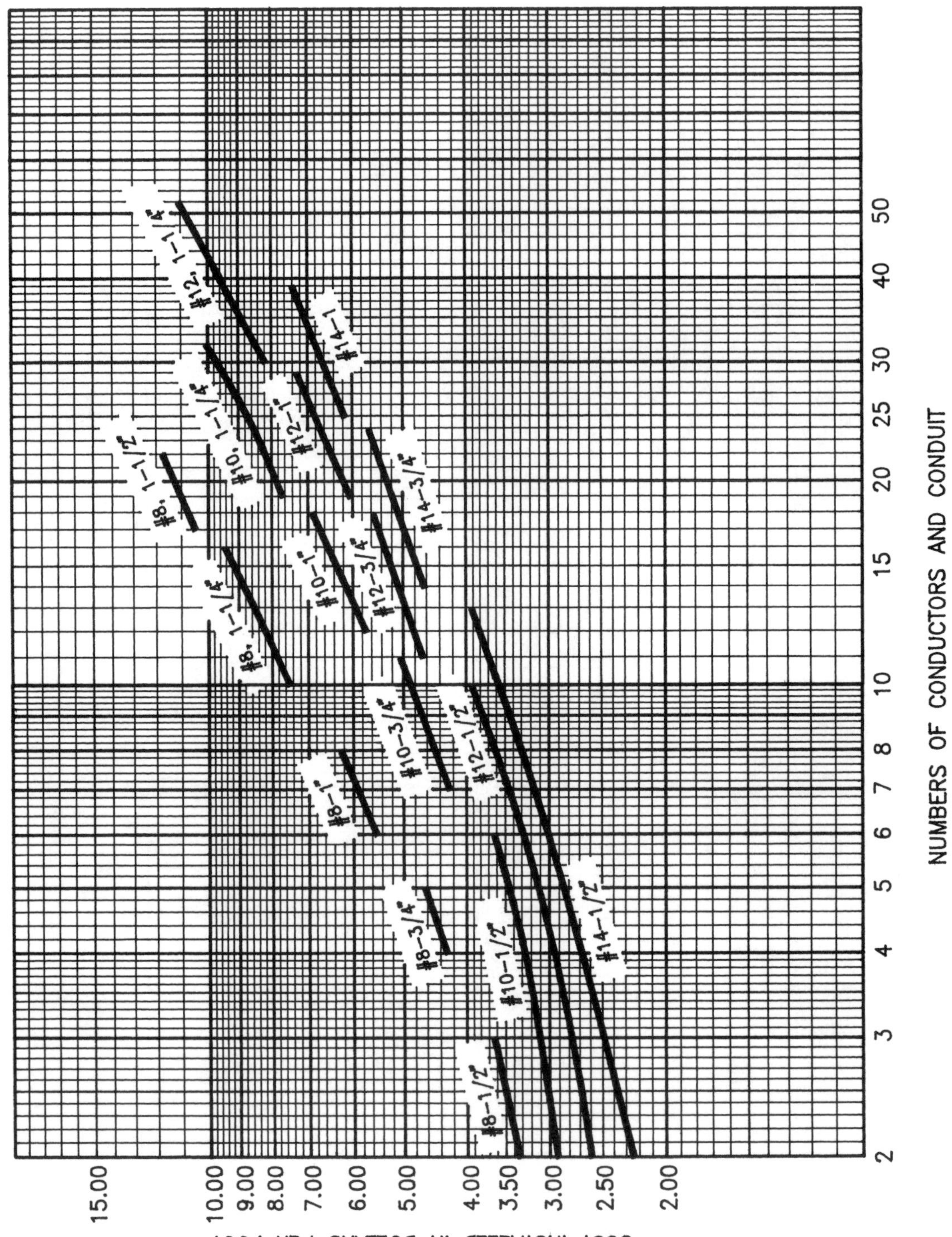

The costs shown for the IMC and GRC conduit with THWN/THHN wire include the published contractors' book price and labor for installation of both conduit and wire. The graph complies with the 1990 National Code.

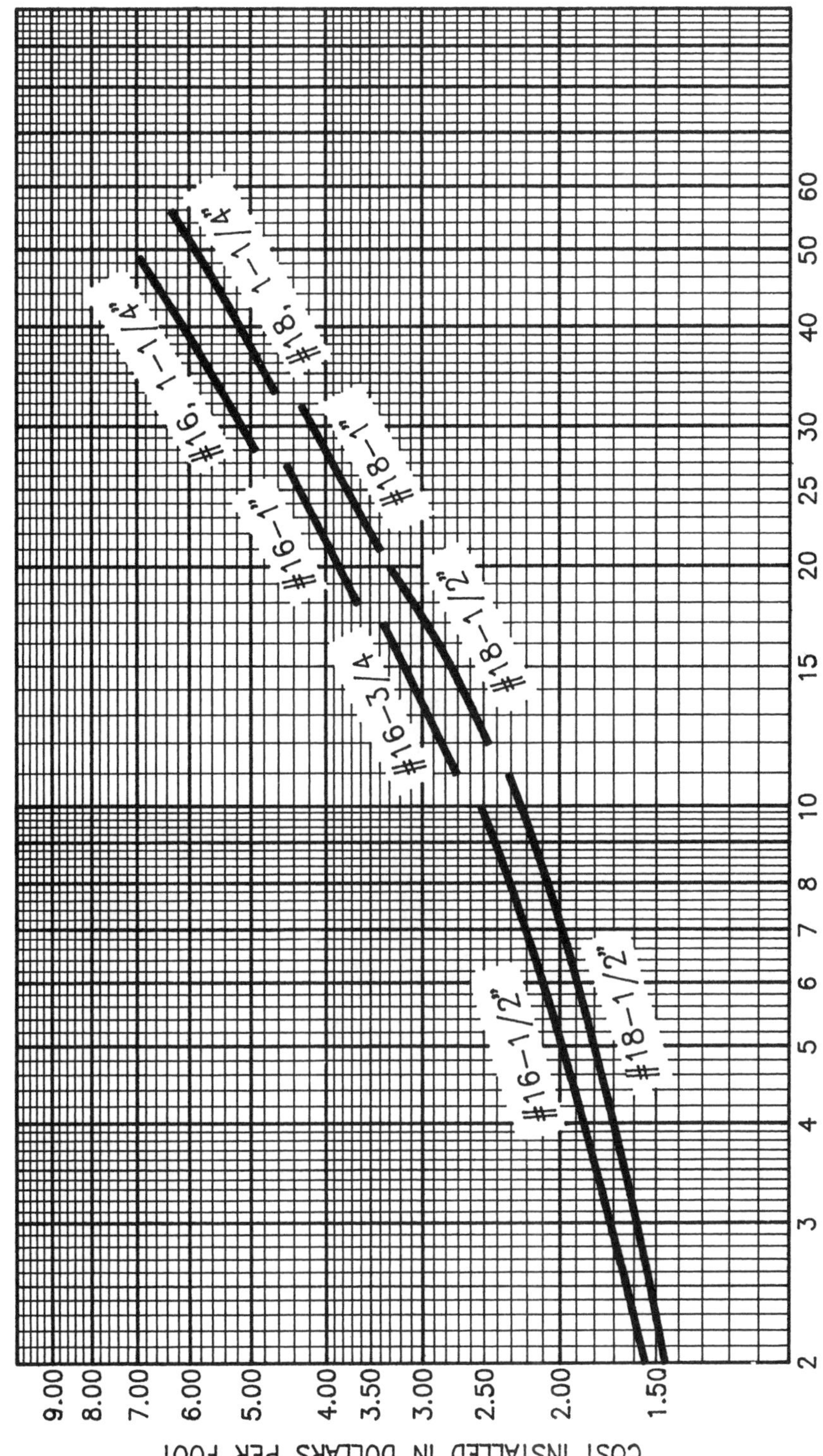

The costs shown for the PVC conduit with TFF wire includes the published contractors' book price and the labor for installation of both conduit and wire. The graph complies with the 1990 National Electrical Code.

COST OF PVC CONDUIT & WIRE

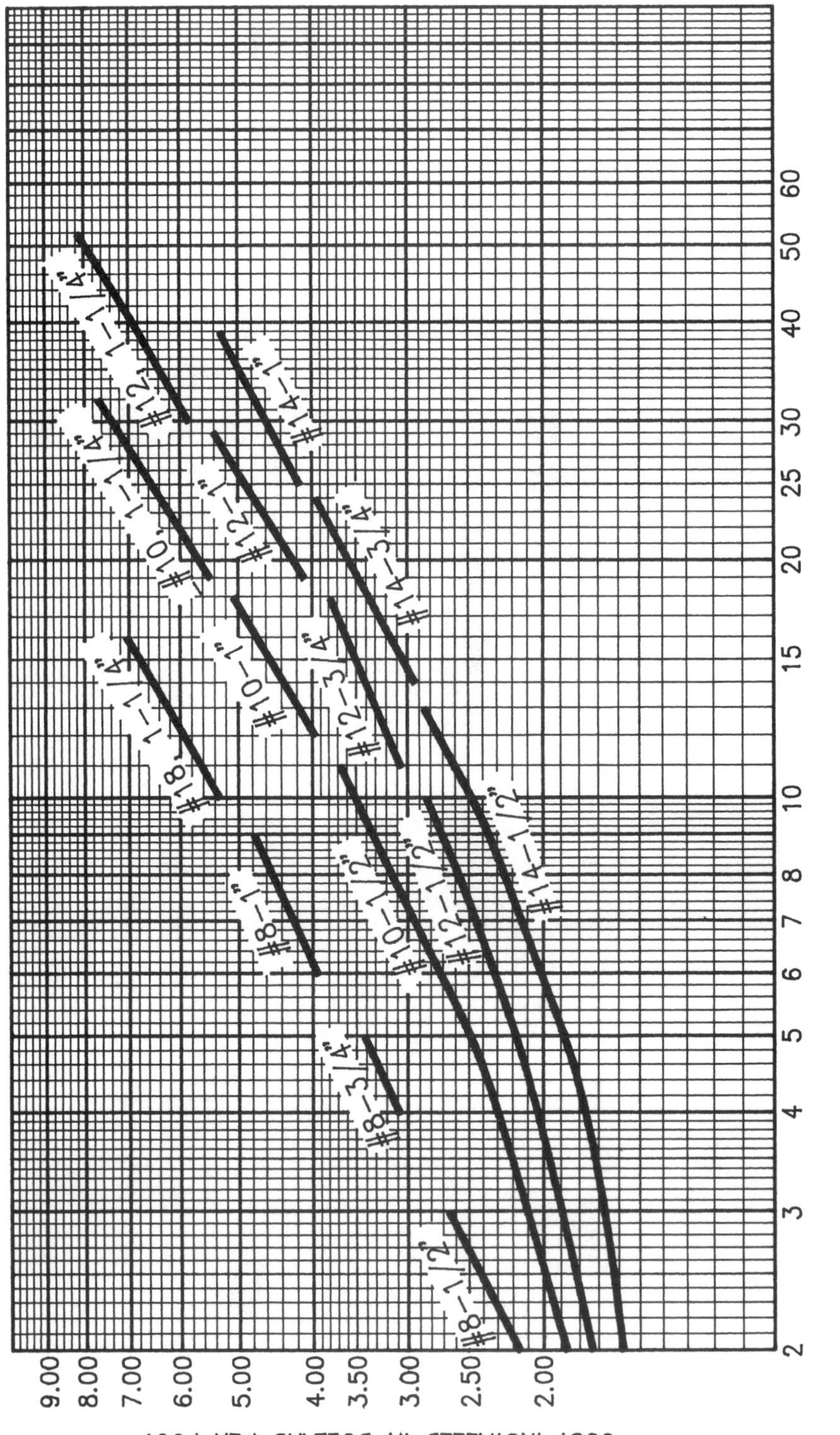

The costs shown for the PVC conduit with THWN/THHN wire include the published contractors' book price and labor for installation of both conduit and wire. The graph complies with the 1990 National Electrical Code.

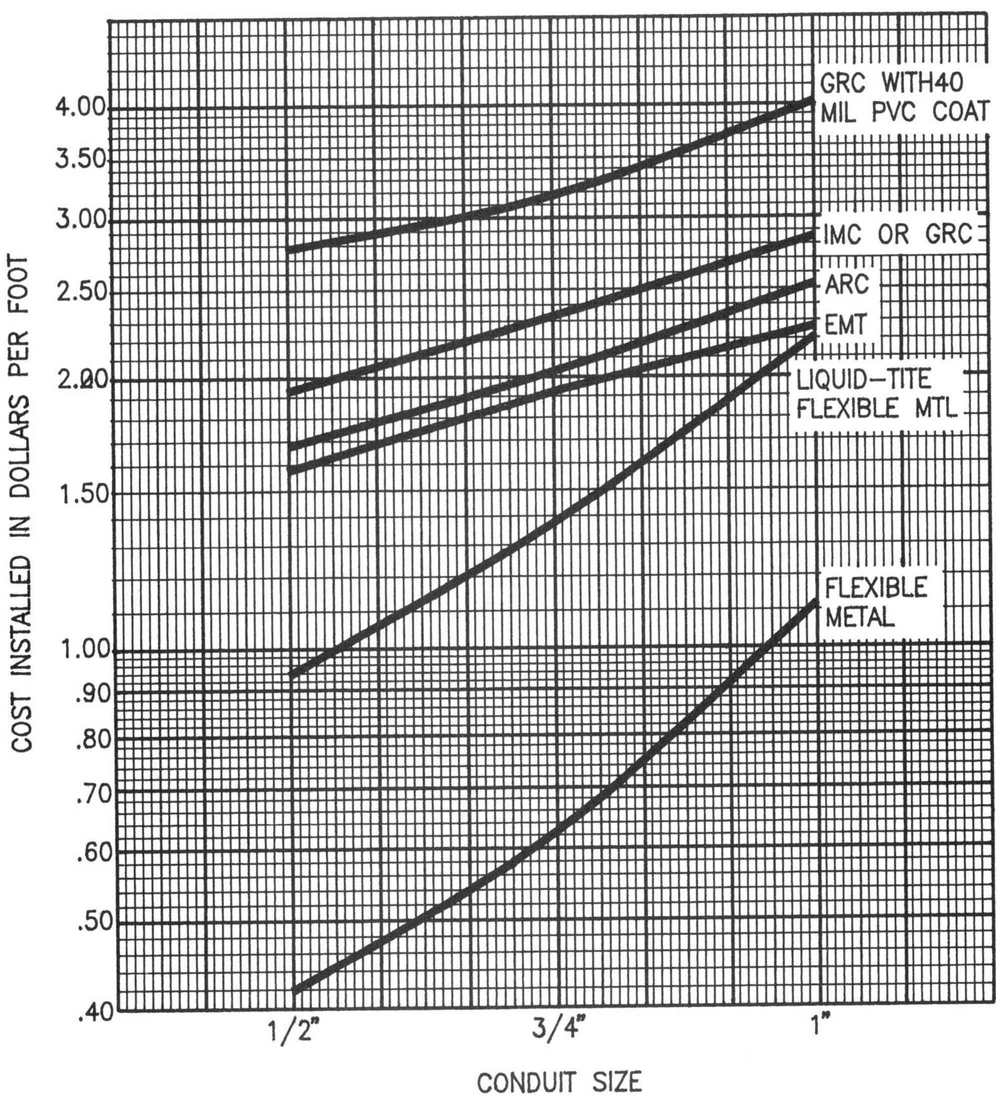

The costs shown for the branch circuit raceways include the published contractors' book price and the labor required for installation.

COST OF NONMETALLIC BRANCH CIRCUIT CONDUITS

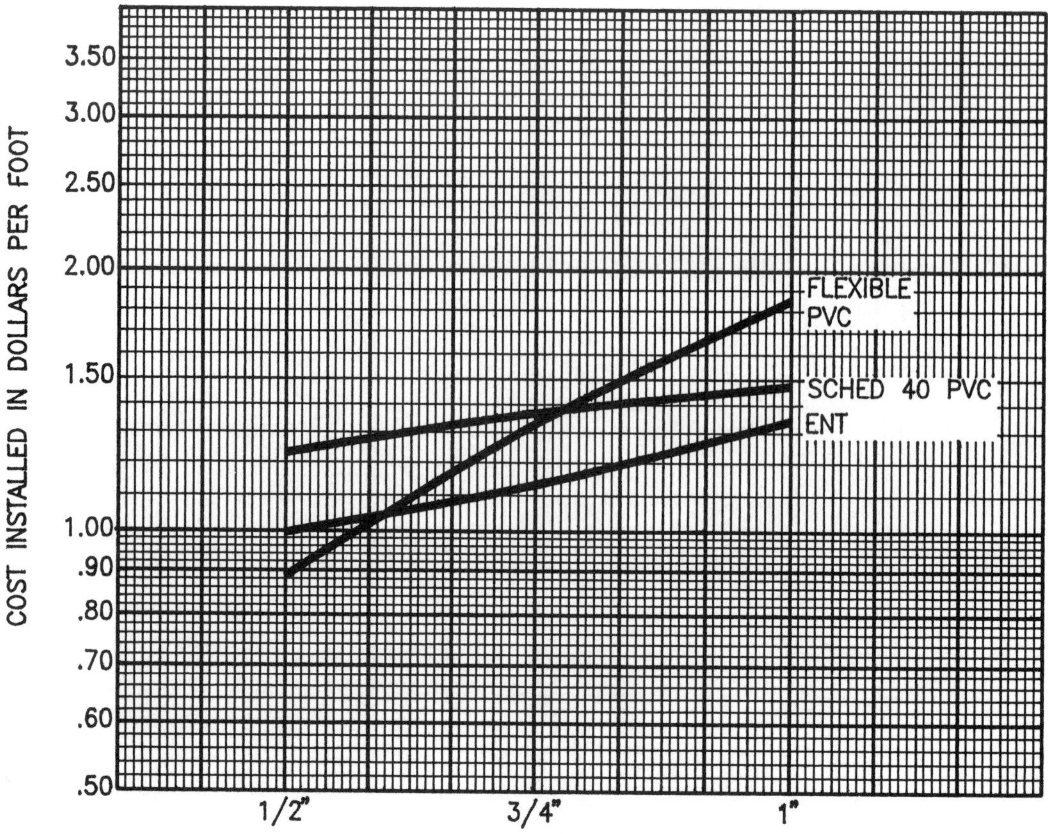

SIZE OF CONDUIT

The costs shown for the branch circuit conduits include the published contractors' book price and the labor required for installation. Electrical Nonmetallic Tubing (ENT) is in the 1990 National Electrical Code, Article 331.

COST OF BRANCH CIRCUIT CONDUIT TERMINALS

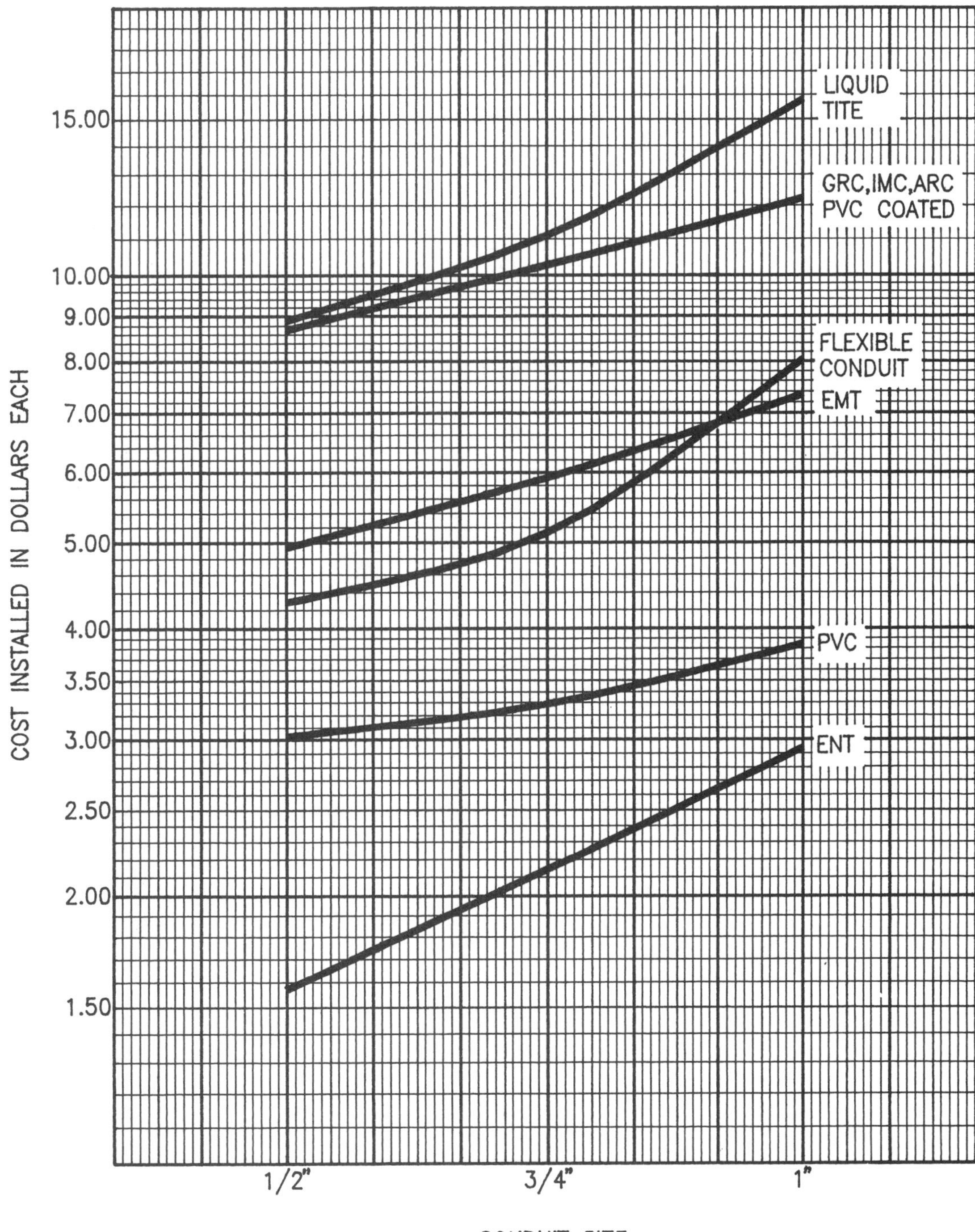

The costs shown for conduit terminals include the published contractors' book price for the type of terminal required, such as locknuts and insulated metallic bushings for IMC and GRC, insulated throat connectors for EMT, plastic connectors for PVC, and connectors for FLEX. They further include the labor required for preparing the end of the conduit either by cutting and threading or by cutting and glueing as needed to satisfy the requirements of the conduit.

COST OF BRANCH CIRCUIT CONDUIT FITTINGS

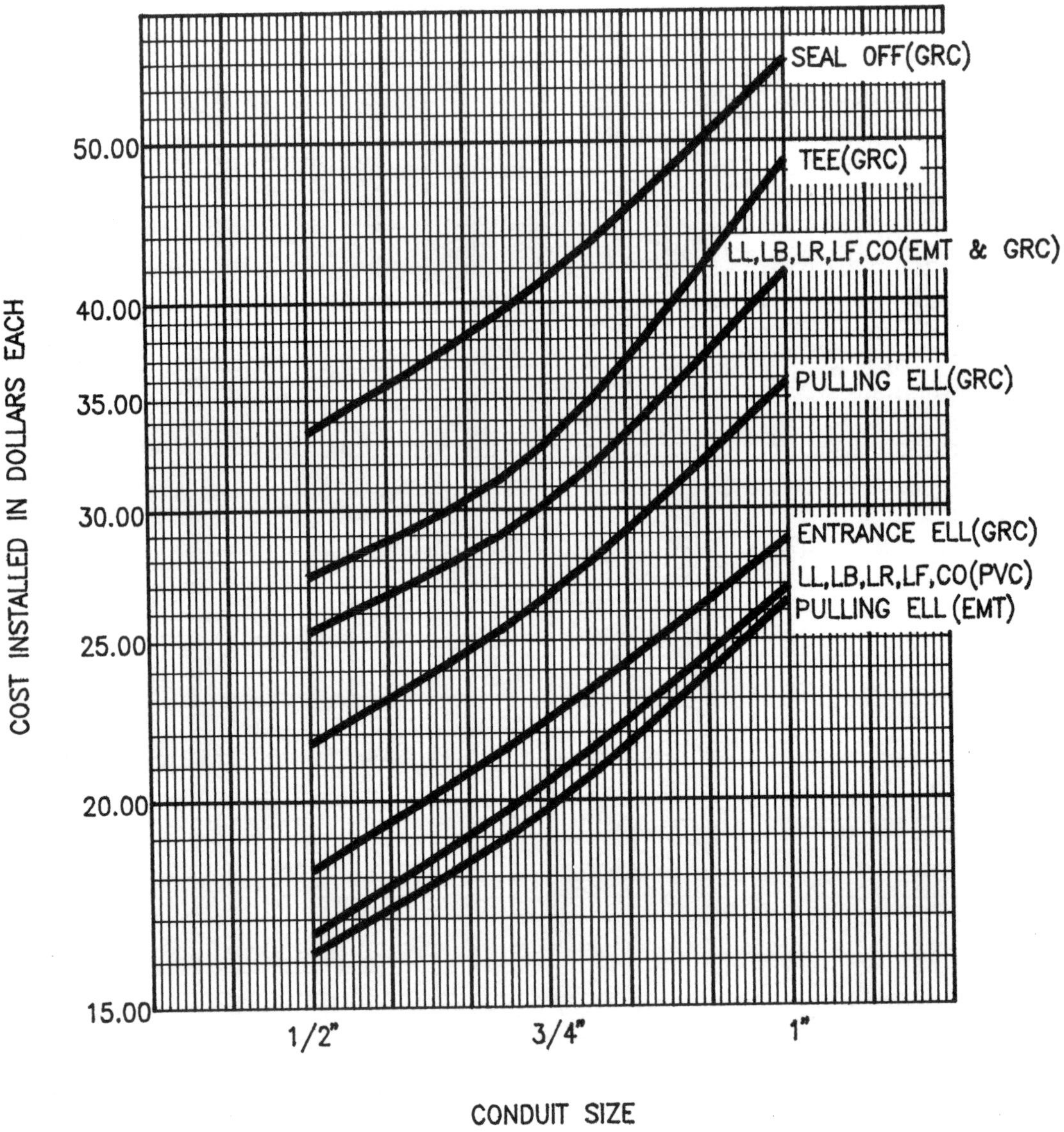

F-10

The costs shown for conduit fittings include the published contractors' book price for the various fittings shown of the gasketed type to suit the kind of conduit required. These fittings are basically LBs, LLs, LRs, and LFs. The cost also includes the labor of preparing the end of the conduit and installing the fitting. Seal-offs are considered to be used with GRC in hazardous applications and include the installation of sealing compound as required.

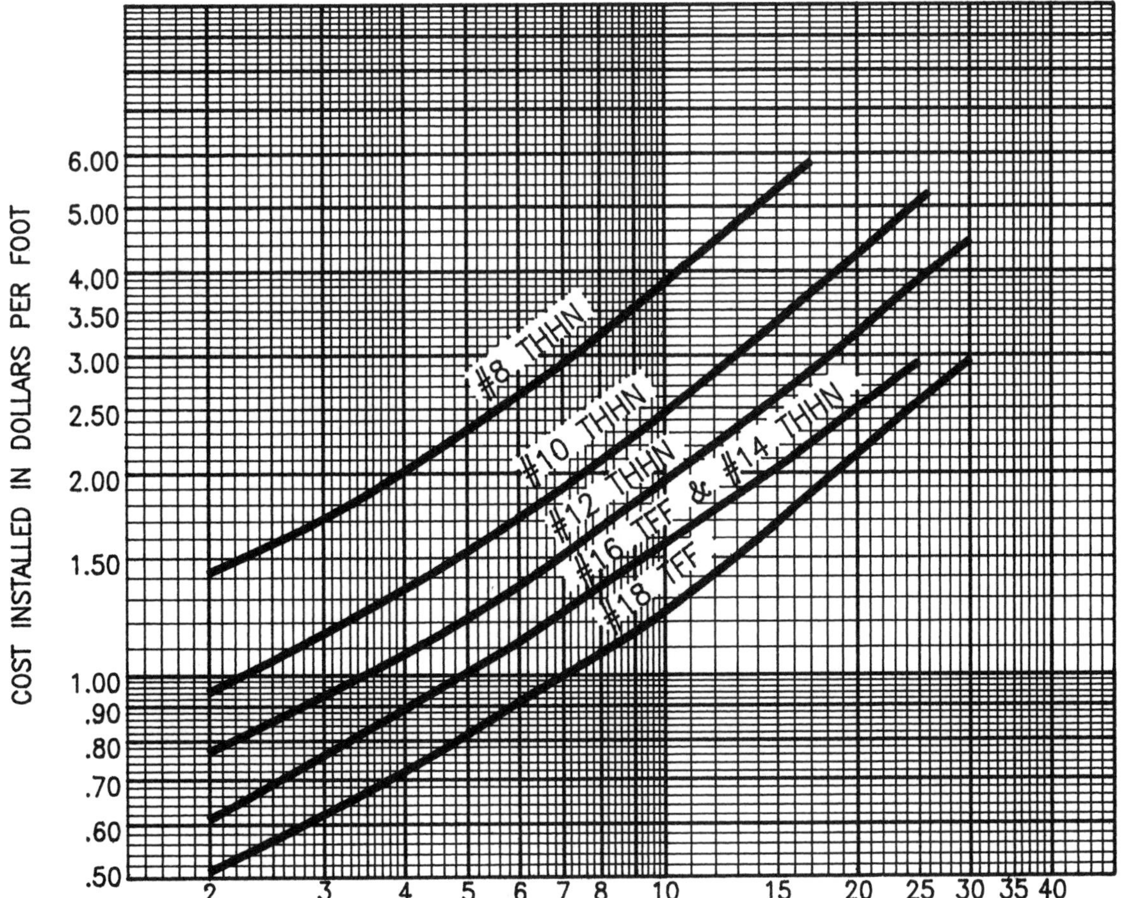

The costs shown for the branch circuit conductors include the published contractors' book price and the required labor for installing the conductors in the raceways.

COST OF THERMOSTAT/ANNUNCIATOR CABLE

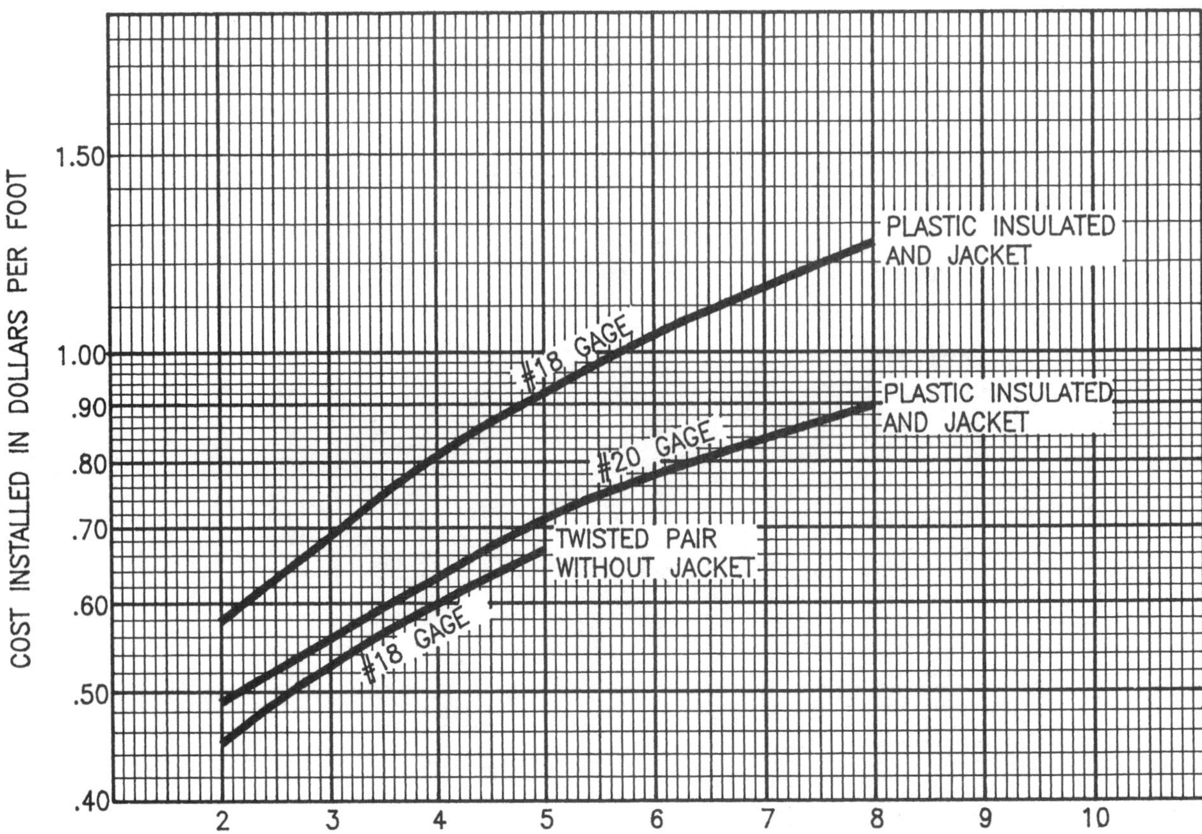

F-12

NUMBER OF CONDUCTORS

The costs shown for the thermostat/annunciator cable are for plastic insulation with or without plastic jacket and include the published contractors' book price and the labor for installing the cable in conduit as one conductor.

COST OF NONMETALLIC SHEATHED CABLE

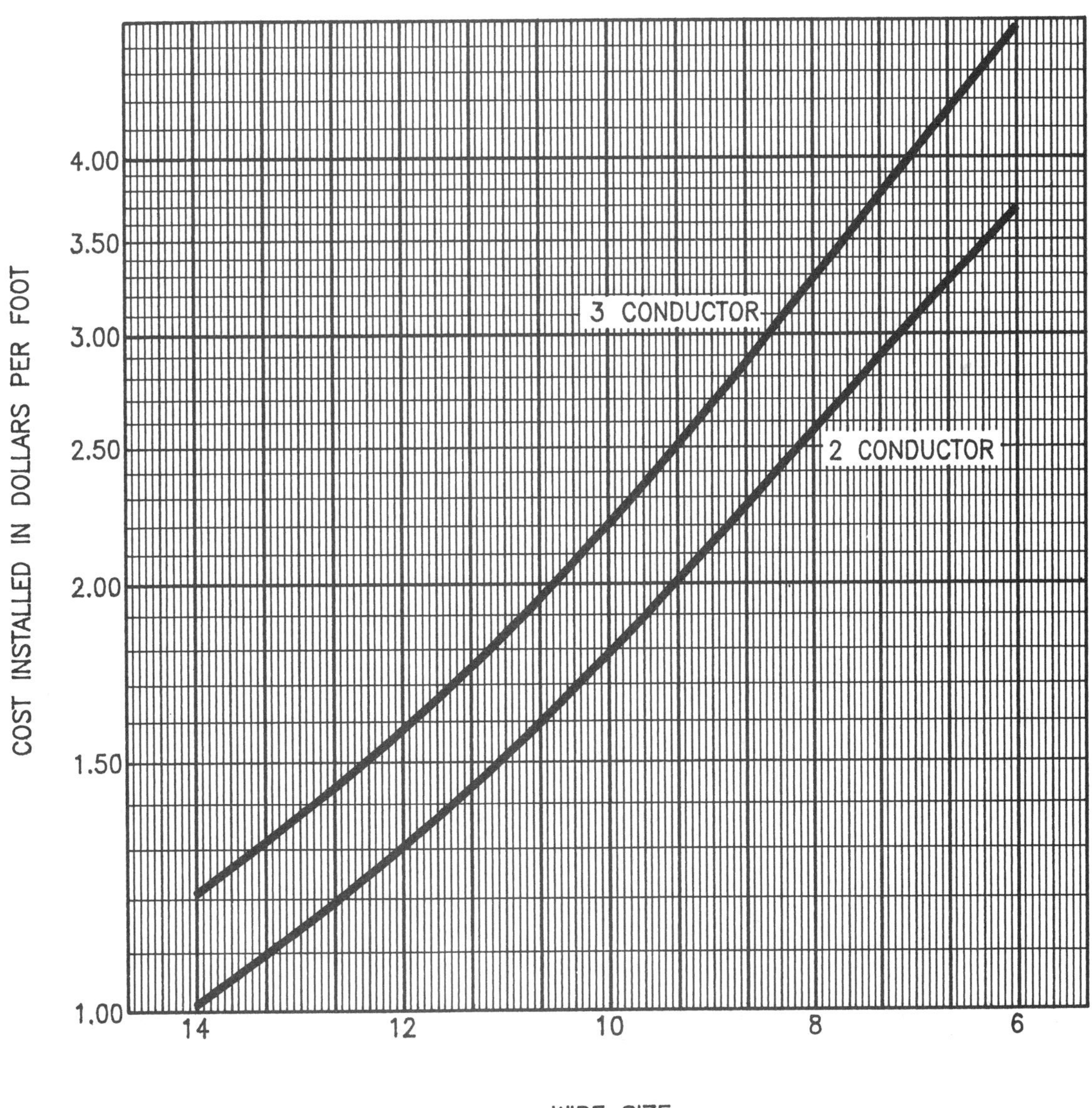

The costs shown for the nonmetallic sheathed cable include the published contractors' book price and also the labor for installing the NMSC on a wood surface or joists supported by staples on 4-foot centers. The grounding conductor is full-size.

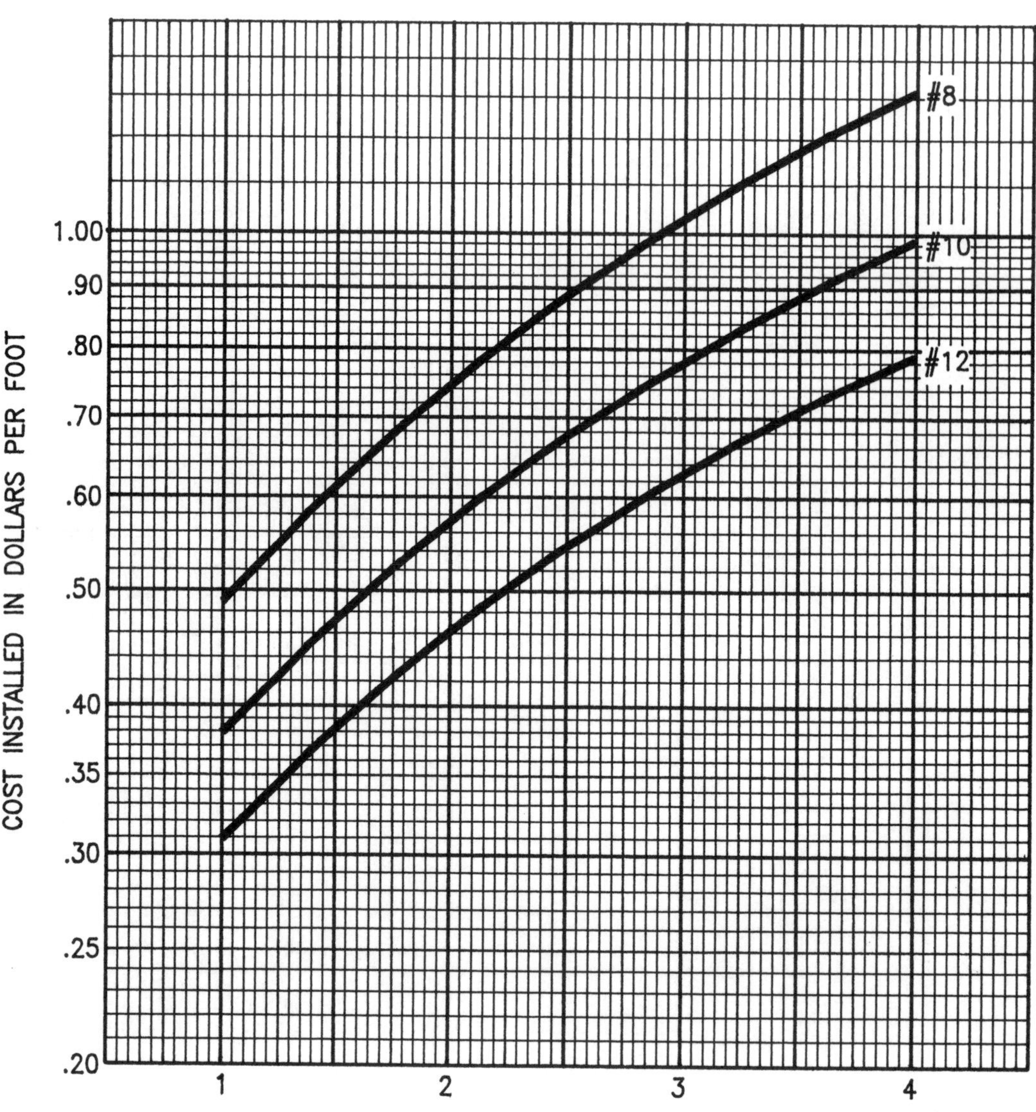

F-14

The costs shown for the direct burial conductors include the published contractors' book price for the kind of insulation shown and the labor for installing in an existing open trench. Trenching and backfilling are not included. See Section L.

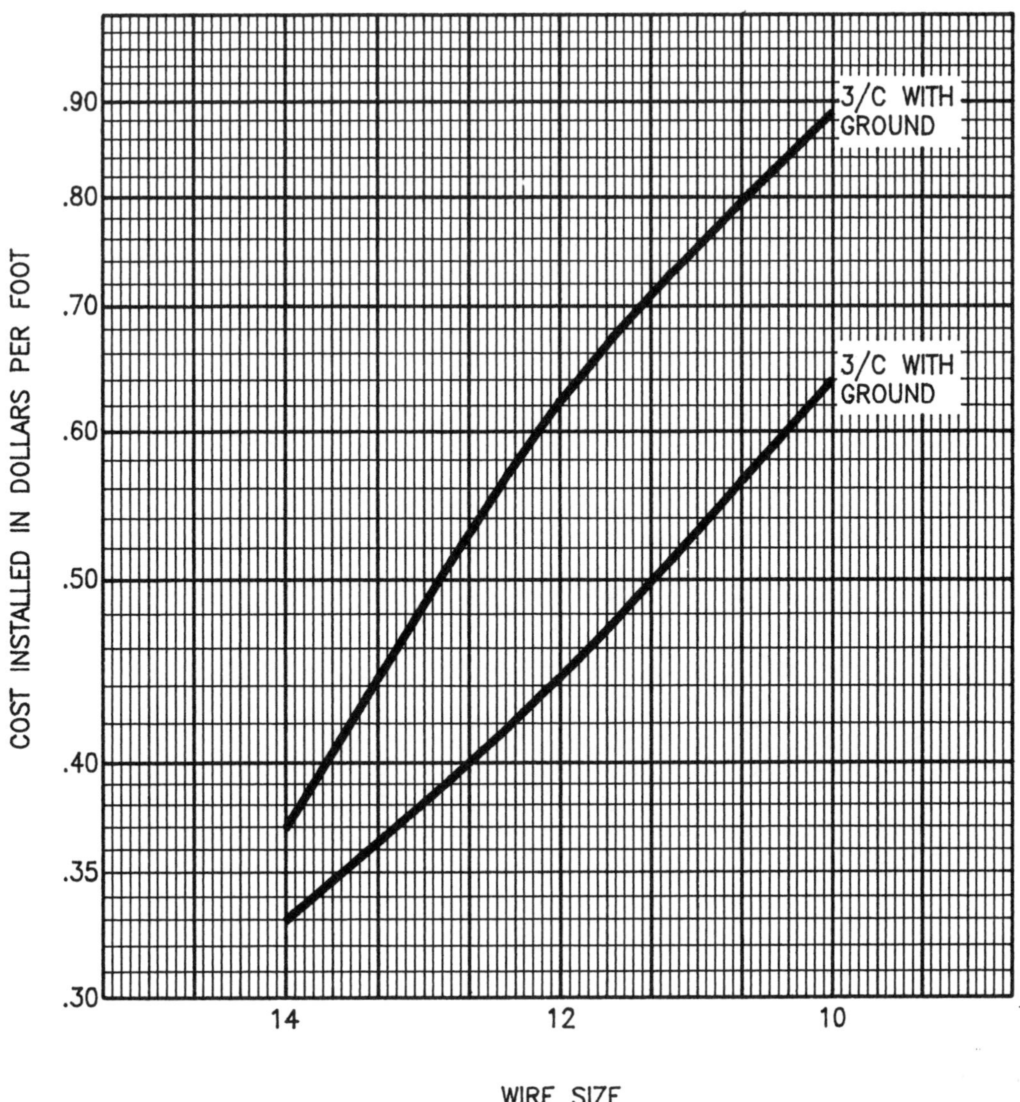

The costs shown for the underground feeder (UF) cable are based upon the contractors' book price for the number of conductors shown, including the grounding conductor. Labor is based upon installing in an existing trench. Trenching and backfilling costs are not included. See Section L for these costs.

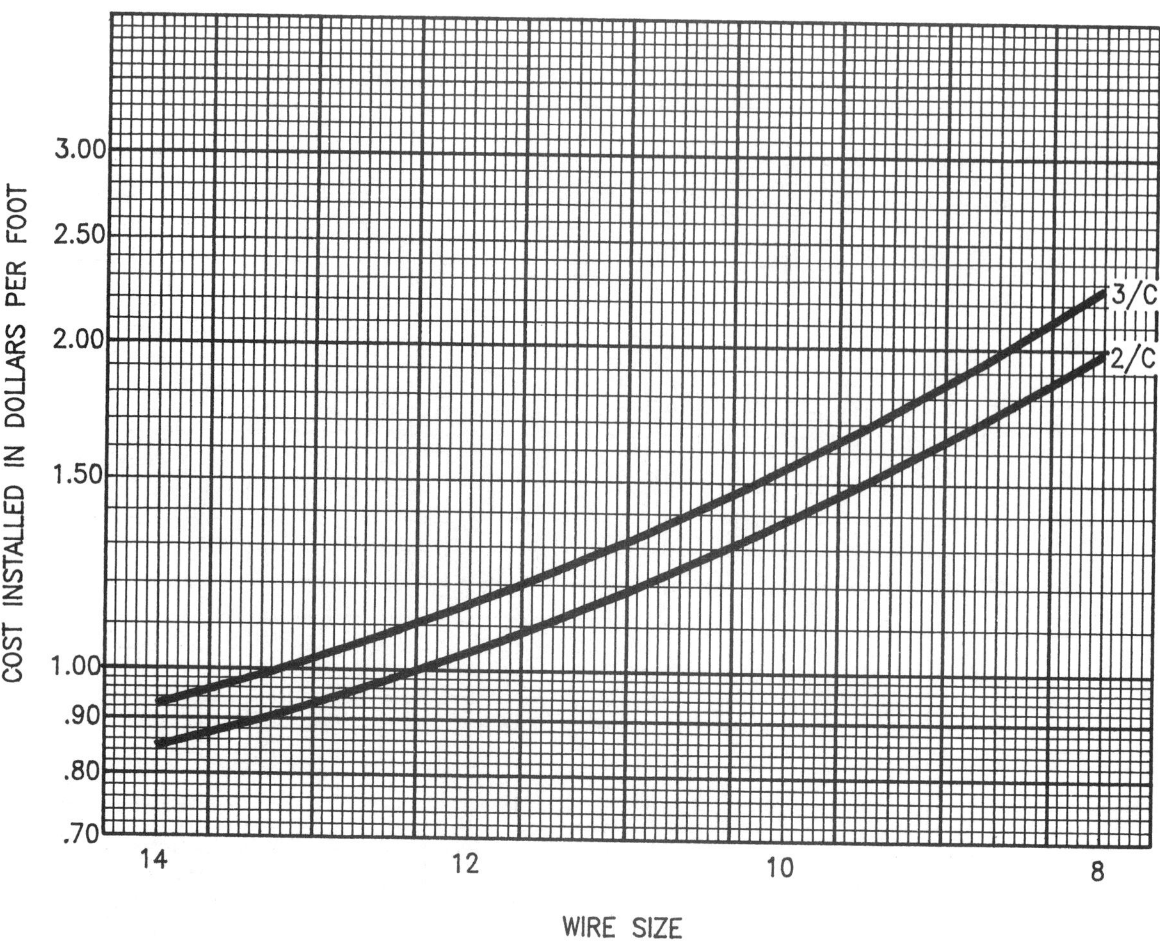

The costs shown for the armored cable include the published contractors' book price and the labor for installation in bored wood joists. Conductors are copper.

COST OF MINERAL–INSULATED WIRING CABLE (NORMAL DUTY)

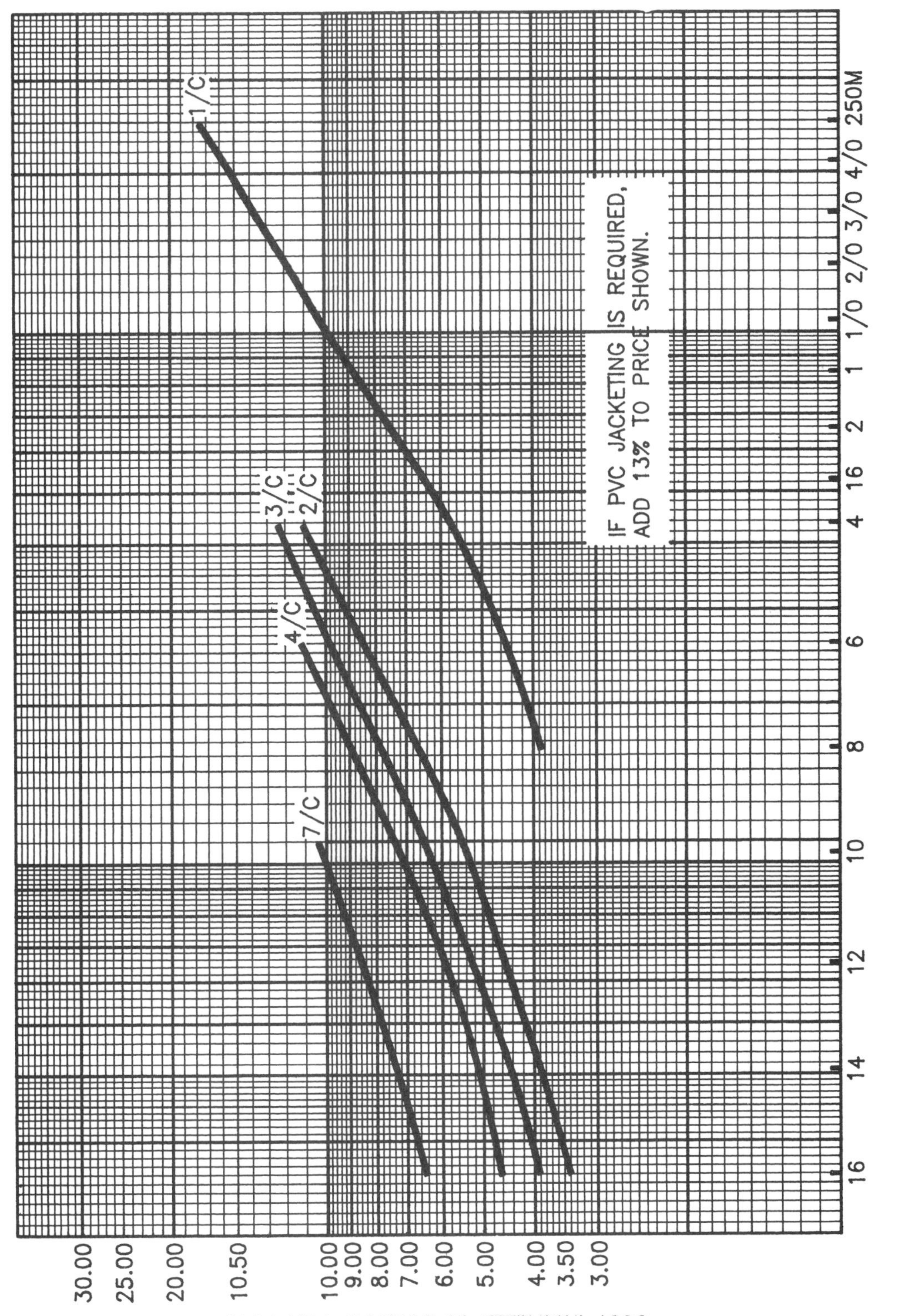

The costs shown for the mineral-insulated cable consist of the published contractors' book price and labor required for installation on the surface with the number and size of conductors shown.

The costs shown for the mineral-insulated cable terminations consist of the published contractors' book price and labor for installation in accordance with the manufacturer's instructions. Some special tools are required.

COST OF MINERAL-INSULATED CABLE TERMINATIONS

COST INSTALLED IN DOLLARS EACH

FITTING SIZE	WIRE SIZE	NUMBER OF CONDUCTORS				
		1	2	3	4	7
1/2"	16	—	17.35	19.89	22.13	30.96
	14	—	18.43	20.65	25.73	32.49
	12	—	19.19	21.80	27.25	34.02
	10	—	23.22	26.30	29.17	48.49
	8	19.60	25.13	28.59	31.46	
	6	21.51	27.42	31.26	46.84	
	4	19.60	41.31	46.90		
3/4"	3	—				
	2	30.21				
	1	32.12				
	1/0	34.03				
	2/0	36.33				
	3/0	38.62				
1"	4/0	53.23				
	250MCM	56.20				

PYROPAK TERMINATION KITS CONTAIN MATERIAL TO TERMINATE BOTH ENDS OF A CABLE RUN. THEY ARE UL APPROVED FOR BOTH HAZARDOUS & NON-HAZARDOUS LOCATIONS.

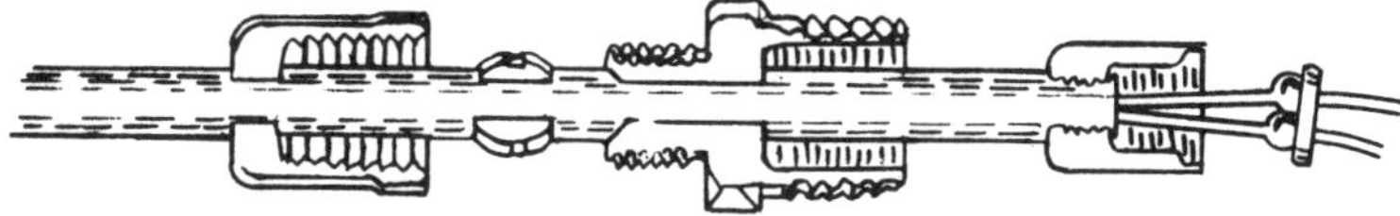

The costs shown for ceiling outlets mounted flush in wood frame construction include a 4-inch octagon box with plaster ring mounted to an adjustable bar hanger with a fixture stud, and two connectors of the type required.

Recessed above the ceiling, the outlet is designed for use with a recessed fixture and consists of a 4-inch square box and blank cover, bar hanger, two connectors for cable or conduit, a 4-foot piece of 3/8 inch flexible metal conduit with two connectors, and three 6-foot lengths of #12 AF wire.

Flush pan or deck mounting is in concrete and contains a 4-inch concrete ring, plate with fixture stud, and connectors for the type of conduit required.

COST OF FIXTURE OUTLETS

COST INSTALLED IN DOLLARS EACH

CEILING OUTLETS

TYPE TERMINAL	TYPE OF CONSTRUCTION: FLUSH MOUNTING			SURFACE MOUNTING		
	WOOD FRAME	RECESSED ABOVE SUSP. CLG.	FLUSH PAN OR DECK	WOOD	STEEL	CONCRETE
NON–METALLIC SHEATHED CABLE	21.15	—	—	—	—	—
ARMORED CABLE	28.40	—	—	—	—	—
EMT	31.95	40.15	33.10	24.90	25.50	27.65
GRC	—	48.60	41.15	36.05	36.95	41,85

COST INSTALLED IN DOLLARS EACH

WALL OUTLETS

TYPE TERMINAL	TYPE OF CONSTRUCTION: FLUSH MOUNTING				SURFACE MOUNTING			
	WOOD FRAME	METAL STUDS	BLOCK MASONRY	REINF. CONCRETE	WOOD	STEEL	CONCRETE	BLOCK MASONRY
NON–METALLIC SHEATHED CABLE	11.15	12.35	—	—	—	—	—	—
ARMORED CABLE	14.75	17.00	—	—	—	—	—	—
EMT	27.35	33.70	28.45	45.00	26.05	25.35	31.80	31.80
GRC	36.15	45.17	36.45	52.25	37.50	36.85	43.30	31.80

Receptacles shown on the facing page include much the same materials as described on the preceding page, but in addition the duplex receptacles contain 15-ampere-rated specification-grade devices unless otherwise indicated and painted metal wall plates. Outlets served by nonmetallic sheathed cable or armored cable have standard-grade devices. Surface-mounted 30- and 50- ampere outlets are of the molded-plastic dryer and range type.

COST INSTALLED IN DOLLARS EACH	RECEPTACLES								
	TYPE OF CONSTRUCTION								
	FLUSH MOUNTING				SURFACE MOUNTING				
TYPE TERMINAL	WOOD FRAME	METAL STUDS	BLOCK MASONRY	REINF. CONCRETE	CONDUIT SUPPORT	WOOD	STEEL	CONCRETE	BLOCK MASONRY
DUPLEX									
N.M.S.C.	26.18	24.30	—	—	—	—	—	—	—
ARMORED CABLE	25.85	30.48	—	—	—	—	—	—	—
EMT	37.55	41.95	40.95	56.10	49.40	34.25	34.25	37.80	37.65
GRC	45.90	49.20	48.95	63.70	51.20	45.70	45.70	49.30	49.15
WEATHERPROOF DUPLEX									
N.M.S.C.	34.35	32.50	—	—	—	—	—	—	—
ARMORED CABLE	34.00	38.65	—	—	—	—	—	—	—
EMT	45.70	47.05	48.90	—	74.90	—	—	—	—
GRC	53.90	54.65	56.90	—	76.70	—	—	—	—
SINGLE									
20A–3W–EMT	55.15	57.25	55.35	73.20	64.75	51.10	50.75	53.75	53.35
GRC	63.15	64.15	64.25	80.45	66.55	64.15	61.80	65.25	64.80
30A–3W–RX/BX	55.15	57.25	55.35	—	—	61.50	—	—	—
EMT	63.15	64.15	64.25	80.45	87.50	52.10	51.75	66.26	54.40
GRC	67.75	59.75	66.90	85.05	89.30	63.55	63.25	66.25	65.90
50A–3W–RX/BX	72.65	—	—	—	—	61.50	—	—	—
EMT	73.10	70.60	70.00	87.75	73.10	61.50	—	78.00	64.55
GRC	81.80	78.00	78.65	95.95	78.74	74.95	—	78.00	78.00

DUPLEX, WEATHERPROOF DUPLEX, AND SINGLE RECEPTACLES

COST OF RECEPTACLES WITH BUILT–IN GROUND FAULT CIRCUIT INTERRUPTER

GROUND FAULT CIRCUIT INTERRUPTERS		
TYPE	INSTALLED COST EACH	
	INDIV. RECEPT.	FEED THRU TYPE
INDOOR	65.75	69.35
WEATHERPROOF	76.25	80.00

Costs shown include outlet box and single-gang ring mounted in plaster wall and GFI receptacle with painted metal (interior) wall plate.

CLOCK OUTLETS

TYPE TERMINAL	TYPE OF CONSTRUCTION — FLUSH MOUNTING			
	WOOD FRAME	METAL STUDS	HOLLOW MASONRY	REINF. CONCRETE
EMT	64.30	64.80	63.85	81.95
GRC	71.55	71.30	71.10	88.45

FLOOR OUTLETS

TYPE TERMINAL	TYPE OF CONSTRUCTION — FLUSH MOUNTING	
	WOOD FRAME	CONCRETE SLAB
EMT	89.95	111.95
GRC	91.65	111.10

TELEPHONE OUTLETS

TYPE TERMINAL	TYPE OF CONSTRUCTION					
	FLUSH WALL MOUNTED			EXPOSED	FLOOR MOUNTED	
	METAL STUDS	BLOCK MASONRY	REINF. CONCRETE	BLOCK MASONRY	WOOD FLOOR	CONCRETE SLAB FLOOR
EMT	33.50	32.50	48.15	26.10	87.05	116.30

The clock, floor, and telephone outlets are specification-grade devices installed as previously described. Those outlets mounted in the slab are pressed-steel floor boxes of the adjustable type and concrete-tight. The receptacles are flush in the floor.

COST INSTALLED IN DOLLARS EACH	TYPE OF CONSTRUCTION							
	FLUSH MOUNTING				SURFACE MOUNTING			
TYPE TERMINAL	WOOD FRAME	METAL STUDS	BLOCK MASONRY	REINF. CONCRETE	WOOD	STEEL	CONCRETE	BLOCK MASONRY
<u>SINGLE POLE</u>								
N.M.S.C.	29.85	31.05	—	—	—	—	—	—
ARMORED CABLE	33.50	35.80	—	—	—	—	—	—
EMT	42.85	49.50	47.40	61.60	40.15	48.60	42.85	42.85
GRC	50.95	60.40	54.70	68.10	52.50	50.60	53.65	54.05
<u>3 WAY SWITCH</u>								
N.M.S.C.	35.20	36.45	—	—	—	—	—	—
ARMORED CABLE	41.15	41.15	—	—	—	—	—	—
EMT	48.60	55.00	55.00	66.45	46.10	45.75	47.80	49.20
GRC	56.35	65.80	60.05	73.45	57.85	56.60	58.61	57.00
<u>DOOR SWITCH</u>								
N.M.S.C.	86.35	—	—	—	—	—	—	—
ARMORED CABLE	88.75	—	—	—	—	—	—	—
EMT	93.50	—	—	—	—	—	—	—
GRC	101.25	—	—	—	—	—	—	—
FLEX. METAL	91.95	—	—	—	—	—	—	—

The switches shown in this table include much the same materials as previously described, but, in addition, contain a 15-ampere-rated specification-grade quiet type of switch with a painted metal wall plate. All devices priced in this table are of specification-grade quality. No residential-grade or standard-grade devices are used in pricing.

COST OF POKE–THRU FLOOR OUTLETS

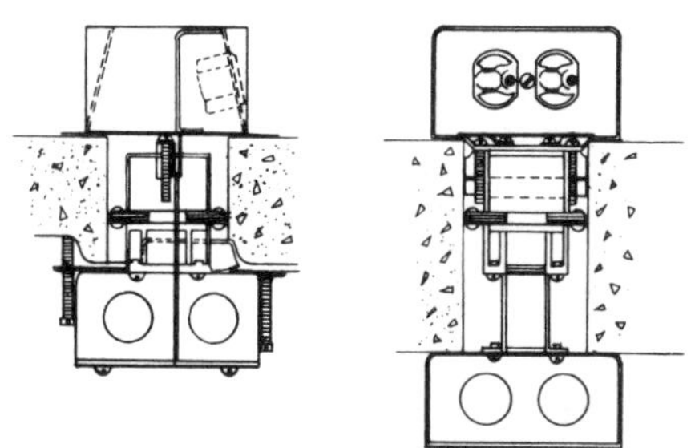

CONCRETE SLAB THICKNESS	COST INSTALLED EACH		
	TELEPHONE	DUPLEX RECEPTACLE	TELEPHONE & RECEPTACLE
4"	170.60	184.65	208.20
6"	178.25	231.20	268.45
8"	191.60	257.75	298.00

Costs of fittings include the published contractors' book price for the assembly, including the combination power-telephone-service fitting and the cost of core-drilling the concrete floor slab. Abandon plate includes the labor expense of fitting removal.

COST OF APPLIANCE CONNECTIONS

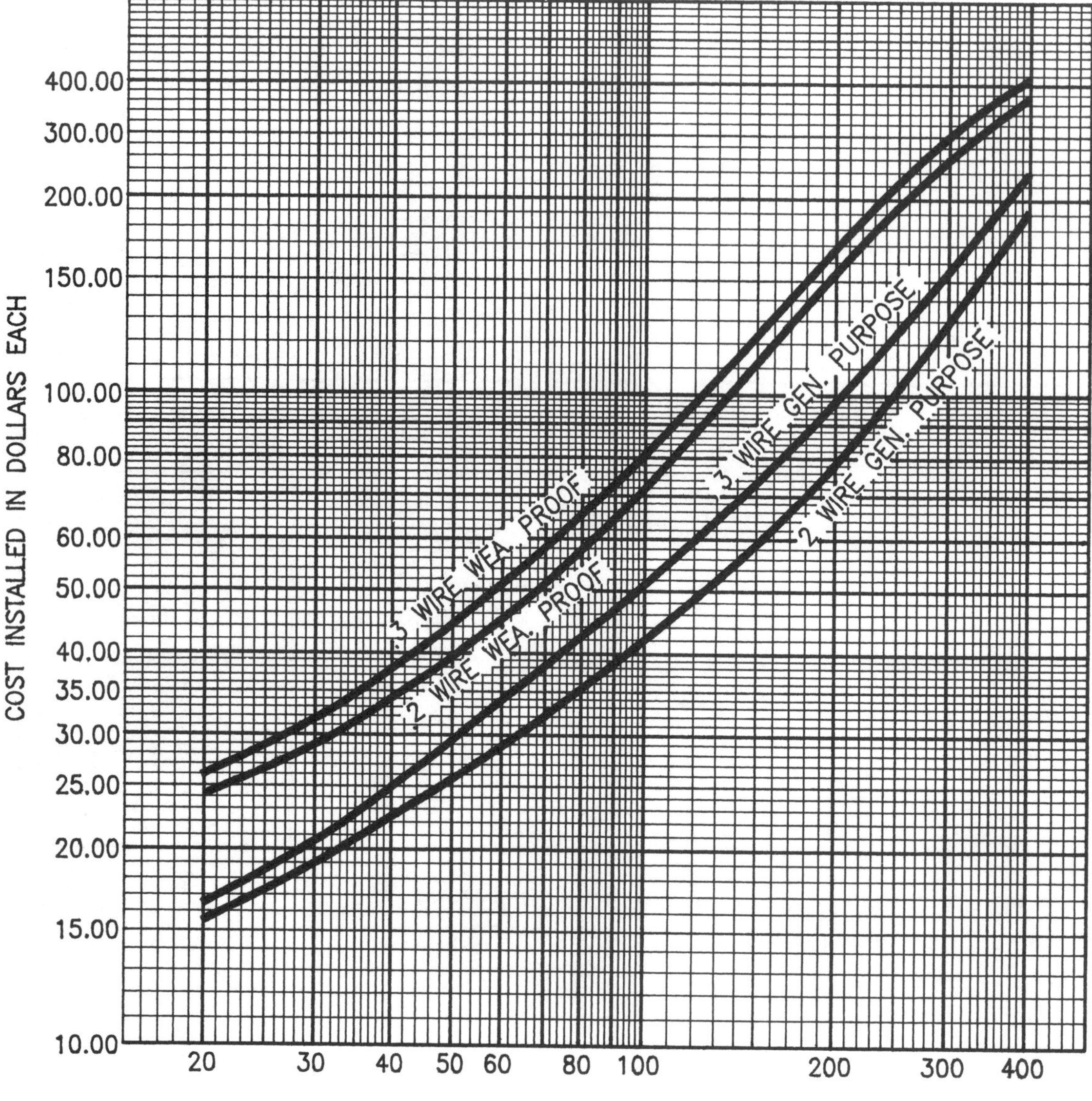

F-25

The costs shown for an appliance connection consist of 3 feet of flexible metal conduit for general-purpose use, or liquidtight flexible metal conduit for weatherproof use, with two connectors of the proper type, 4 feet of two or three conductors, and wire terminals, plus a grounding conductor sized in accordance with NEC Article 250-95. Labor is provided to make the final installation. Add for a safety switch if required.

COST OF MOTOR TERMINAL CONNECTIONS

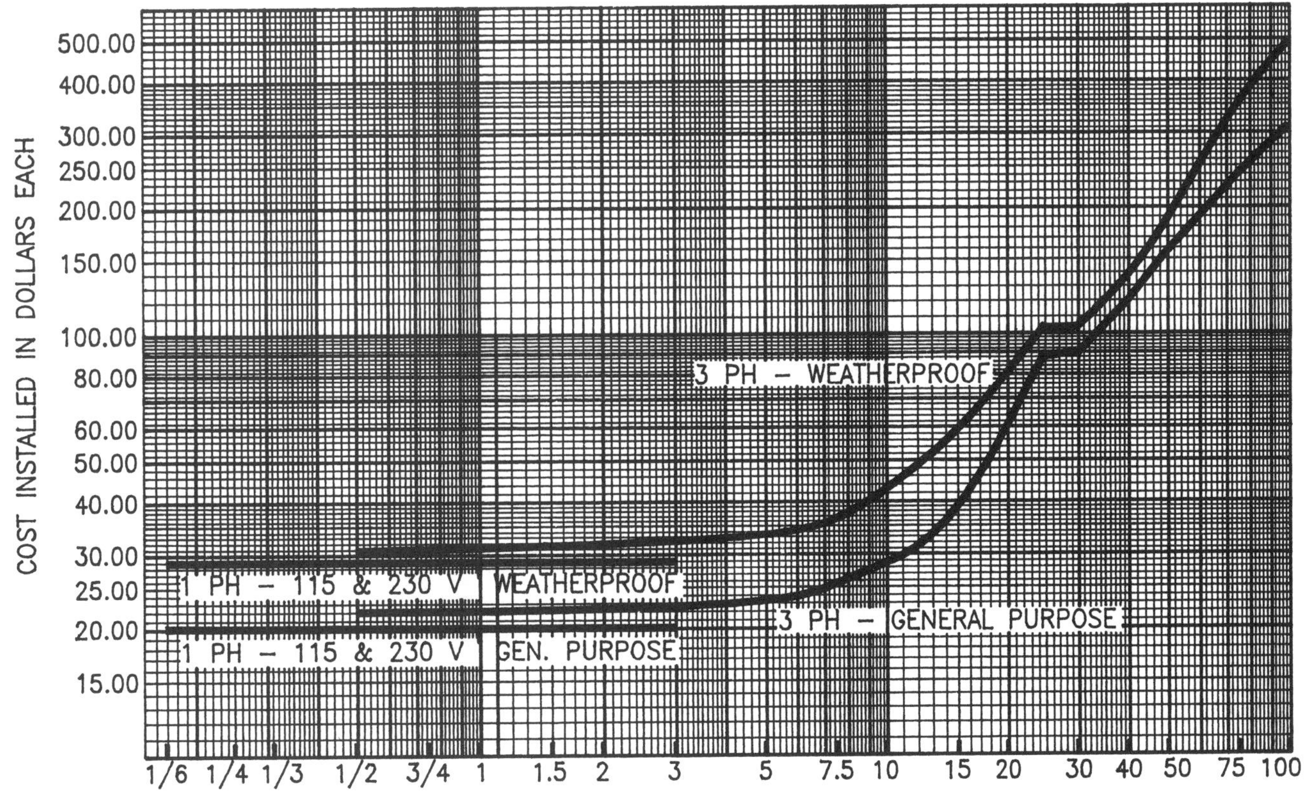

The costs shown for the motor terminal connections consist of 3 feet of flexible metal conduit, two conduit connectors, 4 feet of three conductors, and three lugs for three-phase connections. The weatherproof connection has liquidtight flexible metal conduit with the proper connectors and conductors. Up to 3 horsepower the cost is the same, as shown by the straight horizontal lines. Labor is provided to make the final installation. Conductor and conduit sizes comply with the National Electrical Code.

These costs do not include a motor disconnect switch. If you have priced a magnetic starter, do not include these costs, as they have been included with the starter.

COST OF MOTOR TERMINAL CONNECTIONS

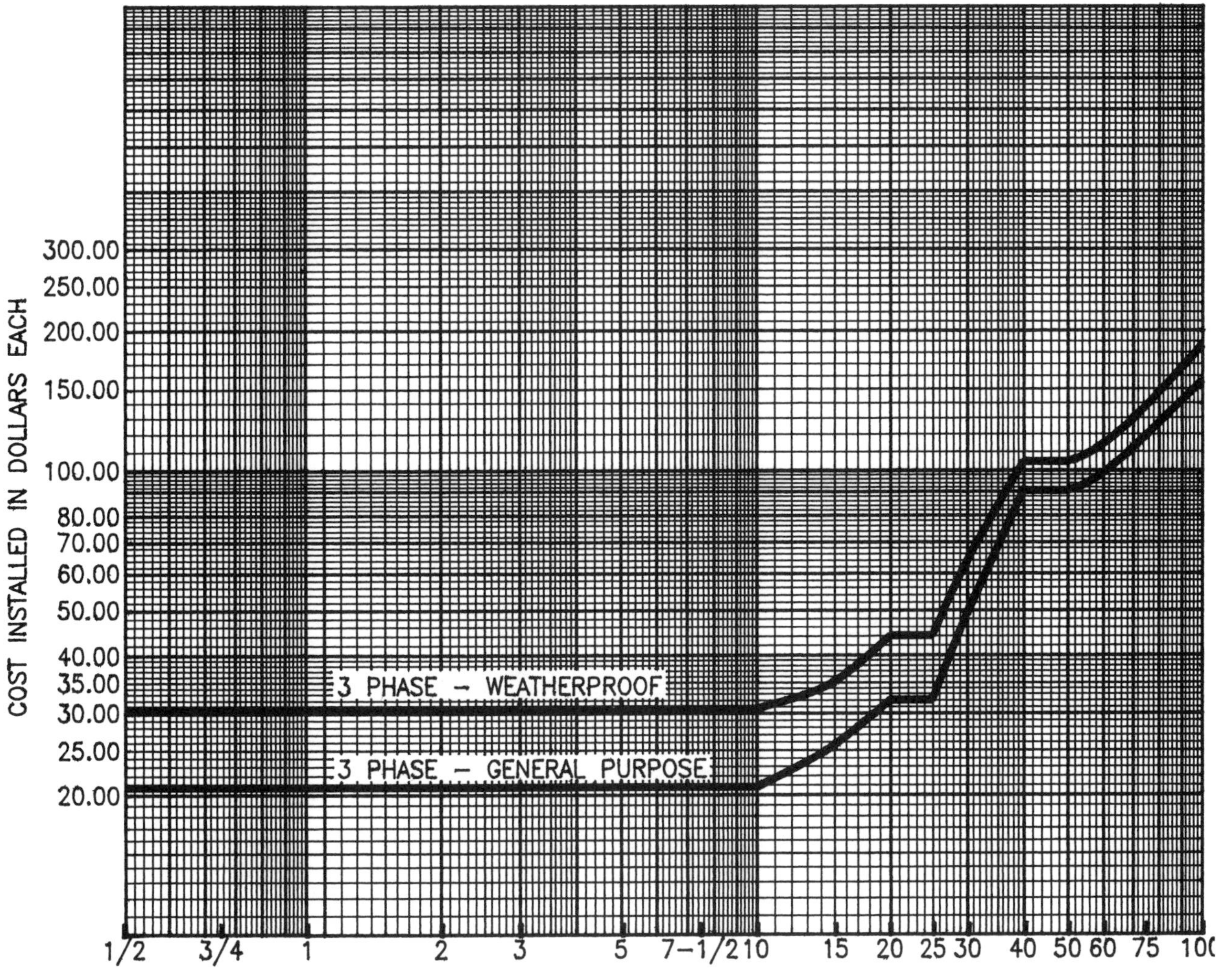

The costs shown for the motor terminal connections consist of 3 feet of flexible metal conduit, two conduit connectors, 4 feet of three conductors, and three lugs for three-phase connections. The weatherproof connection has liquidtight flexible metal conduit with the proper connectors and conductors. Up to 10 horsepower the cost is the same, as shown by the straight horizontal lines. Labor is provided to make the final installation. Conductor and conduit sizes comply with the National Electrical Code.

These costs do not include a motor disconnect switch. If you have priced a magnetic starter, do not include these costs, since they have been included.

The raceway and support systems shown are based upon Unistrut P-2000-H closure strip on top of the raceway, stud nuts for supporting fixtures, 36-inch hanger rod and fittings every 10 feet, connectors, end caps, etc., but no wire or fixtures. Labor is included for installing raceways bnt not fixtures or conductors.

The channel support system is not a raceway system and has a slotted channel. Included are the slotted channel, hangers at 10-foot intervals, and T bolts for supporting fixtures, but no fixtures are provided. Installation labor is provided.

The cost of the channel support system with cable assembly is based on typical runs of 100 feet and includes Wiremold Chan-L-Wire Strut, Chan-L-Wire Flat Cable, junction box, insulated end cap, and couplings. Lighting-fixture-mounting labor is not included.

COST OF SURFACE RACEWAY AND CHANNEL SUPPORT SYSTEMS

TYPE OF UNIT	MANUFACTURER	AMOUNT
RACEWAY AND SUPPORT	UNISTRUT P2000H	$10.95 PER FOOT
CHANNEL SUPPORT	UNISTRUT P2000T	$8.50 PER FOOT
CHANNEL SUPPORT WITH PRE-FABRICATED CABLE ASSEMBLY	WIREMOLD CHAN–L–WIRE STRUT AND FLAT CABLE	$11.05 PER FOOT

COST OF SURFACE RACEWAYS

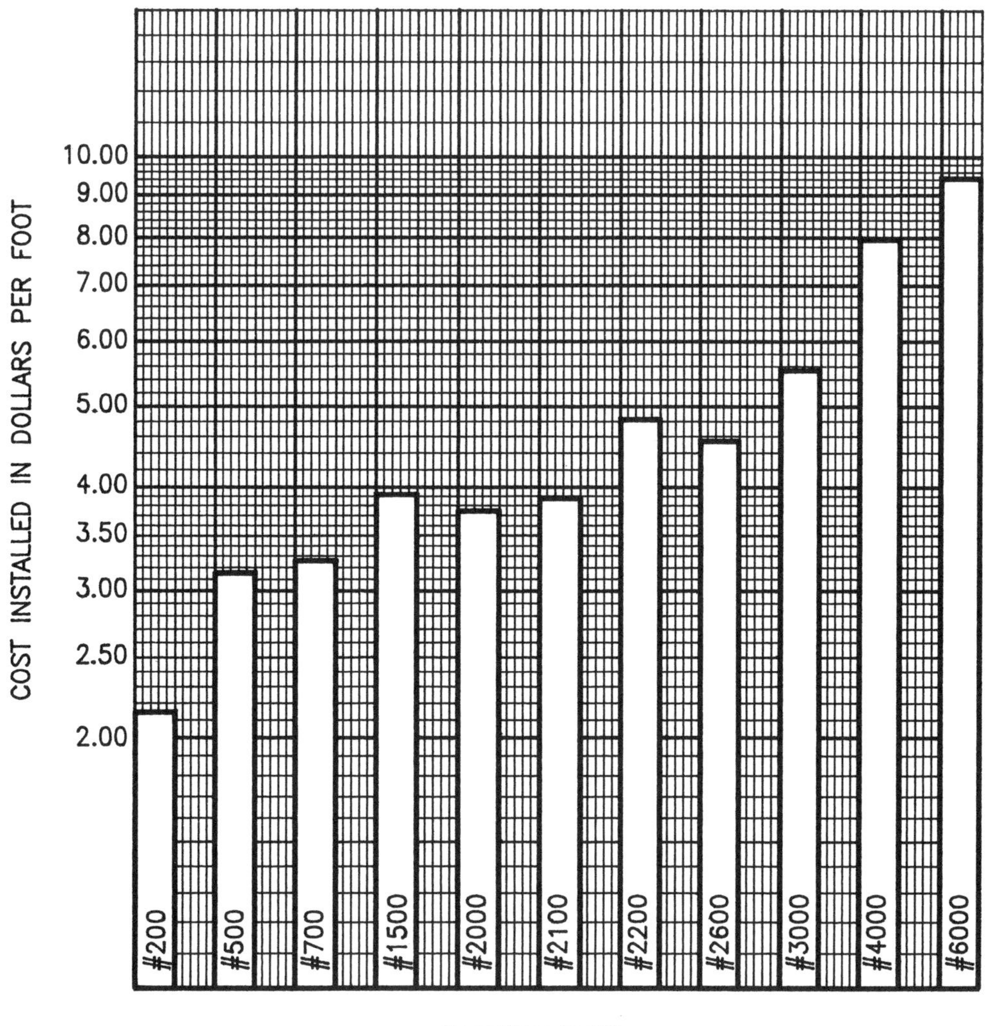

The costs shown for Wiremold raceways and fittings consist of the published contractors' book price and the labor for installation. These raceways and fittings are considered to be mounted on concrete using Rawl plugs and wood screws.

The costs shown for the Wiremold devices consist of the published contractors' book price and the labor for installation. These devices are considered to be mounted on concrete using Rawl plugs and wood screws.

Plugmold:

a. *GB Series: 3-wire, 1-circuit with insulated grounding conductor.*
b. *GBA Series: 4-wire, 2-circuit, outlets wired alternately; has insulated grounding conductor.*
c. *DGBA Series: 4-wire duplex outlets, 2-circuit grounding; each duplex wired alternately; used where multiple circuits are required; and has insulated grounding conductor.*

COST OF SURGE SUPPRESSION DEVICES

WIREMOLD DEVICES	COST INSTALLED IN DOLLARS
RESIDENTIAL & LIGHT COMMERCIAL	
120/240V, 1 PH–3W + G, #AP–1 (<25KVA)	285.
120/208V, 3 PH–4W +G, #AP3	332.
FOR BRANCH SERVICE PANEL 25–500 KVA	
120/240V, 1 PH–3W, + G, #HB120T	754.
120/208V, 3 PH–4W, + G, #HB120Y	1018.
277/480V, 3 PH–4W, + G, #HC277Y	1200.
FOR MAIN SERVICE PANEL <500KVA	
120/240V, 1 PH–3W, + G, #HC120T	1402.
120/208V, 3 PH–4W, + G, #HC120Y	2323.
277/480V, 3 PH–4W, + G, #HC277Y	2681.

The costs shown for the surge and noise suppressors consist of the published contractors' book price and the labor for installation. These units provide protection for solid-state equipment against surges and noise interference, preventing equipment damage and loss of stored data. The equipment is manufactured by the Wiremold Co.

The AMDTP-40 is a two-compartment (power and communication) unit with one 20A 125V dedicated/isolated ground duplex receptacle and one standard 20A 125V duplex receptacle, both specification grade. Length: 10' 0"–10'4". Cross section: 2 1/4" x 2 1/4". Aluminum.

The SMDTP-4 is a two-compartment (power and communication) unit with two specification-grade 20A 125V duplex receptacles. Length: 10' 0"–10' 4". Cross section: 2 1/4" x 2 1/4". Finish: Ivory painted steel.

The SMDTP-4BZ is physically the same as the SMDTP-4, but the power compartment comtains a renewable surge and noise suppressor circuit board with indicator light.

The costs of the above telepower poles include the published contractors' book price and the labor required to assemble, wire and install the pole to a grid ceiling and run 4 feet of flex metal conduit to an existing power junction box. All poles have an adjustable floor gripper pad.

COST OF SURFACE RACEWAY FITTINGS

COST INSTALLED IN DOLLARS EACH

	200	500	700	1500	2000	2100	2200	2600	3000	4000	6000
INTERNAL ELBOW	14.65	20.35	20.55	21.55	15.95	13.40	20.25	24.30	20.05	32.55	43.55
EXTERNAL ELBOW	12.90	14.60	14.60	21.85	12.95	19.05	18.10	—	22.30	40.25	43.55
FLAT ELBOW	14.65	20.20	20.25	21.45	19.15	21.95	30.80	21.10	27.50	32.20	40.05
FIXTURE OR EXTENSION OUTLET	20.50	20.50	29.00	----	----	----	----	----	----	----	----
DUPLEX RECEPTACLE	34.5	41.00	41.00	38.00	----	21.50	----	----	25.25	31.50	----
WALL SWITCH	32.00	39.00	39.00	----	24.00	26.50	----	----	21.00	34.00	----
TELEPHONE OUTLET	----	----	----	35.41	----	36.39	----	----	----	----	----

COST OF PLUGMOLD MULTIOUTLET SYSTEM INSTALLED IN DOLLARS PER FOOT

OUTLET SPACING	SINGLE CIRCUIT – 3 WIRE GROUNDING TYPE	TWO CIRCUIT – 4 WIRE GROUNDING TYPE	TWO CIRCUIT – 4 WIRE–GROUNDING DUPLEX
	20GB	20GBA	20DGBA
6"	10.25	—	—
12"	8.10	8.40	—
18"	6.90	7.45	—
30"	6.45	6.70	7.30
60"	6.00	6.10	6.35

COST OF TELEPOWER POLES

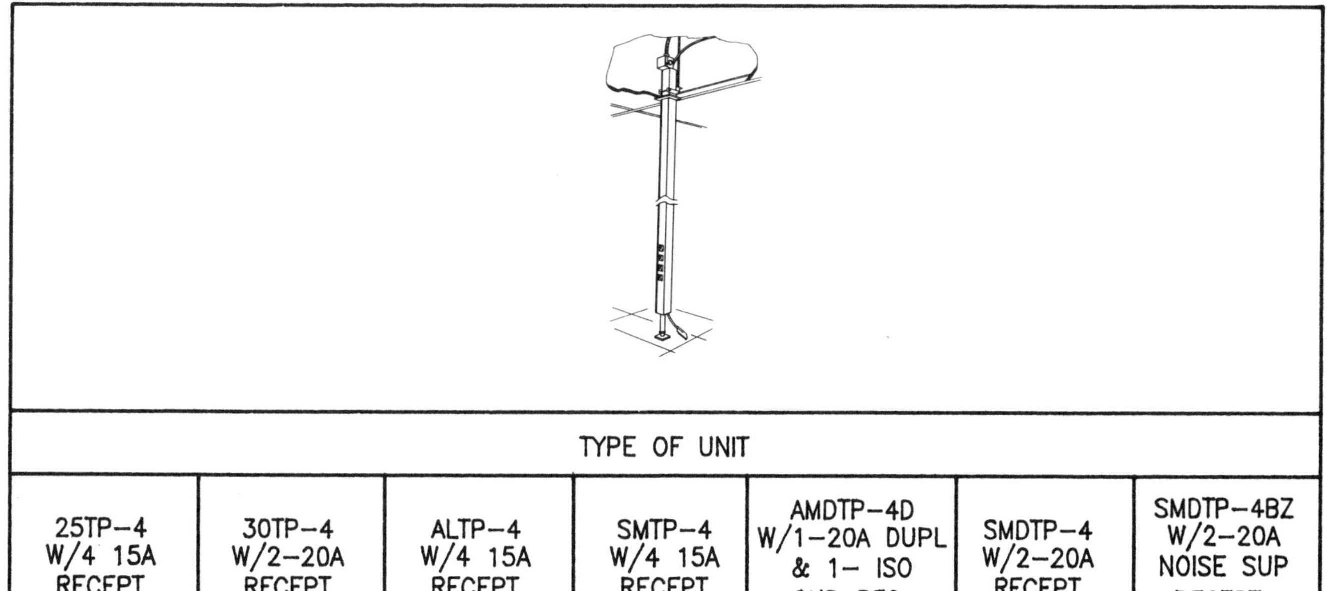

TYPE OF UNIT						
25TP-4 W/4 15A RECEPT	30TP-4 W/2-20A RECEPT	ALTP-4 W/4 15A RECEPT	SMTP-4 W/4 15A RECEPT	AMDTP-4D W/1-20A DUPL & 1- ISO GND REC	SMDTP-4 W/2-20A RECEPT	SMDTP-4BZ W/2-20A NOISE SUP RECEPT
151.00	230.50	218.00	157.25	205.50	160.50	256.75

COST INSTALLED IN DOLLARS EACH

The 25TP-4 is a two-compartment (power and communication) unit with four 15A 125V single receptacles. Length: 10' 5". Cross section: 2 1/8" x 2 1/8". Putty or ivory finish.

The 30TP-4 is a three-compartment (1 power, 2 communication) unit with two specification-grade 20A 125V duplex receptacles. Length: 10' 5 ". Cross section: 2 3/4" x 3". Putty or ivory finish.

The ALTP-4 is a two compartment (power and communications), with four 15A 125V single receptacles. Length: 10'5". Cross section: 2" x 2". Brushed anodized finish.

The SMTP-4 is a two-compartment (power and communication) unit with four specification-grade 15A 125V single receptacles. Length: 10' 0"–10' 4". Cross section: 2 1/4" x 2 1/4". Ivory finish.

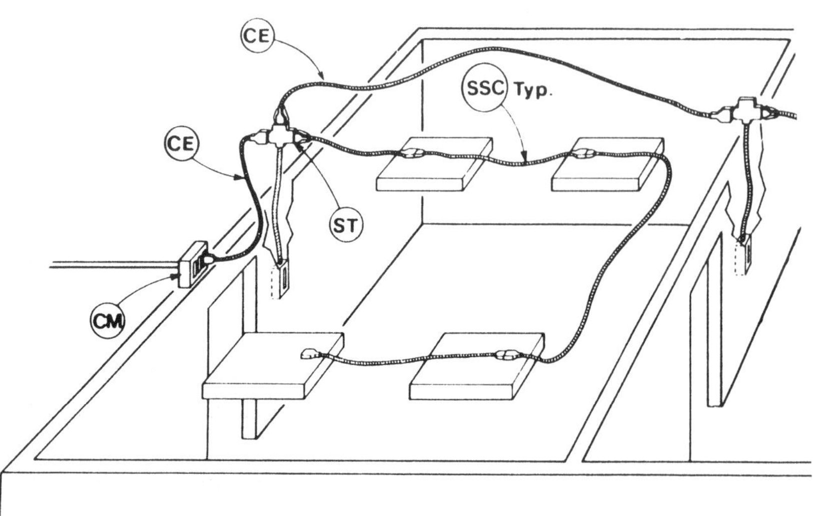

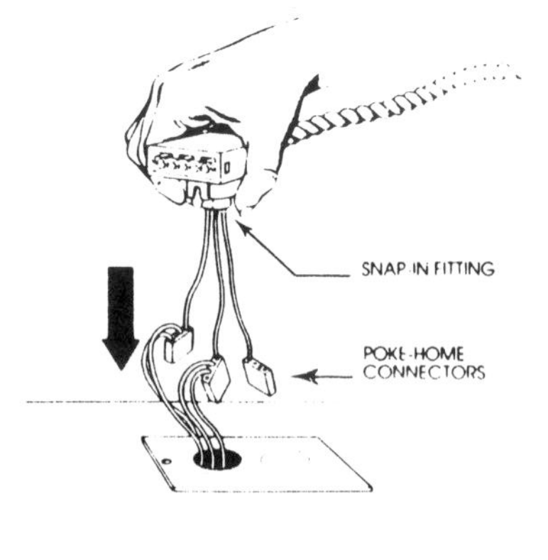

Feed the ballast leads back through the ½″ K.O. one at a time. Snap the SSC into the K.O. The fixture is now completely wired.

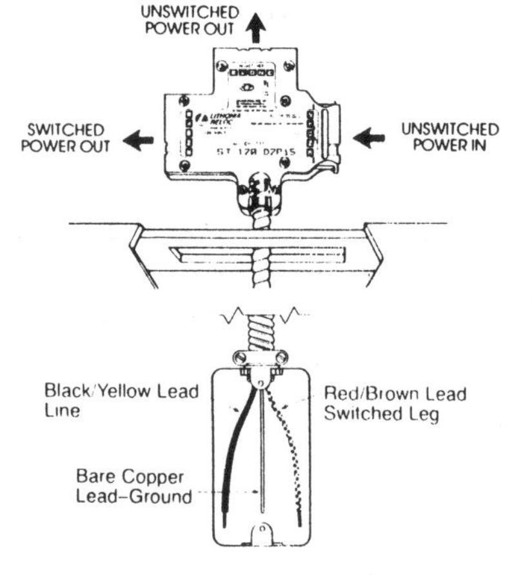

Install the ST above the switch location. The black or yellow lead is used to feed power to the switch. The red or brown lead is the switched leg.

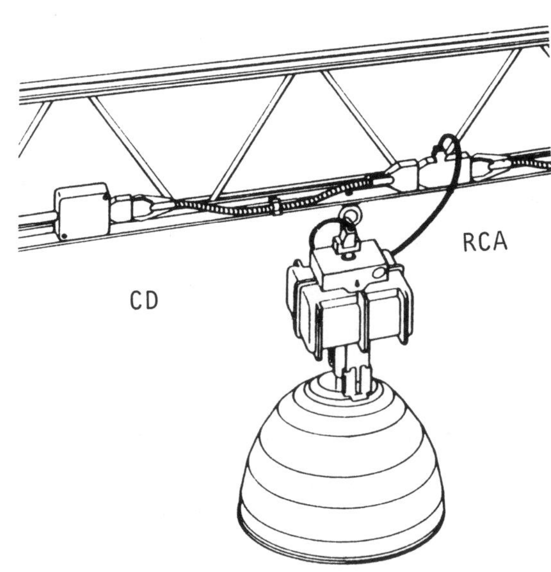

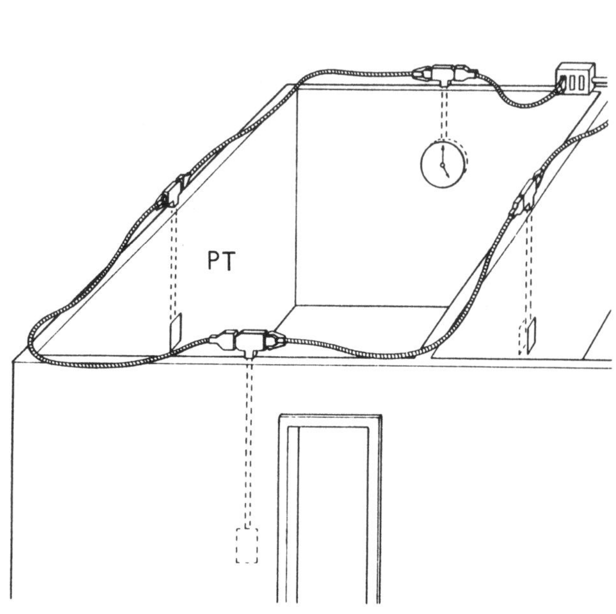

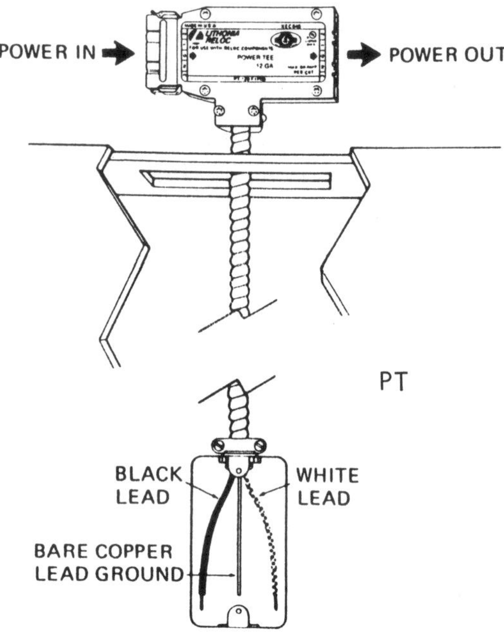

FLEXIBLE CABLE ASSEMBLIES

LENGTH	4 WIRE STD SEL. CABLE (SSC)	5 WIRE STD SEL. CABLE (SSC)	4 WIRE EXT. CABLE SET (CE)	5 WIRE EXT. CABLE SET (CE)	4 WIRE CABLE SET (CS)	5 WIRE CABLE SET (CS)
5	19.70	25.20	18.35	21.45	16.25	19.30
9	23.00	28.90	21.65	25.15	19.60	23.10
11	24.65	31.00	23.30	27.05	21.25	24.95
13	27.00	40.44	26.05	34.30	23.55	36.00
19	35.00	50.00	39.95	46.75	38.55	44.75
25	49.40	59.70	49.15	56.85	47.00	54.70
31	56.10	67.90	55.75	64.20	53.70	63.40

FLEXIBLE CABLE MISCELLANEOUS ITEMS

ITEM	COST
4 WIRE CIRCUIT DISTRIBUTOR (CD)	21.75
5 WIRE CIRCUIT DISTRIBUTOR (CD)	23.85
3 WIRE JUNCTION MODULE (JM)	25.75
4 WIRE JUNCTION MODULE (JM)	26.65
5 WIRE JUNCTION MODULE (JM)	27.60
SPLITTER SPLICE (SS) 5 WIRE ONLY	21.35
5 WIRE RELOC CORD ASSEMBLY (RCA)	30.10
4 WIRE CORD ASSEMBLY	30.10
4 WIRE CONVERSION MODULE (CM)	31.25
4 WIRE DROP CABLE (DC 11')	36.90
POWER TEE (PT 12')	41.65
4 WIRE SWITCHING TEE (ST 6')	32.37

Flexible wiring systems, sometimes referred to as soft wiring systems, are recognized in Article 604 of the National Electrical Code as manufactured wiring systems. They are probably most beneficially applied above a suspended ceiling serving recessed fluorescent luminaires. Switch legs and receptacles can easily be accommodated. The system shown is known as RELOC, manufactured by Lithonia.

The costs shown for the most commonly used components are based upon the contractors' book price and the labor required for the installation of each component.

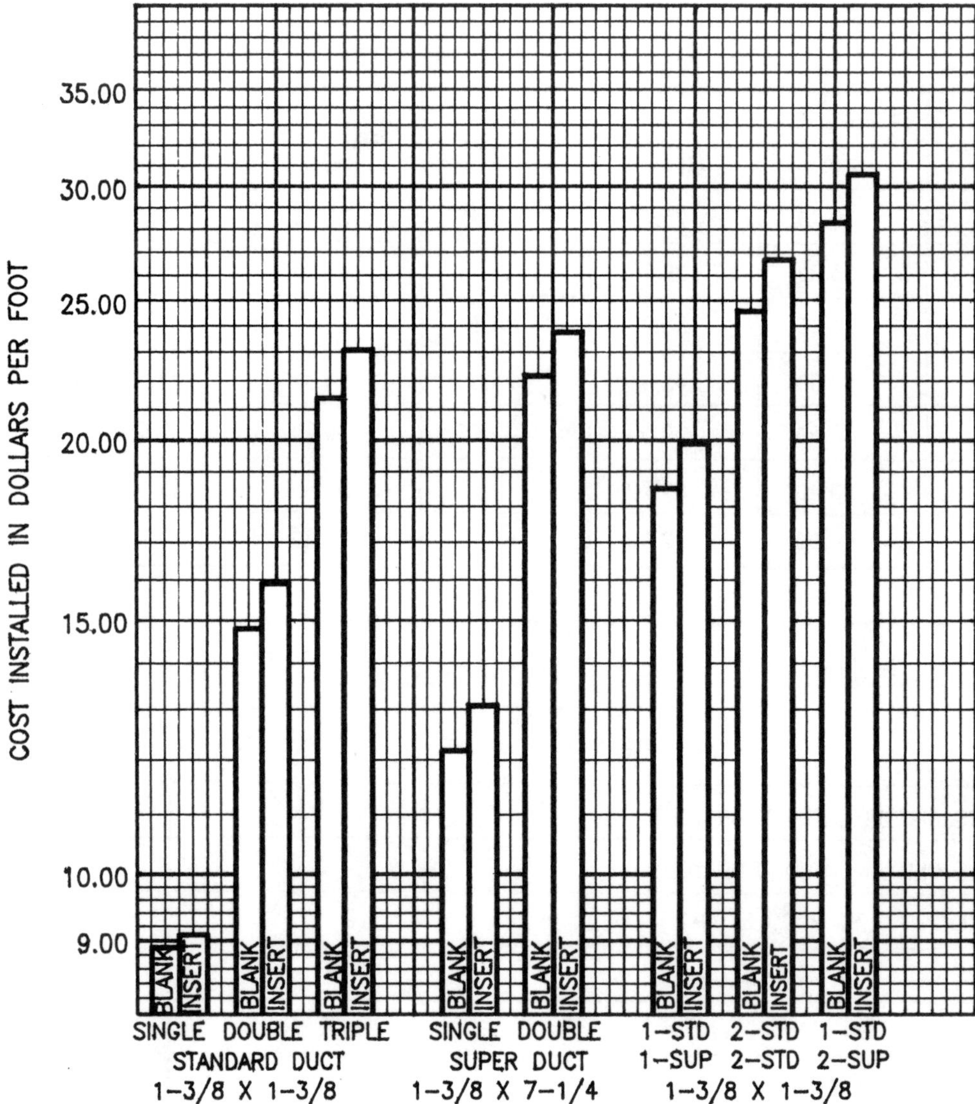

The costs for the underfloor duct consist of the published contractors' book price for the ducts, couplings, duct supports every 5 feet, marker screws for all inserts, sealing compound, and the labor for installation in a 4- to 6-inch concrete floor. It is assumed that one manual cut must be made for each 100 feet of duct. No wiring costs are included. The duct is manufactured by Square D Co.

COST OF UNDERFLOOR DUCT JUNCTION BOXES AND FITTINGS

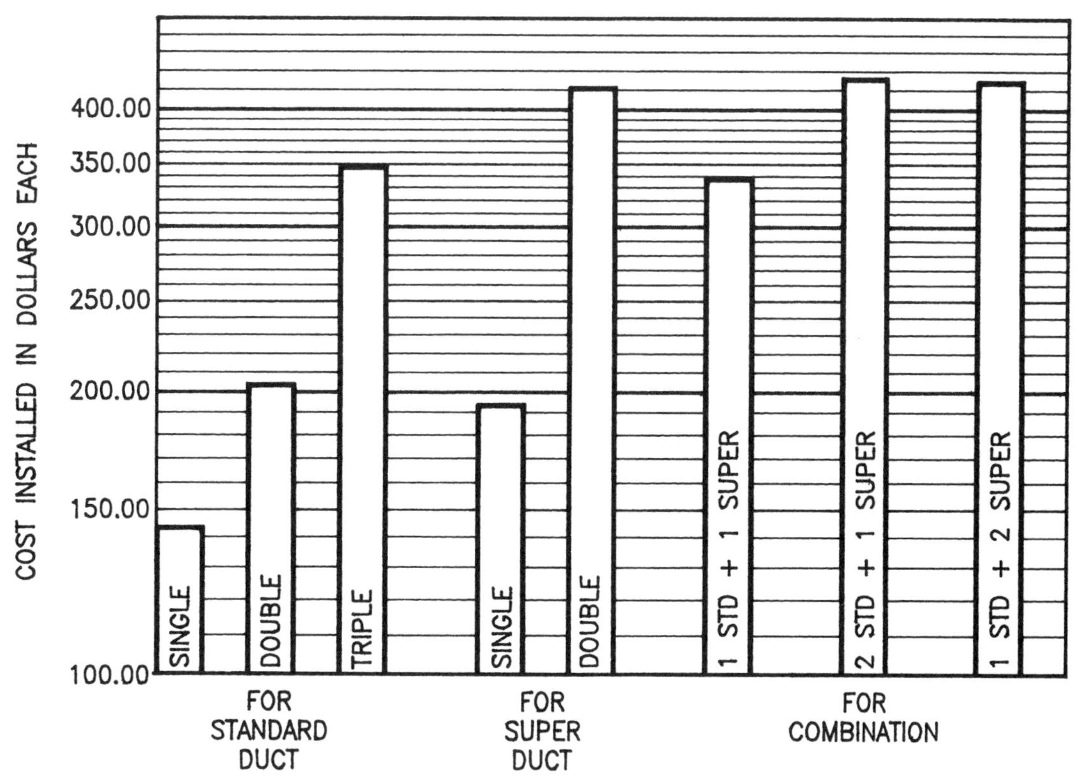

FITTINGS

FLAT ELBOWS FOR STANDARD DUCT	$78.25
FLAT ELBOWS FOR SUPER DUCT	63.55
INTERNAL ELBOWS FOR STANDARD DUCT	39.45
INTERNAL ELBOWS FOR SUPER DUCT	43.25
TELEPHONE OUTLET: PRESET INSERT	53.00
AFTERSET INSERT	158.95
DUPLEX REC: PRESET INSERT	132.95
AFTERSET INSERT	168.50

The costs shown for the single-level underfloor duct junction boxes and fittings consist of the published contractors' book price for the boxes and fitting shown. They also include the labor for installation in a 4- to 6-inch concrete floor.

COST OF TRENCH DUCT

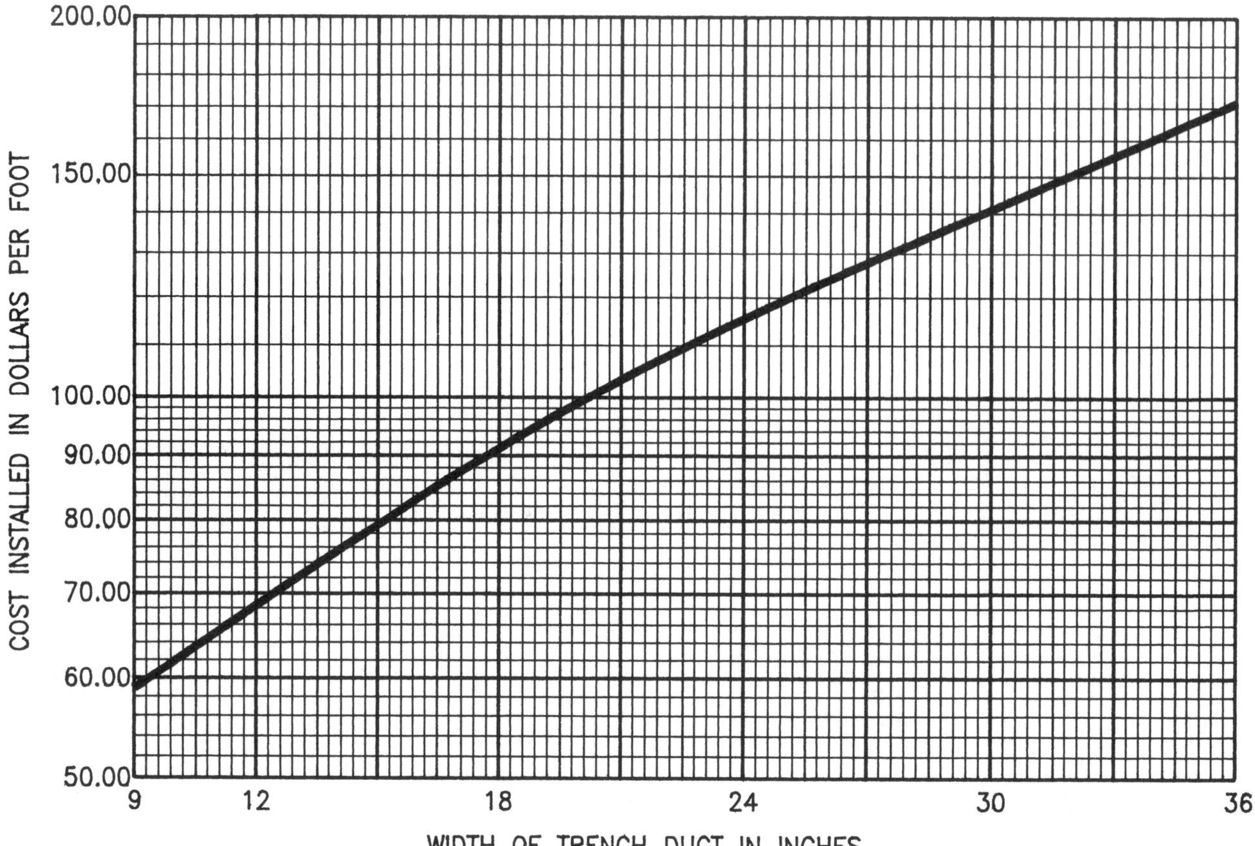

F-37

ADDITIONS AND SPECIAL FEATURES	
ITEM OR FEATURE	COST PER FOOT OF TRENCH DUCT
ADJUSTABLE PARTITION	$12.18
DOUBLE TILE TRIM ON TWO SIDES OF COVER PLATE ADD	18.27
FOR EACH INCH OF DEPTH BEYOND 3–4" ADD	5.48
DOUBLE TILE TRIM ON ALL FOUR SIDES ADD	54.81
DUCT CONNECTION INTO BOTTOM	51.82

The costs shown for the trench duct consist of the published contractors' book price for the sizes shown. Labor for installation is included, but freight is not included. The trench duct shown here is as manufactured by Square D Co. It is considered to be tack-welded to a cellular floor system. The standard straight lengths are 10 feet long and include five cover plates 2 feet long and 1/4 inch thick, of painted steel, for each 10-foot length of duct. The nominal trench width is actually the cover plate width, and the actual inside trench width is about 2 inches less. The standard duct is furnished with single-tile trim for 1/8 inch floor tile. The trench is single-compartment with an adjustable depth (before pouring concrete) from 2 3/8 to 3 3/8 inches.

COST OF TRENCH DUCT FITTINGS

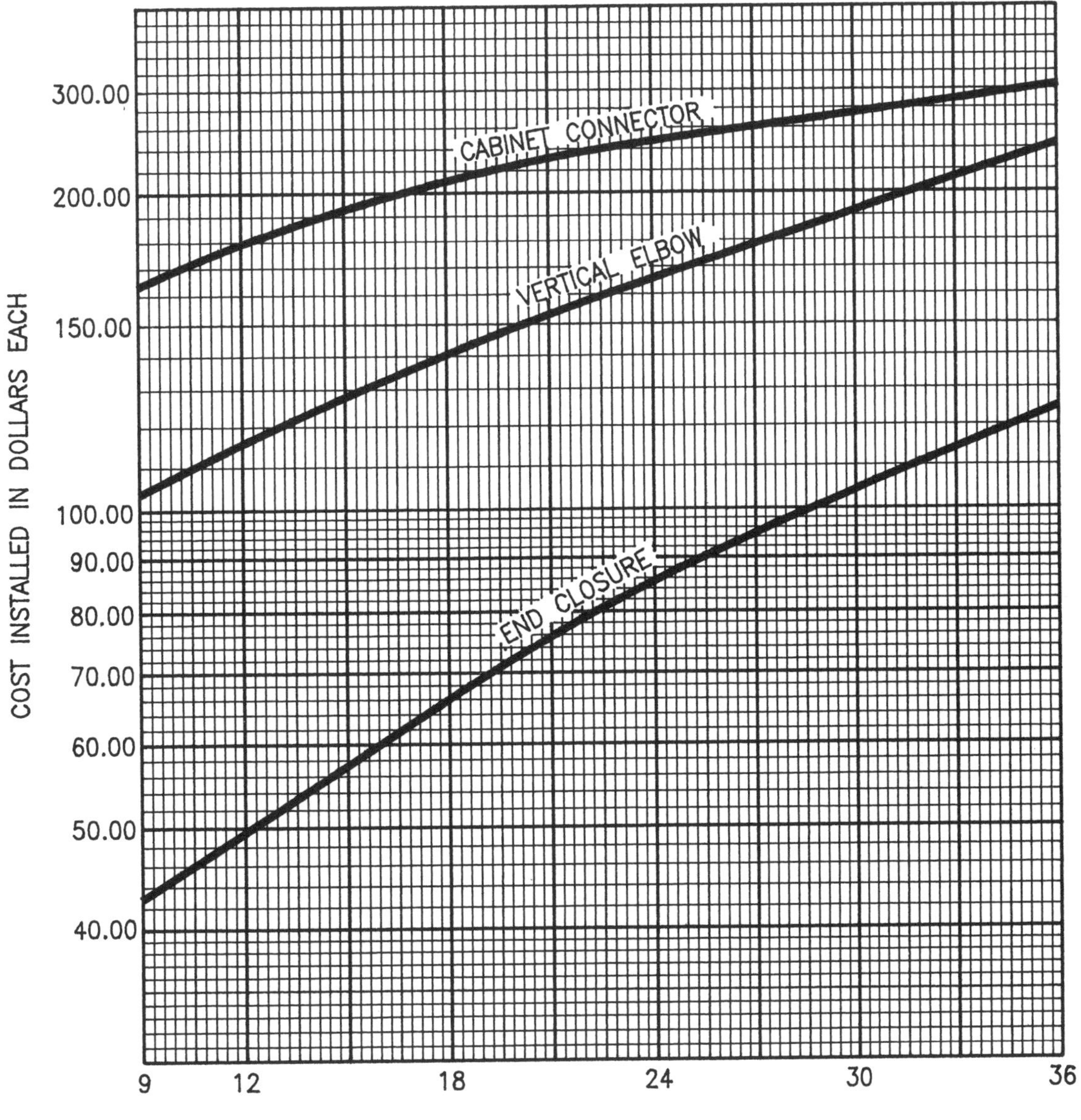

The costs shown for the trench duct fittings consist of the published contractors' book price for the sizes indicated and the required labor for the installation. These are all companion fittings to the duct and are essentially self-explanatory. The riser/cabinet connector, vertical elbow, and end closure are for connecting the duct system to a telephone, signal, or power panel.

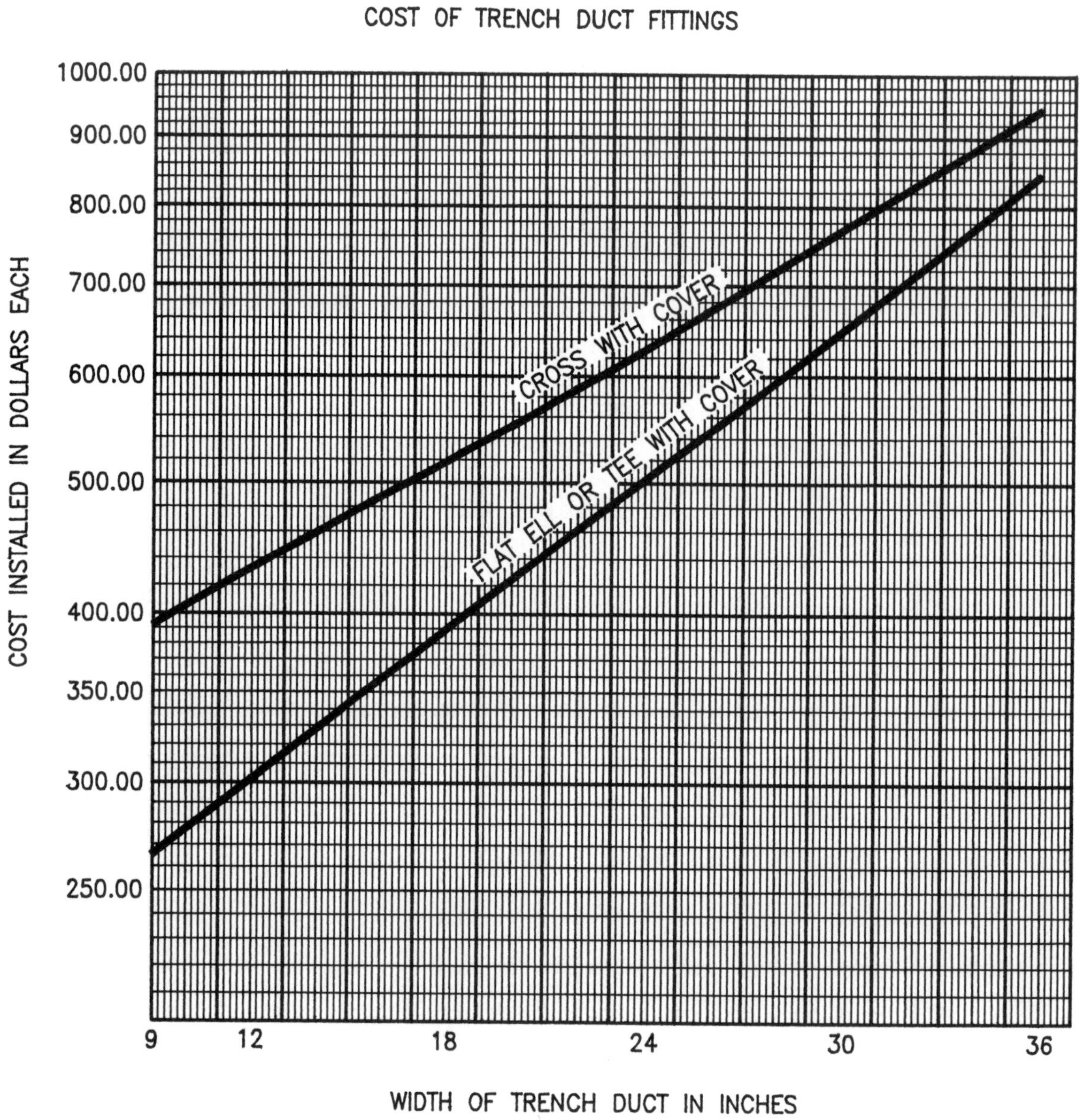

COST OF TRENCH DUCT FITTINGS

The costs shown for the trench duct fittings consist of the published contractors' book price for the sizes indicated and the labor for installation. These are all companion fittings to the duct and are self-explanatory.

Control Equipment

MOTOR CONTROL CENTERS

LOCAL CONTROL SWITCH	COST INSTALLED IN DOLLARS EACH				
	TYPE OF PLATE	NORMAL SWITCH		KEY OPERATED SWITCH	
		NO PILOT LIGHT	WITH PILOT LIGHT	NO PILOT LIGHT	WITH PILOT LIGHT
1 POSITION, 1 GANG	NYLON	45.75	49.60	50.95	56.45
	STAINLESS	47.10	50.95	52.30	57.80
2 POSITION, 1 GANG	NYLON	55.10	64.15	65.60	76.55
	STAINLESS	56.45	65.40	66.90	77.90
3 POSITION, 2 GANG	NYLON	66.90	78.50	82.65	97.25
	STAINLESS	70.40	82.00	86.10	101.45
4 POSITION, 2 GANG	NYLON	58.30	76.85	79.25	104.25
	STAINLESS	62.85	81.35	83.80	108.80
8 POSITION, 2 GANG MASTER SWITCH	ANODIZED ALUMINUM	137.25	168.25	176.15	210.85

The costs shown for the low-voltage control system components consist of the published contractors' book price and the labor for installation. All equipment is now specification-grade.

Local switches are considered to be installed flush in a masonry wall in either single- or a two-gang box with a deep tile ring, two 1/2 inch terminals, the necessary low-voltage switches, and the appropriate wall plate.

The master sequencer is an updated version of the older motorized master with more flexibility. It mounts in a standard GE component cabinet.

The telephone override allows any Touch-Tone phone to override an individual relay or group of relays, and is mountable in an RBS-2 GE component cabinet.

The component cabinets for the relays and other items are considered to be installed flush in a masonry wall.

All equipment is manufactured by General Electric Co.

DESCRIPTION	INSTALLED COST	DESCRIPTION	INSTALLED COST
WALL SWITCH: Conventional		SILICON RECTIFIER	$32.60
Momentary ON–OFF–ON	$36.00		
Locking Type	$45.00		
		BLANK SWITCH INSERT	$6.00
		RED PILOT LIGHT	$14.40
WALL SWITCH: Interchangeable	$33.40	COMPONENT CABINETS	
		RBS–1 8" X 12" W/COVER	$82.45
8 POSITION MASTER SWITCH			
8 Pos. no pilot lt.–Alum. Plate	$137.25	RBS–2 12" X 12" W/COVER	$99.40
8 Pos. w/ pilot lt.–Alum. Plate	$168.25		
8 Pos. key oper. no p.l.–Alum. Plate	$176.15		
8 Pos. key oper. w/ p.l.–Alum Plate	$210.90		
MASTER SEQUENCER		RB3EZ 18" X 24" W/COVER	$541.30
8 Output device	$285.40		
16 Output device	$344.25		
32 Output device	$466.90		
TELEPHONE OVERRIDE		FRAMES	
2 Input, 8 Output Chnls	$965.50	#RRF78EZ (1–8 relays)	$48.10
2 Input, 16 Output Chnls	$1342.00		
RELAYS		#RFT178EZ (4 relays & 120.V power supply)	$142.00
RR–7 (no P.L. sw.)	$30.55		
RR–8 (w/P.L. sw.)	$34.50	#RFT278EZ (4 relays & 277V. power supply)	$166.70
RR–9 (w/ isol. P.L. sw.)	$38.45		
INDIVIDUAL LOW VOLTAGE SWITCHES		TRANSFORMERS	
Ivory unlighted	$9.35		
Ivory lighted	$14.00		
Ivory w/ pilot light	$9.35	RT–1 120/24V	$90.30
Key oper. unlighted	$14.60		
Key oper. lighted	$20.85	RT–2 277/24V	$115.45
Key oper. w/pilot light	$20.85		

COST OF LOW-VOLTAGE REMOTE CONTROL SYSTEM

DESCRIPTION	INSTALLED COST
PHOTO CONTROL SWITCHES	
Indoor switch (#BPHOTO-4)	$326.00
Indoor/outdoor switch (#BPHOTO-5)	$220.25
TWISTED PAIR (No Jacket) INDOOR WIRE	
3/c (PVC) insulated	$.66 /FT.
3/c (plenum rated)	$.75 /FT.
4/c (PVC) insulated	$.76 /FT.
5/c (plenum rated)	$.91 /FT.
5/c (PVC) Insulated)	$.86 /FT.
5/c (plenum rated)	$1.05 /FT.
DATA & PANEL WIRE	
Datawire (#DATAWIRE-2SP)	$.90 /FT.
Panel wire 1/c #18 (for wrg. cbts.)	$.10 /FT.

The costs shown for these switches consist of the published contractors' book price and the labor for installation onto the surface of a masonry wall. These switches are manufactured by Tork.

DESCRIPTION		INSTALLED COST
7 DAY DIAL	SPST STANDARD MECH.	$180.00
	DPDT W/RESERVE POWER	$368.00
	3PST W/ RESERVE POWER	$367.00
PHOTO/TIME	RESERVE POWER & HAND–OFF–AUTO SWITCHES	
	2 CIRCUIT – DUSK/TIME, DUSK/DAWN	$867.00
	3 CIRCUIT – DUSK/TIME, DUSK/DAWN, TIME/TIME	$917.00
TURN–LOCK TYPE	PHOTOELECTRIC CONTROL	
	2000 WATT, 120 VOLT, (INCLUDES MTG. BRACKET)	$52.40
CONDUIT TYPE	PHOTOELECTRIC CONTROL	
	2000 WATT, 120 VOLT	$66.50
FLUSH MOUNTING	PHOTOELECTRIC CONTROL	
	1800 WATT, 120 VOLT	78.80
CONTACTOR TYPE	PHOTOELECTRIC CONTROL	
	6000 WATT, 120 VOLT, DPDT, WITH TURN–LOCK PHOTOELECTRIC CONTROL, AND RAINTIGHT CONTACTOR ENCLOSURE	$189.25
	SPRING WOUND TIMER	
	FLUSH MOUNTED 5, 15, 30, OR 60 MIN.	$114.75
	FLUSH MOUNTED 2,4,6, OR 12 MIN.	$126.00

DESCRIPTION		INSTALLED COST
24 HOUR DIAL	STANDARD UNITS – 40 AMP. ON–OFF	
	Indoor – SPST	$126.50
	Indoor – DPST	$132.75
	Raintight – SPST	$151.00
	Raintight – DPST	$157.25
	Program time switch – SPDT	$156.75
	STANDARD UNITS WITH SKIP–A–DAY FEATURE	
	Indoor – SPST	$143.50
	Indoor – DPST & SPDT	$153.91
	Indoor – 3PST & DPDT	$190.50
	STANDARD UNITS WITH SKIP–A–DAY & RESERVE POWER	
	Indoor – SPDT	$333.25
	Indoor – SPST	$333.25
	Indoor – DPST	$390.25
	Indoor – 3PDT	$390.75
ASTRONOMIC DIAL	SKIP–A–DAY FEATURE	
	Indoor – SPDT	$181.00
	Indoor – DPST	$181.00
	Indoor – 3PDT	$245.00
	SKIP–A–DAY AND RESERVE POWER	
	Indoor – SPST	$414.50
	Indoor – SPDT	$414.50
	Indoor – 3PDT	$461.25

G-5

The costs shown for these time switches consist of the published contractors' book price with anchors and the labor for installing the switches onto the surface of a masonry wall. The switches shown are manufactured by Tork.

COST OF SOLID STATE TIME SWITCHES

DESCRIPTION		INSTALLED COST
24 HOUR DIAL	Standard – SPDT	$239.25
	Momentary Contact – SPDT	$257.25
	7 Day Signal Timer – SPDT	$301.25
	Standard 20a – SPDT	$221.75
ASTRONOMIC DIAL	7 Day Clock – DPDT	$278.00
	7 Day Momentary Contact – SPDT	$306.25
	4 Channel – SPDT (can be used as astro or w/P.C.)	$632.25

The costs shown for these digital solid-state time switches consist of the published contractors' book price with anchors and the labor for installing the switches onto the surface of a masonry wall. These switches provide flexibility not available in the mechanically operated types.

The switches shown are manufactured by Tork.

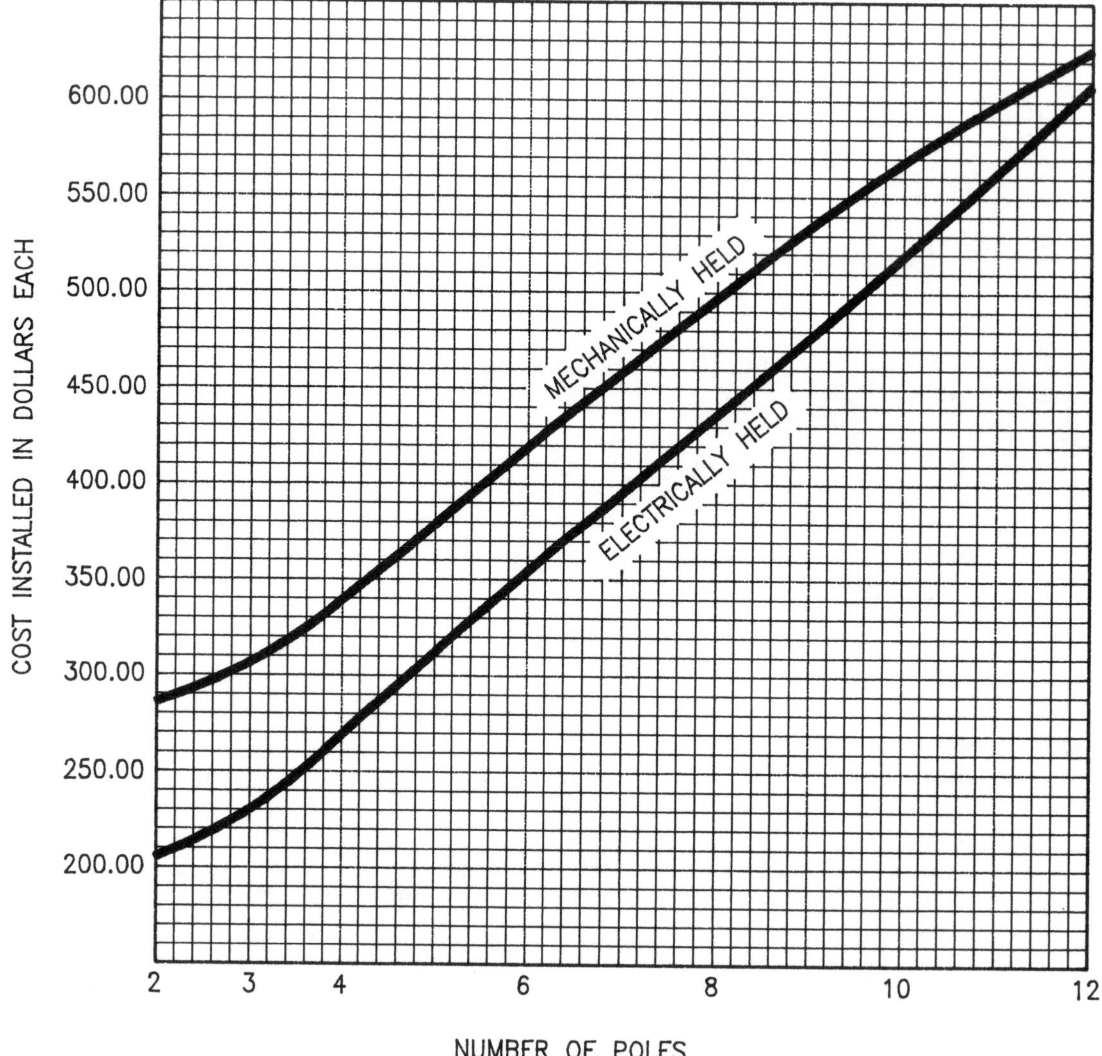

G-7

The light-duty lighting contactors or relays of the multipole type are a Square D 8903 Series with 20-ampere poles mounted in a general-purpose enclosure and fastened to a masonry wall. Included are conduit terminals and wire within the enclosure. No control switch for either the electrically or the mechanically held unit is included. The units are rated for 480-volt-maximum line voltage, and the contacts are such that you may apply full ampere rating for tungsten, fluorescent, or mercury vapor lighting fixtures.

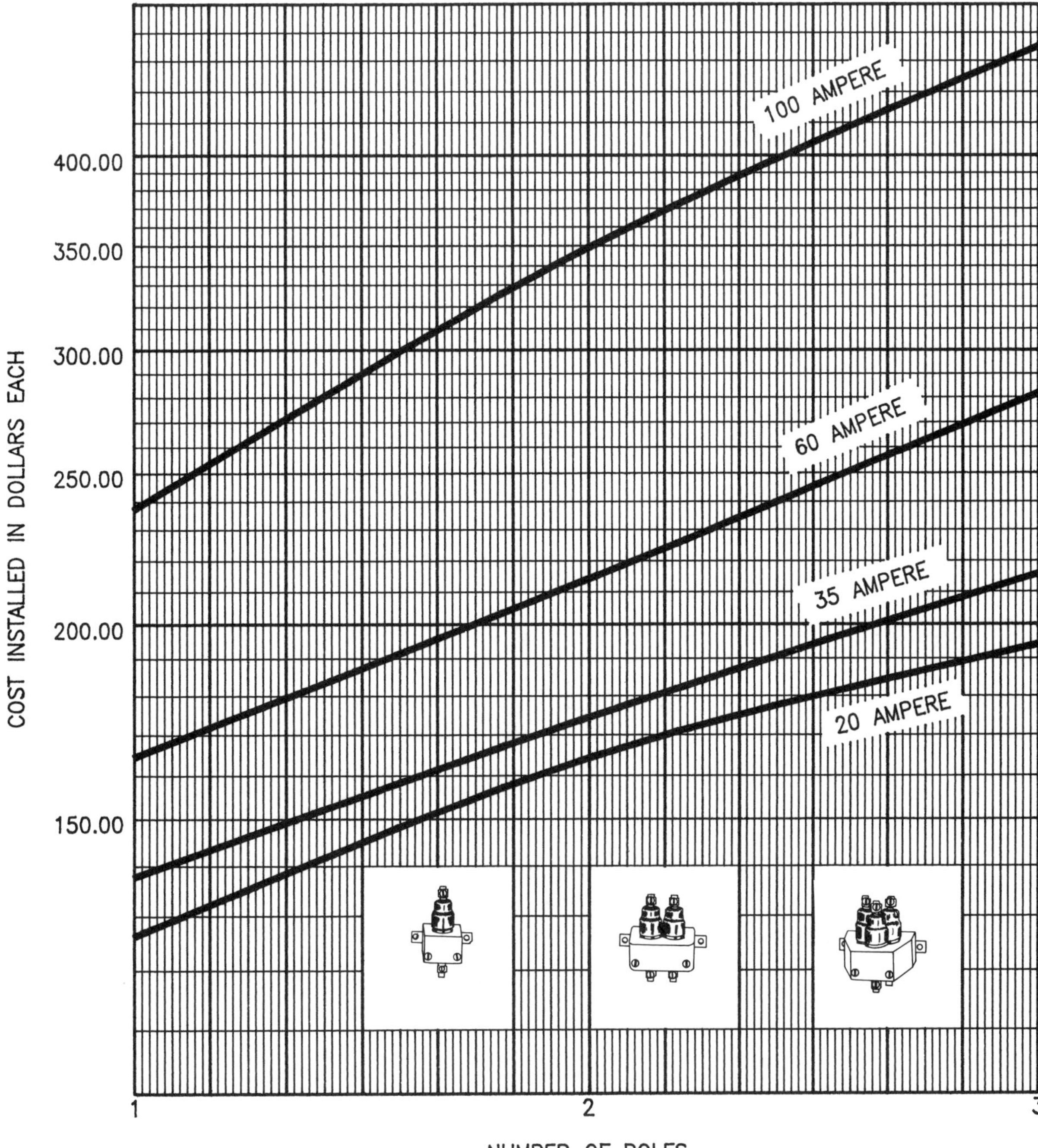

The costs shown for these relays consist of the published contractors' book price for the size and number of poles shown. These relays are manufactured by Mercury Displacement Industries, Inc. of Edwardsburg, MI 49112.

Included: (material and labor)

1. *Screw-cover junction box of a size to accept a relay with fastening devices for surface mounting*
2. *EMT terminals to suit conduit size required*
3. *Sufficient wire of size and length to suit the requirements inside the unit for making connections*

The costs shown for these electrically held contactors consist of the published contractors' book price for the items shown. The units are rated for 480-volt-maximum line voltage. These units are manufactured by Square D Co. and are Class 8903 in a general-purpose enclosure. Full ampere rating may be applied to the contacts.

Included: (material and labor)

1. *Fastening devices and mounting to a masonry wall*
2. *EMT terminals to suit conduit size*
3. *Sufficient wire of size and length to suit requirements inside the unit and for making connections*

COST OF LIGHTING CONTACTORS

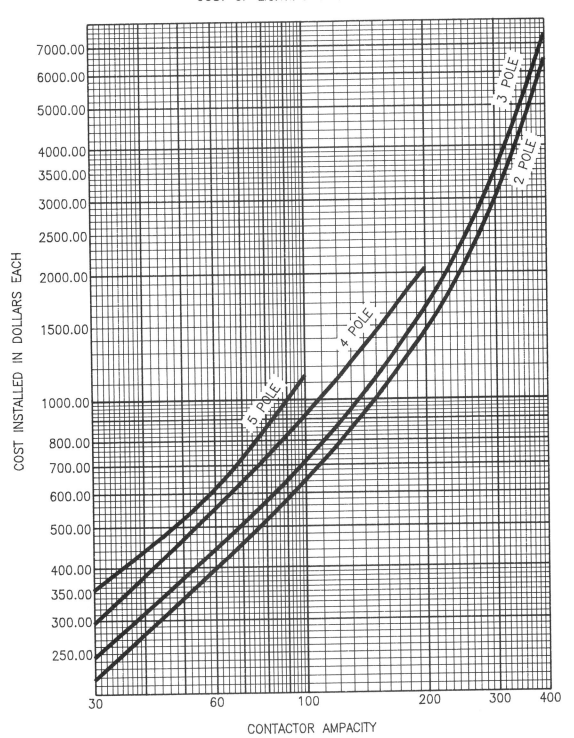

COST INSTALLED IN DOLLARS EACH

7000.00
6000.00
5000.00
4000.00
3500.00
3000.00
2500.00
2000.00
1500.00
1000.00
800.00
700.00
600.00
500.00
400.00
350.00
300.00
250.00

3 POLE
2 POLE
4 POLE
5 POLE

30
60
100
200
300
400

CONTACTOR AMPACITY

The costs shown for these mechanically held contactors consist of the published contractors' book price for the items shown. The units are rated for 480-volt-maximum line voltage. These units are manufactured by Square D Co. and are Class 8903 in a general-purpose enclosure. Full ampere rating may be applied to the contacts.

Included: (material and labor)

1. *Fastening devices and mounting to a masonry wall*
2. *EMT terminals to suit conduit size*
3. *Sufficient wire of size and length to suit requirements inside the unit and for making connections*

COST OF LIGHTING CONTACTORS

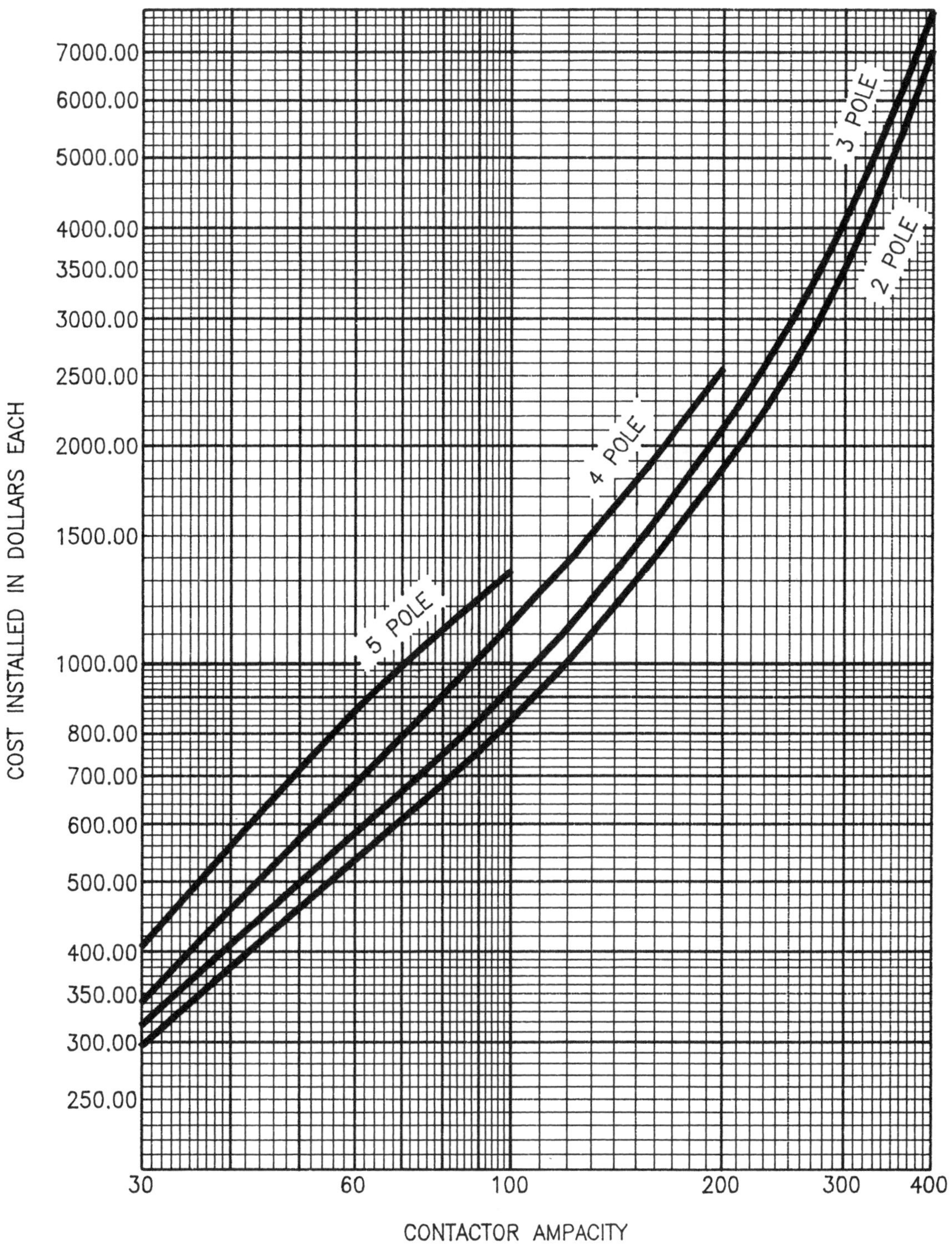

COST INSTALLED IN DOLLARS EACH

7000.00
6000.00
5000.00
4000.00
3500.00
3000.00
2500.00
2000.00
1500.00
1000.00
800.00
700.00
600.00
500.00
400.00
350.00
300.00
250.00

3 POLE
2 POLE
4 POLE
5 POLE

30
60
100
200
300
400

CONTACTOR AMPACITY

G

G-10

COST OF INCANDESCENT WALL DIMMERS

LOW VOLTAGE, SPEC. GRADE

120V., SPEC. GRADE

120 V., STANDARD GRADE, ROTARY

COST INSTALLED IN DOLLARS EACH

250.00
200.00
150.00
100.00
90.00
80.00
70.00

500 1000 1500 2000

SIZE OF DIMMER IN WATTS

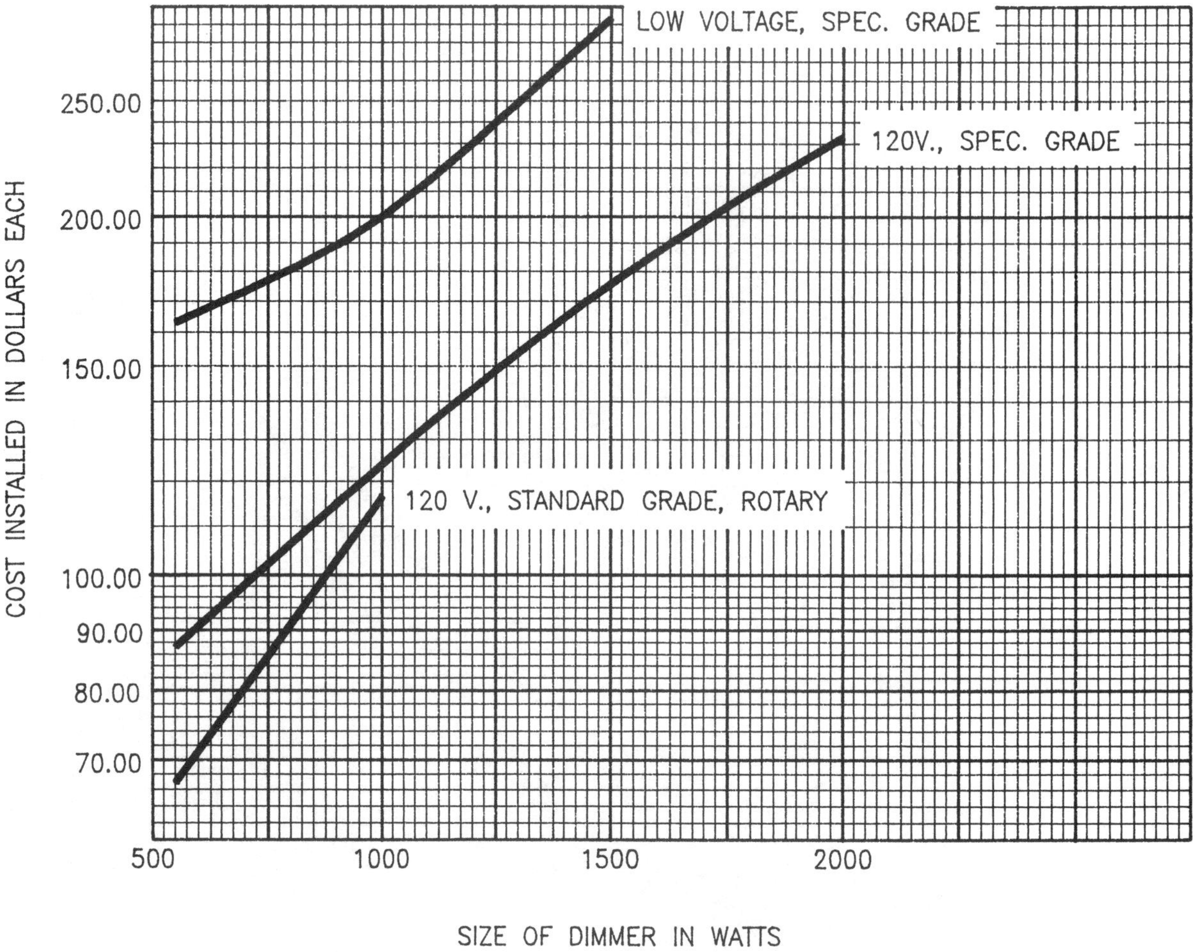

G-11

The costs shown for the incandescent wall dimmers consist of the published contractors' book price for the units shown. The costs also include a flush wall box with two conduit terminals. These dimmers are are manufactured by Lutron Electronics Co. The specification grade has a slider type of control with an ON-OFF switch, while the standard grade has a rotary control with a push-type ON-OFF switch.

COST OF INCANDESCENT DIMMERS – MANUAL REMOTE

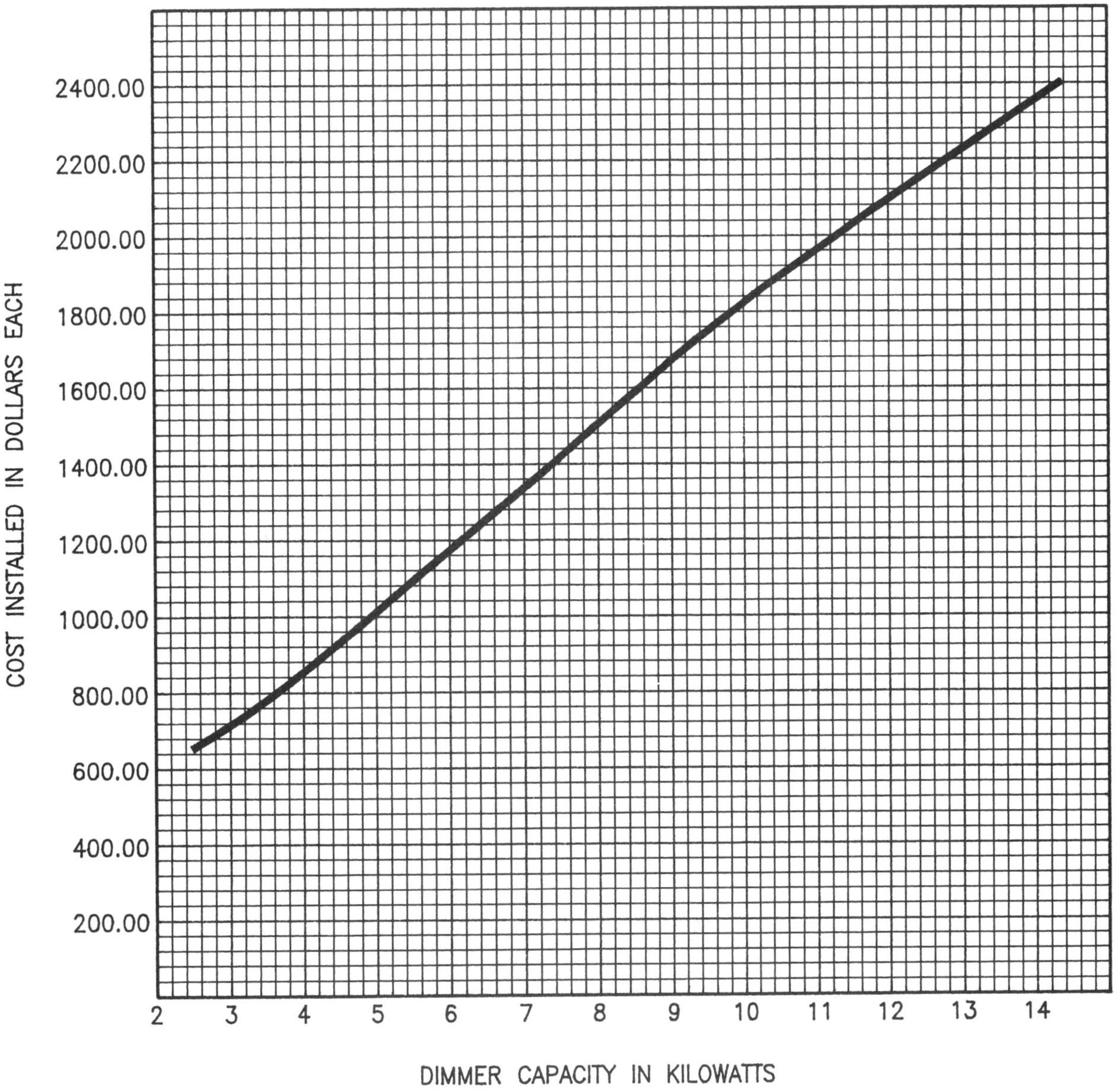

The cost of these dimmers includes the published contractors' book price and the labor for installing the units on the wall and connecting the wires in the units. No interconnecting raceway is included.

These single-phase manual remote incandescent dimmers are made up of modules including the lighting control station, master control card, and lighting controllers. The lighting control station looks like a low-powered wall dimmer. These units are manufactured by Lutron Electronics Co.

COST OF INCANDESCENT DIMMERS – MANUAL REMOTE

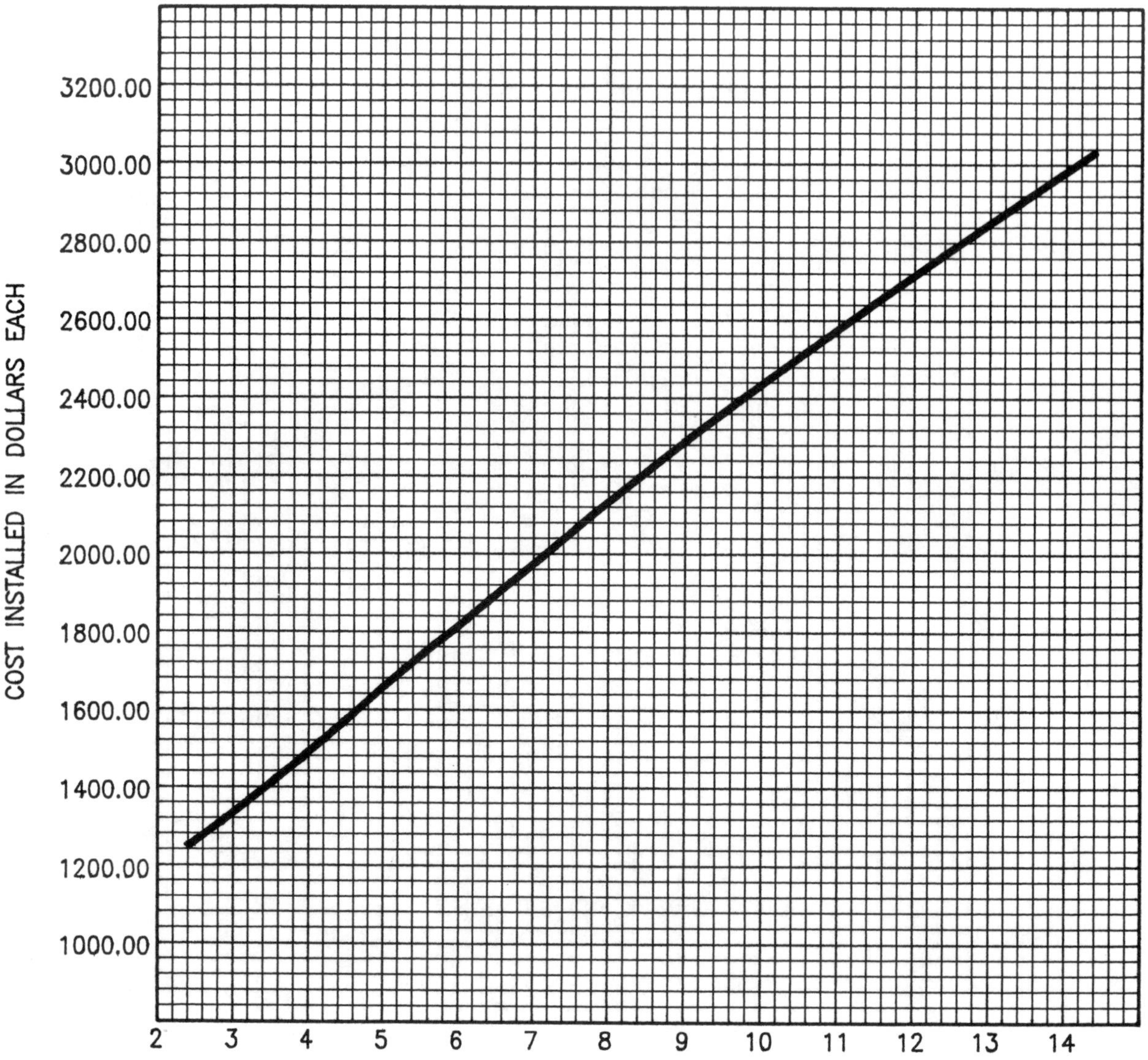

COST INSTALLED IN DOLLARS EACH

3200.00
3000.00
2800.00
2600.00
2400.00
2200.00
2000.00
1800.00
1600.00
1400.00
1200.00
1000.00

2 3 4 5 6 7 8 9 10 11 12 13 14

DIMMER CAPACITY IN KILOWATTS

G-13

The cost of these dimmers includes the published contractors' book price and the labor for installing the units on the wall and connecting the wires in the units. No interconnecting raceway is included.

These single-phase manual remote incandescent dimmers are made up of modules including the lighting control station, master control card, and lighting controllers. The lighting control stations look like low-powered wall dimmers. These units are manufactured by Lutron Electronics Co.

COST OF INCANDESCENT DIMMERS – MANUAL REMOTE

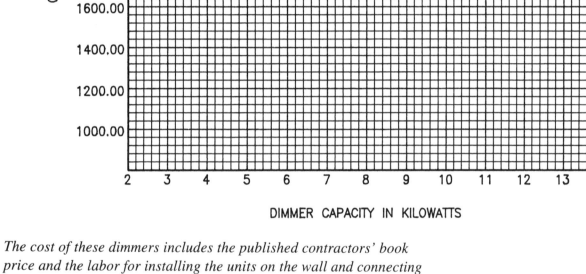

COST INSTALLED IN DOLLARS EACH

3200.00
3000.00
2800.00
2600.00
2400.00
2200.00
2000.00
1800.00
1600.00
1400.00
1200.00
1000.00

2 3 4 5 6 7 8 9 10 11 12 13 14

The cost of these dimmers includes the published contractors' book price and the labor for installing the units on the wall and connecting the wires in the units. No interconnecting raceway is included.

These single-phase wireless remote incandescent dimmers are made up of modules including the lighting control station, master control card, and lighting controllers. The lighting control stations look like low-powered wall dimmers. Receivers may be wall mounted and/or ceiling mounted; however, the transmitter is a hand-held infrared unit. These units are manufactured by Lutron Electronics Co.

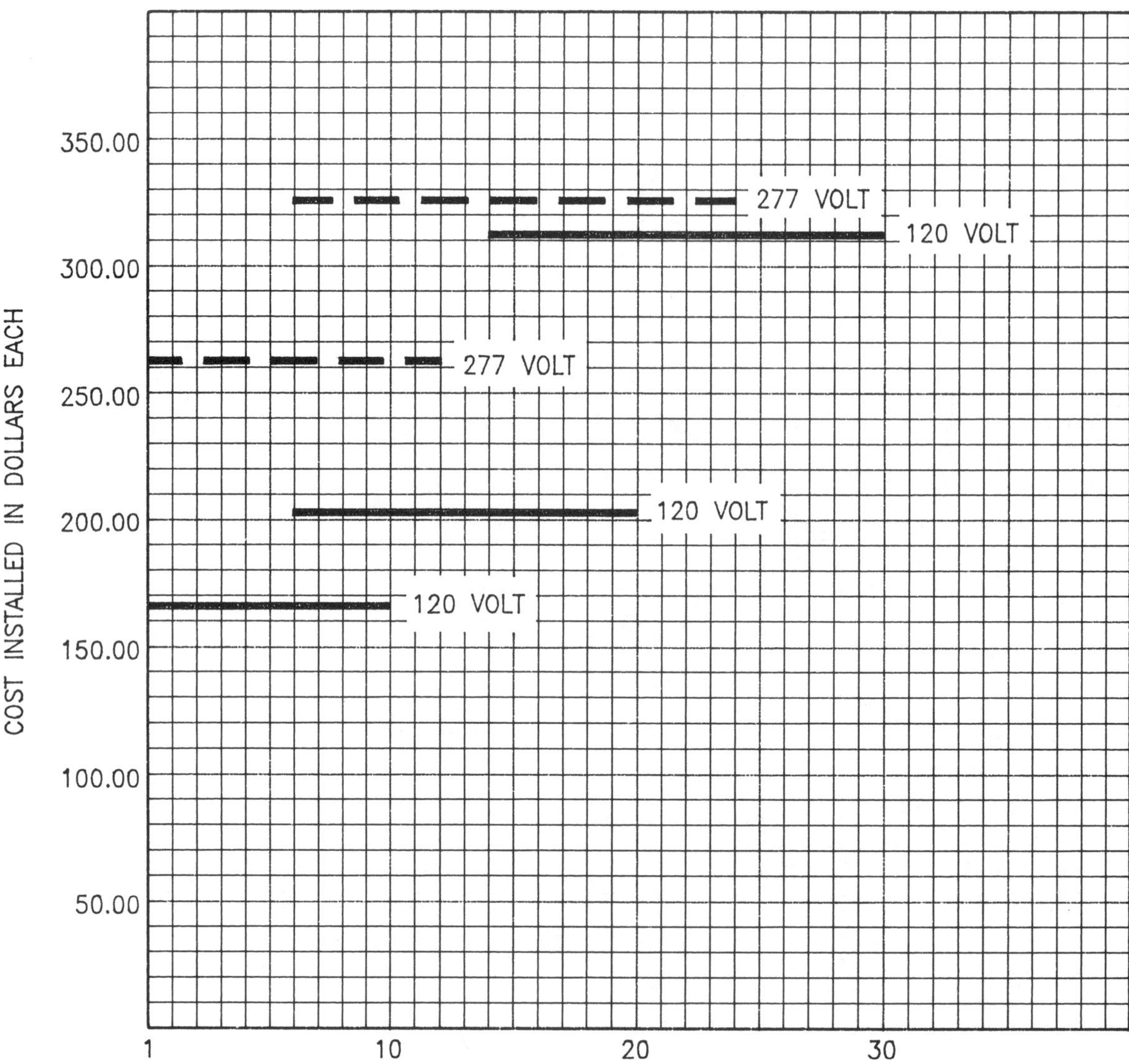

G-15

The costs shown for the fluorescent wall dimmers consist of the published contractors' book price for the units shown and the associated labor for installation. The costs also include a flush wall box with two conduit terminals. These dimmers have a slider type of control with ON-OFF switch. Manufactured by Lutron Electronics Co.

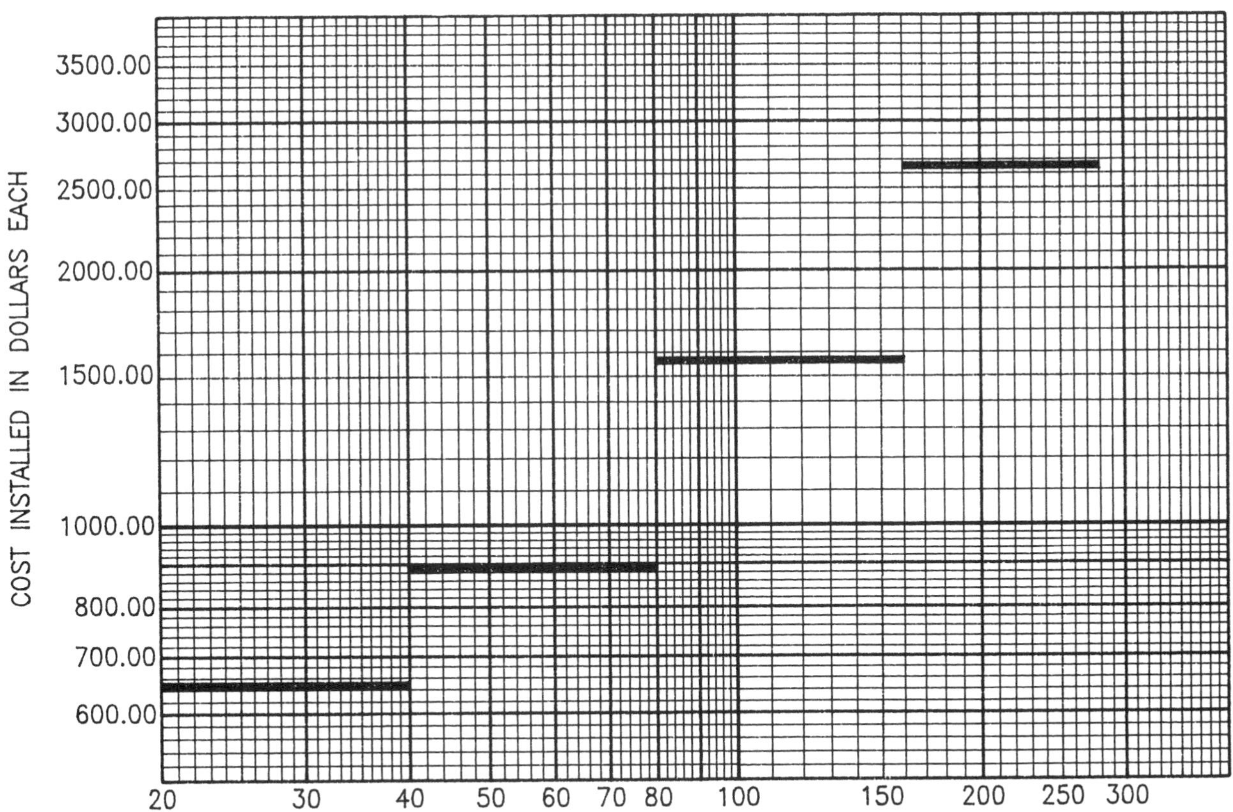

The cost of these dimmers includes the published contractors' book price and the labor for installing the units on the wall and connecting the wires in the units. No interconnecting raceway is included.

These single-phase manual remote fluorescent dimmers are made up of modules including the lighting control station, master control card, and lighting controllers. The lighting control station looks like a low-powered wall dimmer. These units are manufactured by Lutron Electronics Co.

COST OF FLUORESCENT DIMMERS – MANUAL REMOTE

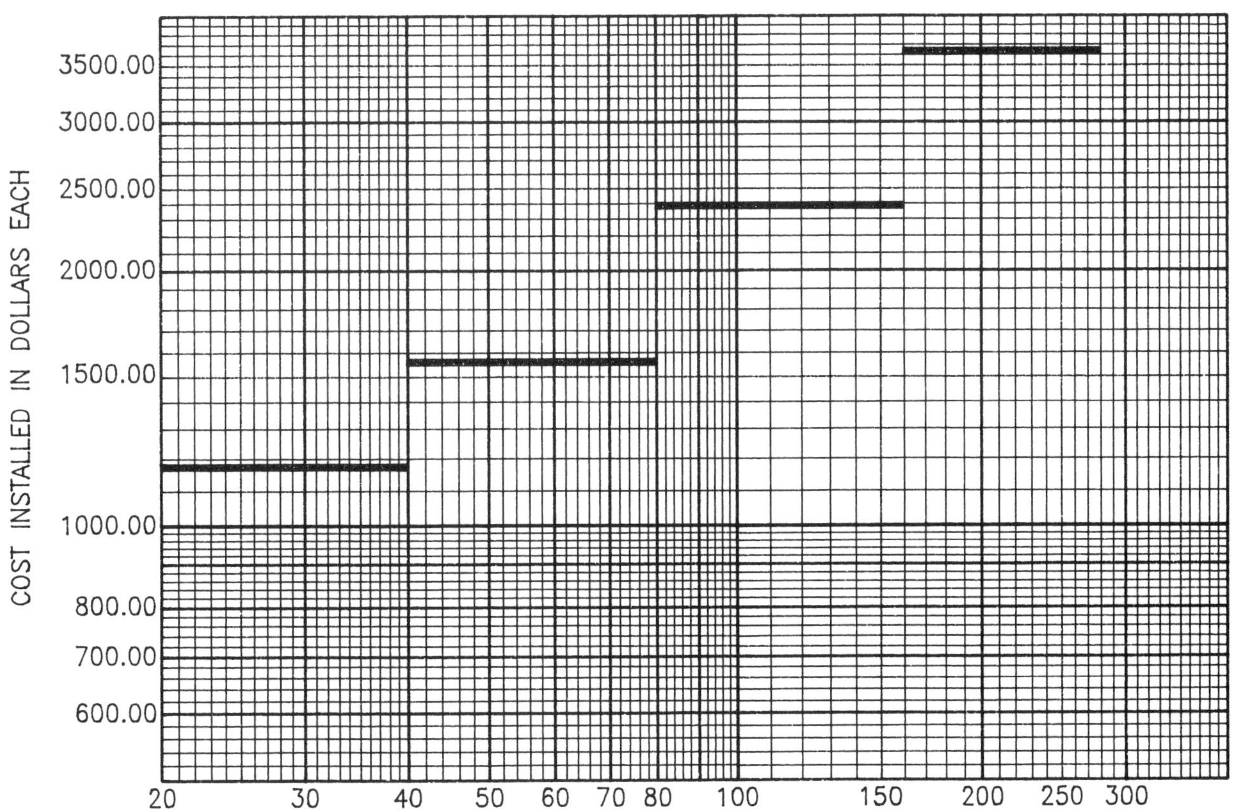

NUMBER OF CONTROLLED 40 WATT LAMPS

The cost of these dimmers includes the published contractors' book price and the labor for installing the units on the wall and connecting the wires in the units. No interconnecting raceway is included.

These single-phase manual remote multistation control fluorescent dimmers are made up of modules including the lighting control station, master control card, and lighting controllers. The lighting control station looks like a low-powered wall dimmer. These units are manufactured by Lutron Electronics Co.

HAND MOTOR STARTER AND HOOK–UPS	115 VOLT – 1 POLE		208 OR 230 VOLT 2 POLE		208 OR 230 VOLT 3 POLE	
	GENERAL PURPOSE	WEATHERPROOF	GENERAL PURPOSE	WEATHERPROOF	GENERAL PURPOSE	WEATHERPROOF
1/6 – 1.0 H.P.	$89.50	$156.25	$95.25	$162.25	N/A	N/A
1–1/2 – 3 H.P.	N/A	N/A	$176.75	$356.75	$295.00	$89.50
5 – 7–1/2 H.P.	N/A	N/A	N/A	N/A	$213.00	393.00

CONTROL SWITCHES			
DESCRIPTION		STANDARD DUTY	HEAVY DUTY
PUSHBUTTON	SINGLE UNIT	$61.00	$121.00
	TWO UNIT	74.50	139.50
	THREE UNIT	110.50	195.50
	TWO UNIT W/ PILOT LIGHT	152.75	192.50
SEL. SWITCH TYPE	TWO POSITION	63.50	201.25
	THREE POSITION	78.75	205.00

The costs shown for these hand motor starters and hookups consist of the published contractors' book price for the switches required and the labor for the installation. The prices include the heating elements, a 3-foot length of flexible steel conduit, wire, and wire connectors. These units are the Allen-Bradley 600 and 609 Series.

NEMA SIZE	LINE VOLTAGE		
	HORSEPOWER RANGE		
	200–VOLT MOTOR	230–VOLT MOTOR	460–VOLT MOTOR
00	0 TO 1–1/2	0 TO 1–1/2	0 TO 2
0	2 TO 3	2 TO 3	3 TO 5
1	4 TO 7–1/2	4 TO 7–1/2	6 TO 10
2	8 TO 10	8 TO 15	11 TO 25
3	11 TO 25	16 TO 30	26 TO 50
4	26 TO 40	31 TO 50	51 TO 100
5	41 TO 75	51 TO 100	101 TO 200
6	76 TO 150	101 TO 200	201 TO 400

The costs shown for these motor starters consist of the published contractors' book price for the motor starters required for the horsepower and voltages shown. They further include fastening devices for securing to a masonry wall, a 3-foot length of flexible metal conduit with 4 feet of conductor, the necessary fittings, wire terminals, and the labor for making a complete installation. When the starter is furnished by others, it is considered that only the starter, with the appropriate heaters, is furnished to the electrical contractor.

COST OF MOTOR STARTER AND HOOK-UP

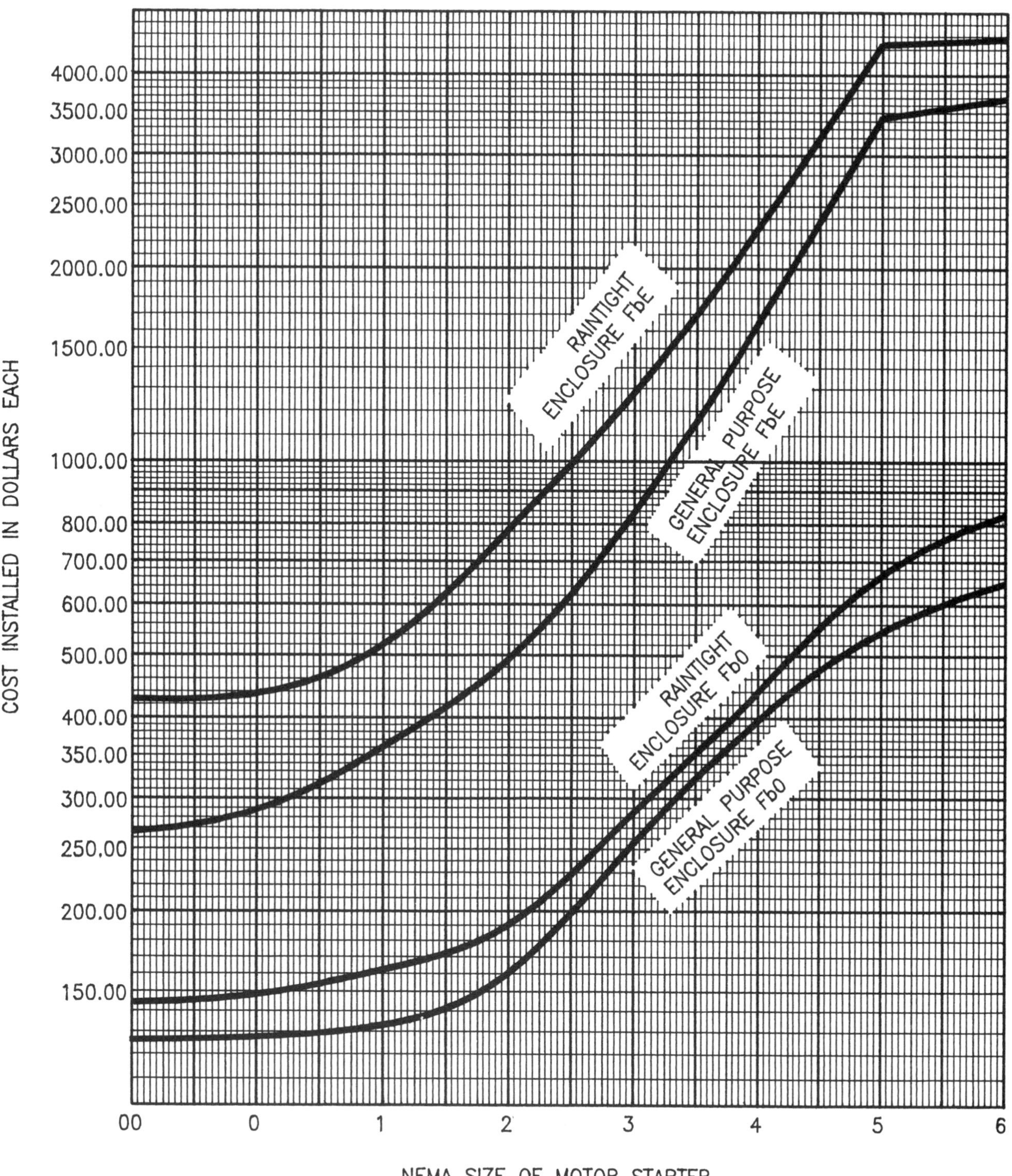

200, 230, AND 460 VOLT AC LINE VOLTAGE MAGNETIC STARTER – 3 PHASE

The costs shown for the combination motor starters consist of the published contractors' book price for the motor starters required for the horsepower and voltages shown. The starters are Square D 8538 Series. They include fastening devices for securing to a masonry wall, a 3-foot length of flexible metal conduit with 4 feet of conductor at the motor, the necessary fittings and wire terminals, and the labor for making a complete installation with the exception of the length of conduit and wire run from the starter to the motor. Weatherproof installations provide liquidtight flexible metal conduit.

LINE VOLTAGE			
NEMA SIZE	HORSEPOWER RANGE		
	200–VOLT MOTOR	230–VOLT MOTOR	460–VOLT MOTOR
0	0 TO 3	0 TO 3	0 TO 5
1	4 TO 7–1/2	4 TO 7–1/2	6 TO 10
2	8 TO 10	8 TO 15	11 TO 25
3	11 TO 25	16 TO 30	26 TO 50
4	26 TO 40	31 TO 50	51 TO 100
5	41 TO 75	51 TO 100	101 TO 200
6	76 TO 150	101 TO 200	201 TO 400

COST OF COMBINATION MOTOR STARTER – SWITCH & FUSE TYPE

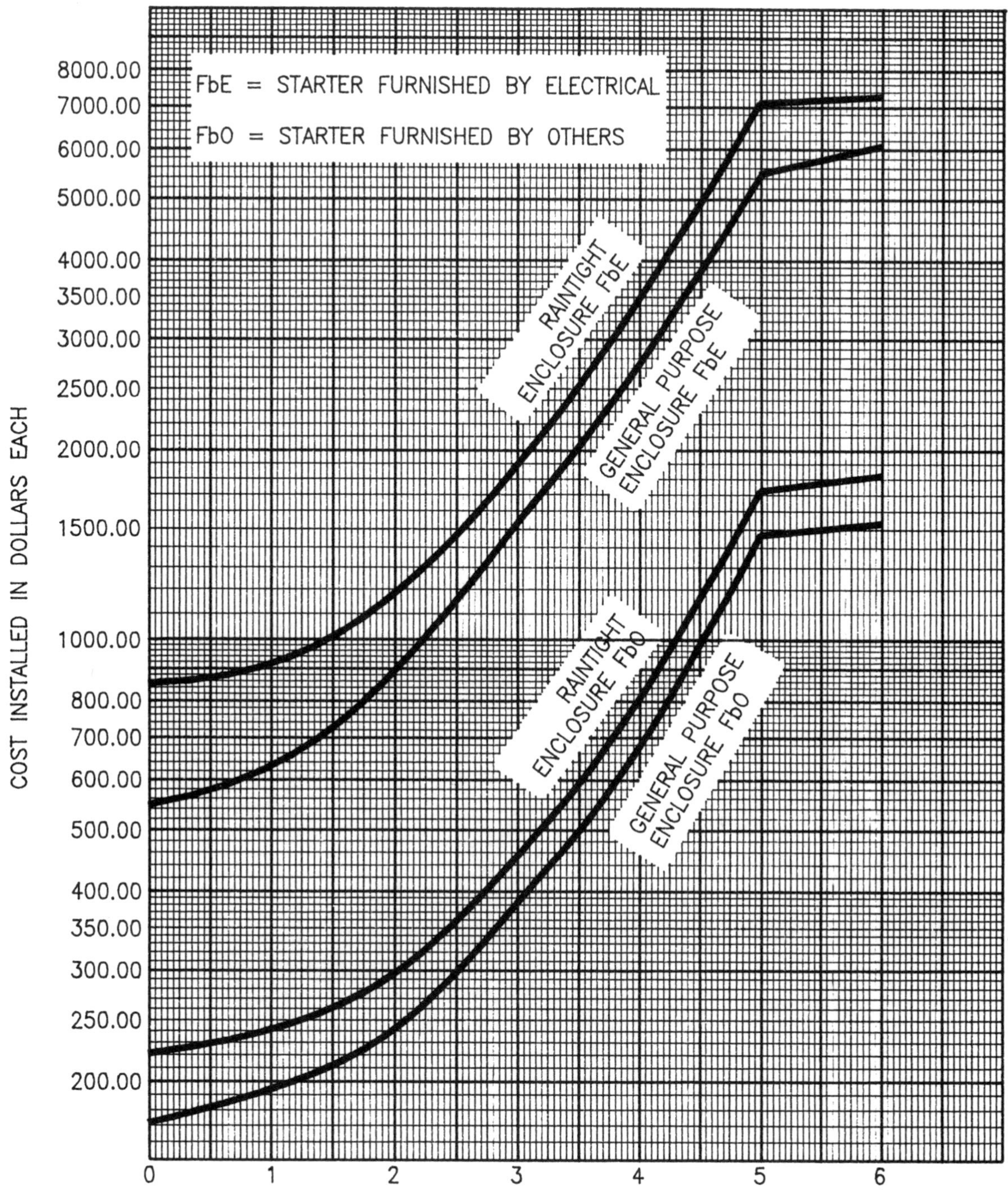

G

G-2

The costs shown for the autotransformer type of reduced-voltage starters are based upon the published contractors' book price. These are Square D Class 8606.

Included: (material and labor)

1. *Start/stop pushbutton in the cover*
2. *Pilot light*
3. *Toggle bolts for mounting to a masonry wall*
4. *Conduit terminals*
5. *Sufficient conductor of proper size and length required in the starter enclosure for connections*
6. *3 feet of flexible conduit, terminals, 4 feet of the number and size of conductors required. and connections*
7. *3 overload thermal units*

AUTOTRANSFORMER			
NEMA SIZE	HORSEPOWER		
	200–VOLT MOTOR	230 VOLT MOTOR	460 VOLT MOTOR
2	0–10	1–15	0–25
3	11–25	16–30	26–50
4	26–40	31–50	51–100
5	41–75	51–100	101–200
6	76–150	101–200	201–400

COST OF REDUCED VOLTAGE STARTER

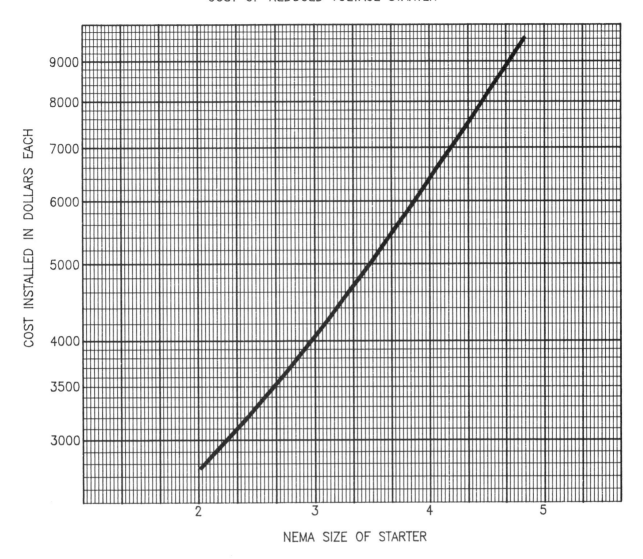

COST INSTALLED IN DOLLARS EACH

9000
8000
7000
6000
5000
4000
3500
3000

2 3 4 5

NEMA SIZE OF STARTER

REDUCED VOLTAGE STARTER — AUTOTRANSFORMER — CLOSED TRANSITION

The costs shown for the wye-delta type of reduced-voltage starters are based upon the published contractors' book price. These are Square D Class 8630.

Included: (material and labor)

1. *Start/stop pushbutton in the cover*
2. *Pilot light*
3. *Toggle bolts for mounting to a masonry wall*
4. *Conduit terminals*
5. *Sufficient conductor of proper size and length required in the starter enclosure for connections*
6. *3 feet of flexible conduit, terminals, 4 feet of the number and size of conductors required and connections*
7. *3 overload thermal units*

WYE DELTA			
NEMA SIZE	HORSEPOWER		
	200-VOLT MOTOR	230 VOLT MOTOR	460 VOLT MOTOR
1YD	0–10	0–10	0–15
2YD	11–20	11–25	15–40
3YD	21–40	26–50	41–75
4YD	41–60	51–75	76–100
5YD	61–150	76–150	151–300

COST OF REDUCED VOLTAGE STARTER

COST INSTALLED IN DOLLARS EACH

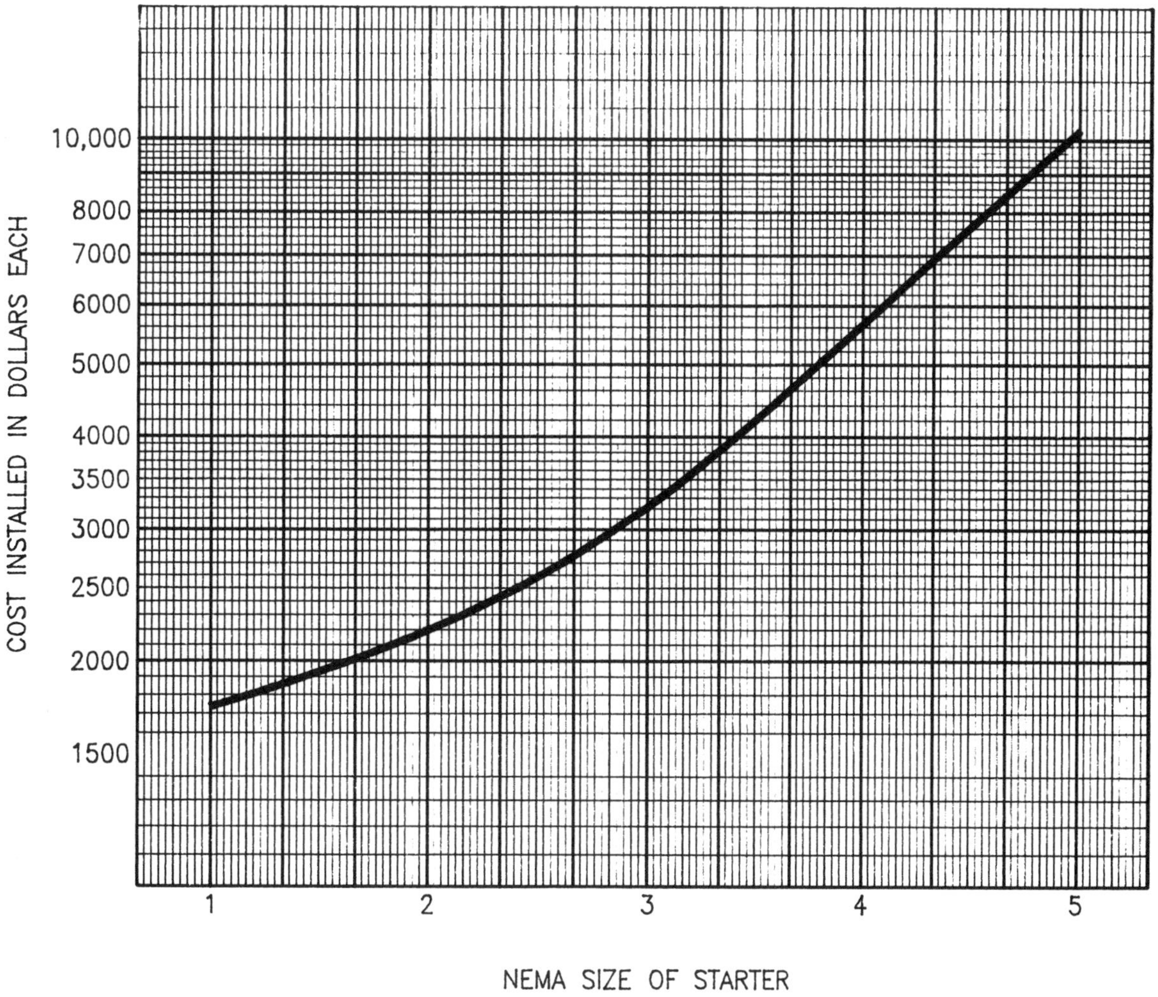

10,000
8000
7000
6000
5000
4000
3500
3000
2500
2000
1500

1 2 3 4 5

NEMA SIZE OF STARTER

REDUCED VOLTAGE STARTER – WYE–DELTA TYPE – OPEN TRANSITION

The costs shown for the part-winding type of reduced-voltage starters are based upon the published contractors' book price. These are Square D Class 8640.

Included: (material and labor)

1. *Start/stop pushbutton in the cover*
2. *Pilot light*
3. *Toggle bolts for mounting to a masonry wall*
4. *Conduit terminals*
5. *Sufficient conductor of proper size and length required in the starter enclosure for connections*
6. *3 feet of flexible conduit, terminals, 4 feet of the number and size of conductors required. and connections*
7. *3 overload thermal units*

PART WINDING			
NEMA SIZE	HORSEPOWER		
	200–VOLT MOTOR	230 VOLT MOTOR	460 VOLT MOTOR
1PW	0–10	0–10	0–15
2PW	11–20	11–25	15–40
3PW	21–40	26–50	41–75
4PW	41–75	51–75	76–100
5PW	76–150	76–150	151–350
6PW	-----	151–300	351–600

COST OF REDUCED VOLTAGE STARTERS

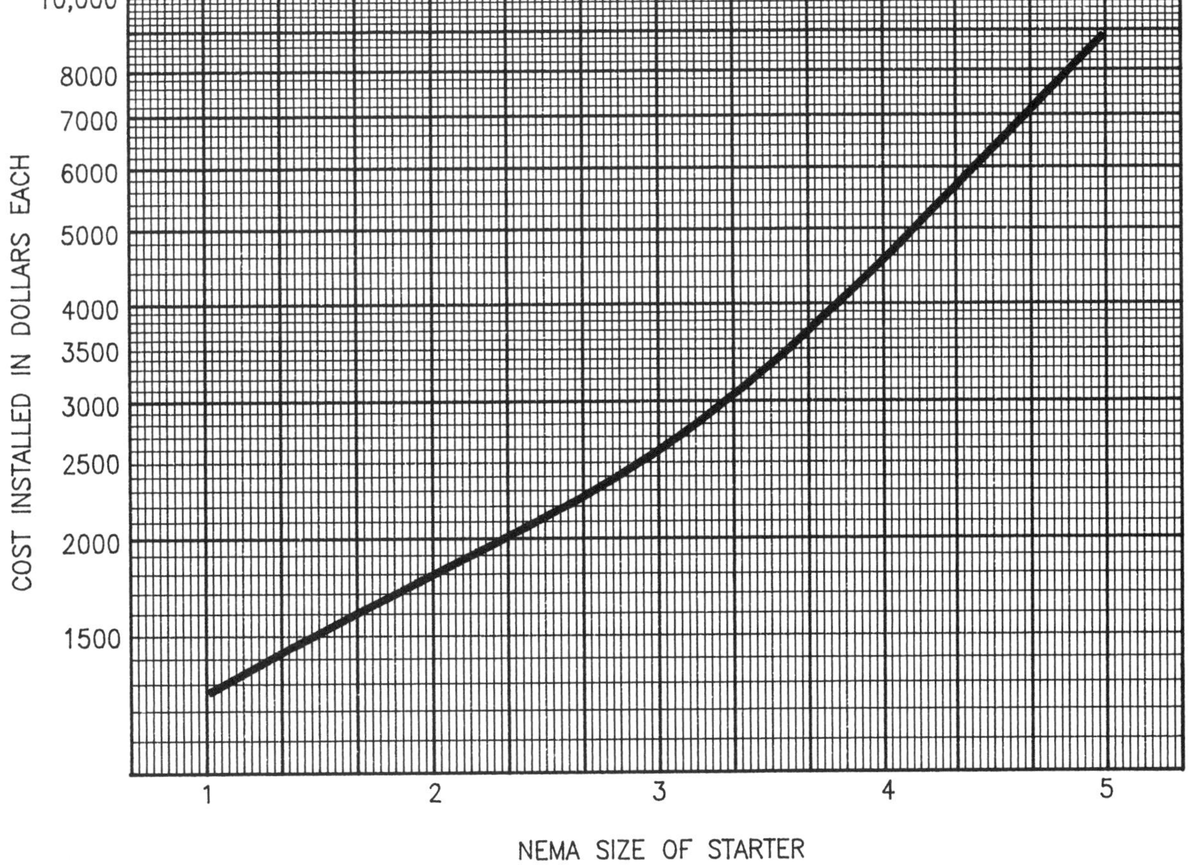

REDUCED VOLTAGE STARTER — PART WINDING TYPE — CLOSED TRANSITION

The costs shown for the primary resistor type of reduced-voltage starters are based upon the published contractors' book price. These are Square D Class 8647.

Included: (material and labor)

1. *Start/stop pushbutton in the cover*
2. *Pilot light*
3. *Toggle bolts for mounting to a masonry wall*
4. *Conduit terminals*
5. *Sufficient conductor of proper size and length required in the starter enclosure for connections*
6. *3 feet of flexible conduit, terminals, 4 feet of the number and size of conductors required and connections*
7. *3 overload thermal units*

PRIMARY RESISTER TYPE			
NEMA SIZE	HORSEPOWER RANGE		
	200–VOLT MOTOR	230 VOLT MOTOR	460 VOLT MOTOR
1	0–7–1/2	0–7–1/2	0–10
2	8–10	8–15	15–25
3	11–25	16–30	26–50
4	26–40	31–50	51–100
5	41–75	51–100	101–200

COST OF REDUCED VOLTAGE STARTERS

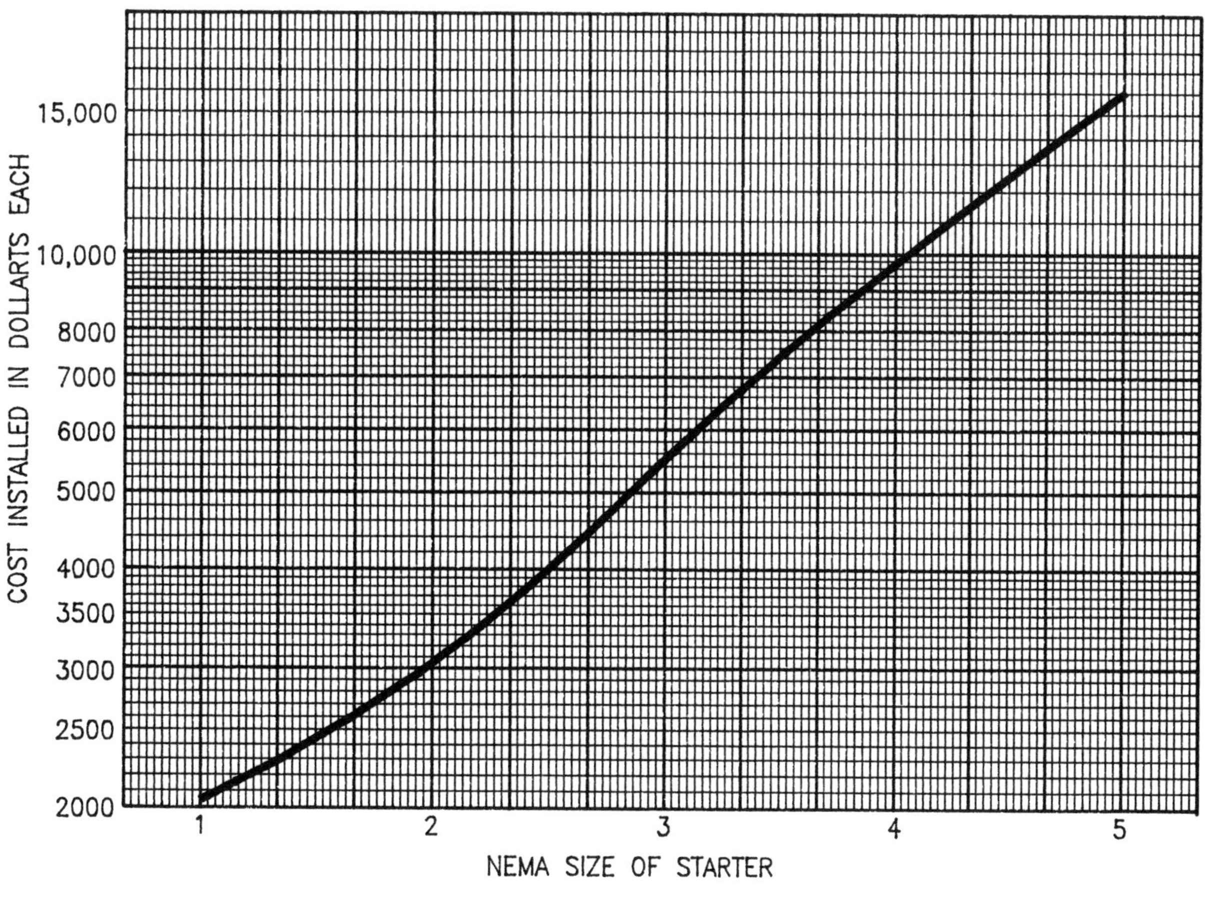

REDUCED VOLTAGE STARTER – PRIMARY RESISTER TYPE – NONREVERSING

COST OF REDUCED VOLTAGE STARTERS

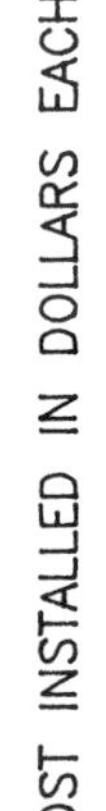

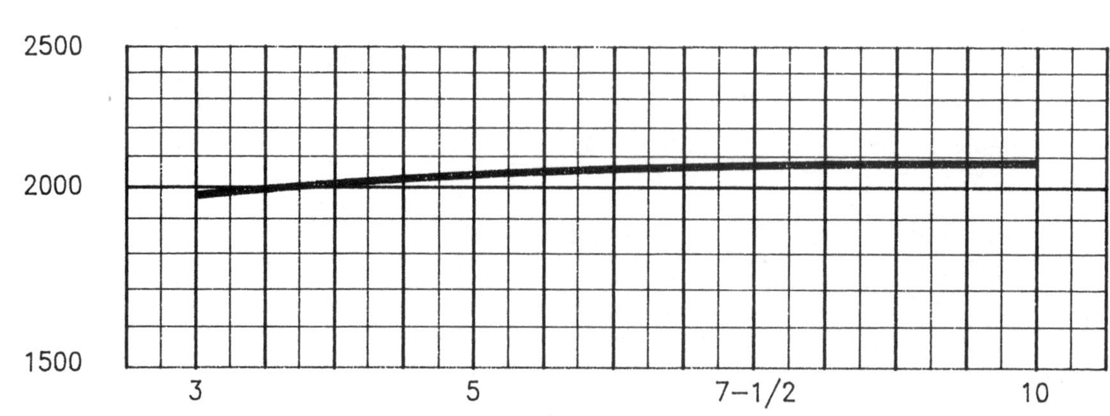

SIZE OF STARTER IN HORSEPOWER

SOLID STATE STARTERS			
MAXIMUM FULL LOAD AMPERES	HORSEPOWER RANGE		
	200-VOLT MOTOR	230 VOLT MOTOR	460 VOLT MOTOR
16	3	3-5	5-10
32	5-10	5-10	5-20
64	5-20	5-20	5-40
128	5-40	5-40	5-100
200	5-60	5-75	5-150
320	5-100	5-125	5-250

REDUCED VOLTAGE STARTER - SOLID STATE TYPE - 200/230, 380/480, & 500 V

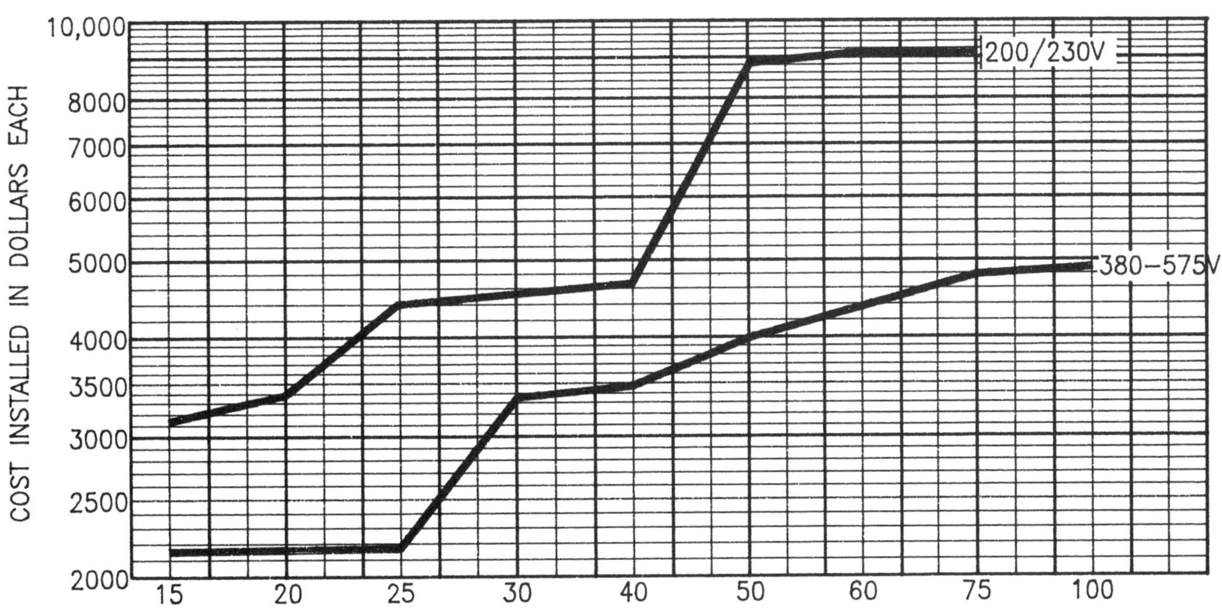

The costs shown for the solid-state type of reduced-voltage starters are based upon the published contractors' book price. These are Square D Class 8660.These starters provide smooth, stepless acceleration of a motor through use of SCRs which provides a "soft start" to the motor.

Included: (material and labor)

1. *Start/stop pushbutton in the cover*
2. *Pilot light*
3. *Toggle bolts for mounting to a masonry wall*
4. *Conduit terminals*
5. *Sufficient conductor of proper size and length required in the starter enclosure for connections*
6. *3 feet of flexible conduit, terminals, 4 feet of the number and size of conductors required. and connections*
7. *3 overload thermal units*

COST OF POWER FACTOR CORRECTING CAPACITORS

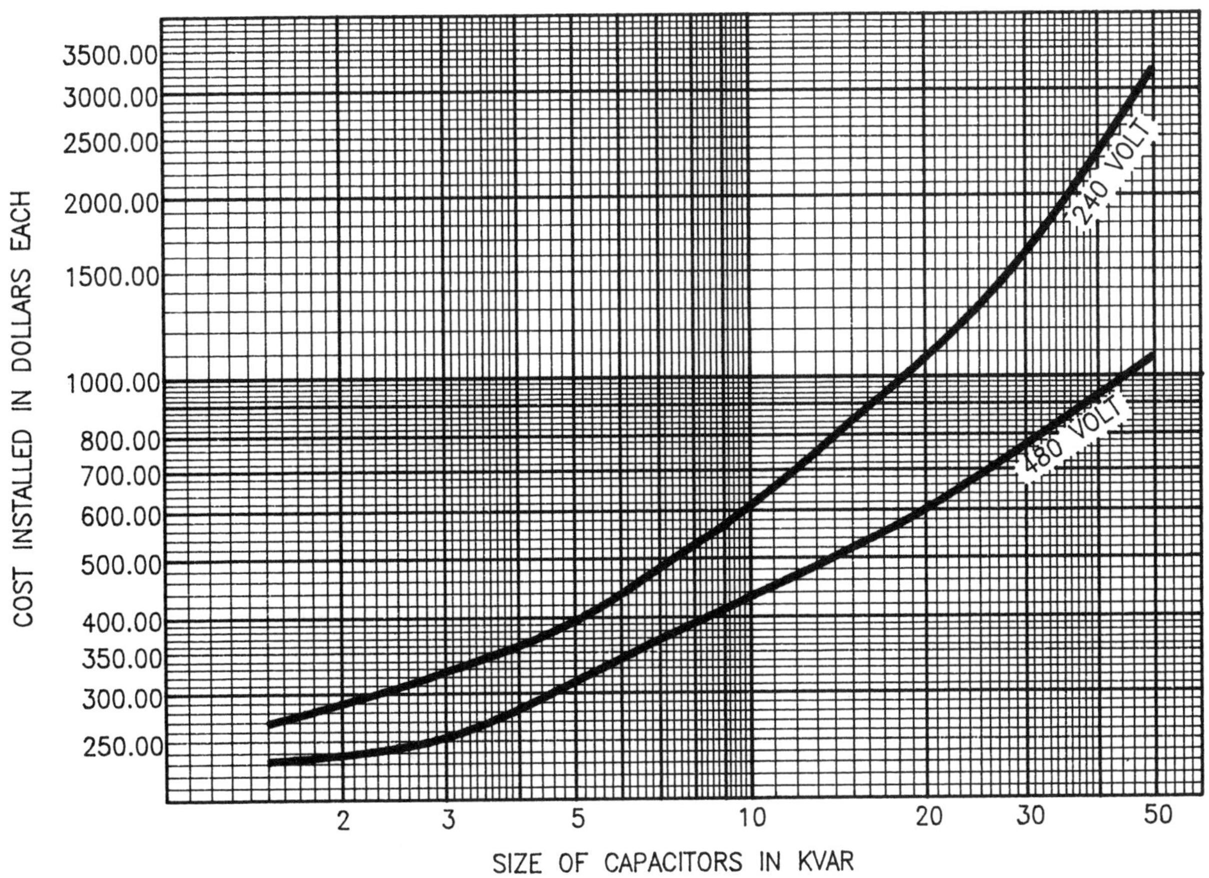

The costs shown for the power factor correcting capacitors consist of the published contractors' book price as manufactured by Square D Co. Included are gasketed covers and discharge resistors.

The control center components used in establishing these graphs are based upon Square D Model 5 control centers. The installed cost of a free-standing type of motor control center can be assembled from the use of a few pages of the essential components, such as

1. *Vertical sections required*
2. *Main and outgoing feeder disconnects*
3. *Motor starters as required*

Prices are based upon Class 1, Type B wiring, which provides factory-wired terminal boards for load and control wire in the starter units. This seems to be the most popular type.

Vertical Section for Incoming Feeders

The vertical section is a general-purpose Type 1 gasketed enclosure 20 inches wide by 20 inches deep by 90 inches high providing 72 inches of mounting space. Busbar bracing is provided for 42,000 amperes RMS. Main buses are tin-plated copper rated at 600, 800, 1200, 1600, and 2000 amperes.

The labor for installation of this vertical section is based upon its being received from the factory with main lugs, main breaker, or main switch installed, moving the unit to a location under favorable conditions, and anchoring to the floor. Material costs are based upon the contractors' book price.

COST OF 20" DEEP MOTOR CONTROL VERTICAL SECTION FOR INCOMING MAIN

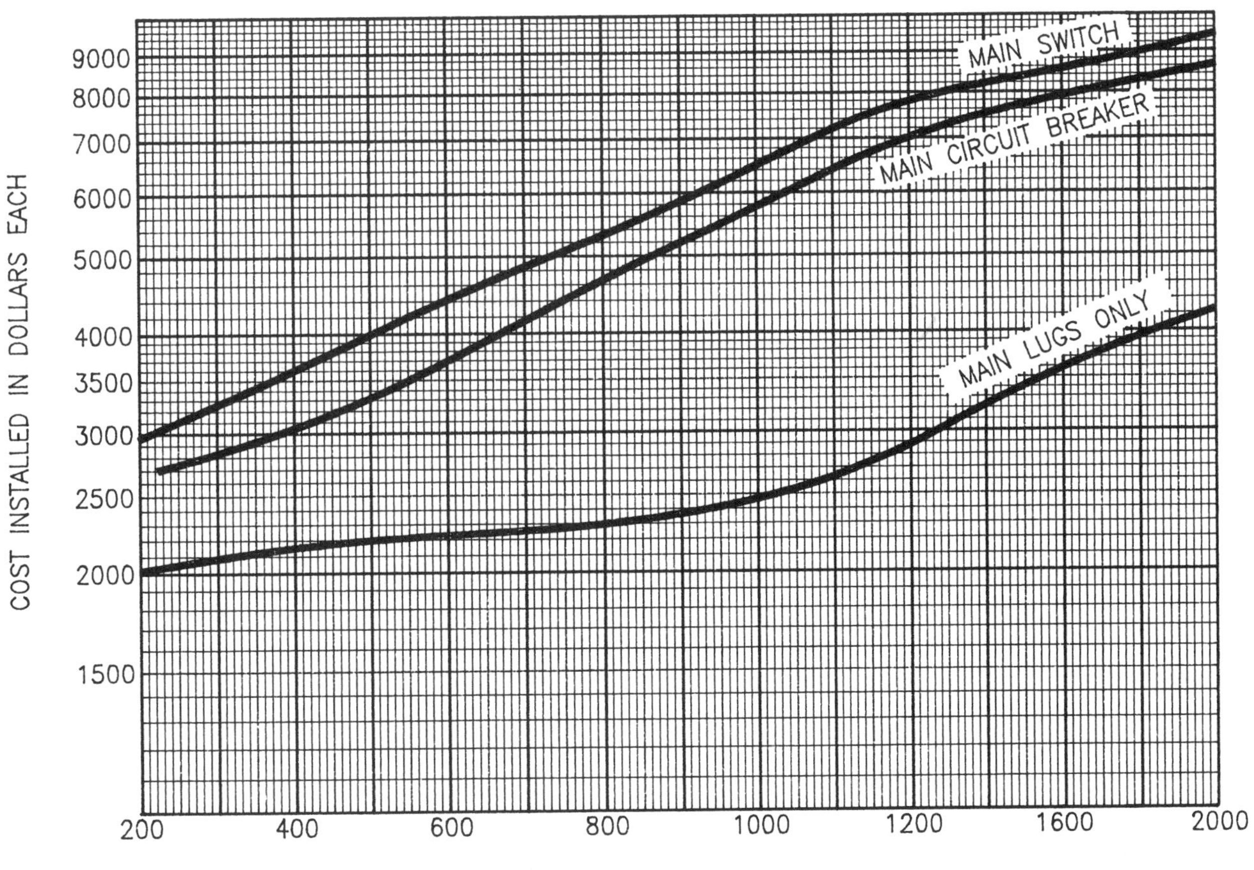

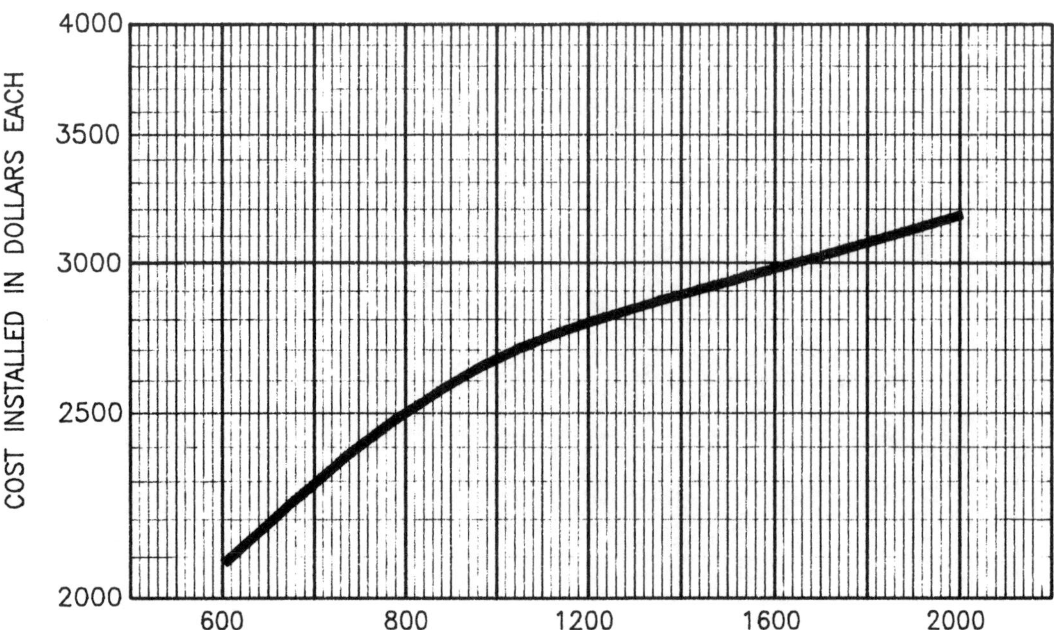

The vertical section is a 20-inch wide by 20-inch deep by 90-inch high structure with a 600, 800, 1200, 1600, or 2000 ampere horizontal bus and a 300-ampere vertical bus. Buses are tin-plated copper braced for 42,000 amperes RMS. These sections have 72 inches of available mounting space for disconnects, starters, and metering. Vertical wiring troughs are also provided.

The labor for installation of this vertical section is based upon moving into location under favorable conditions, and anchoring to the floor. Material costs are based upon the contractors' net book price.

COST OF M.C.C. 600–V BRANCH FEEDER FUSIBLE SWITCHES

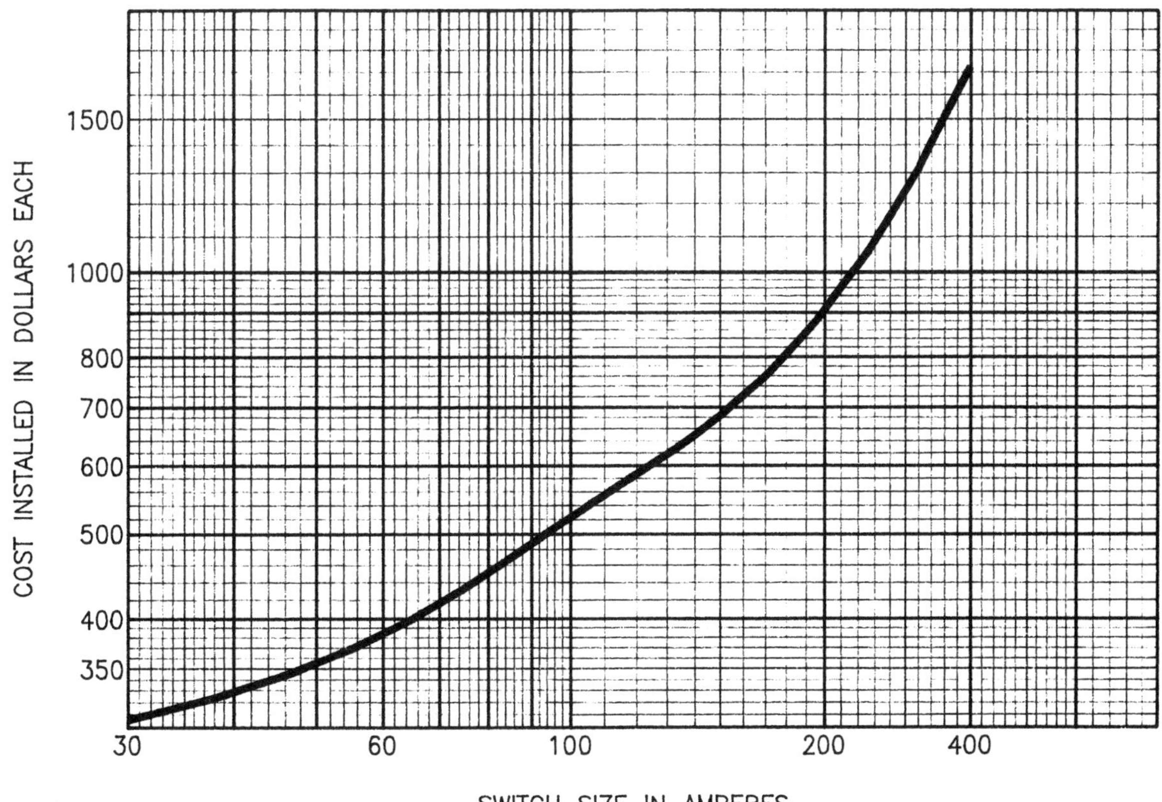

The costs shown for the switch/fuse branch feeder disconnects consist of the published contractors' book price for the units only. Costs for the vertical section are not included with these costs; they are listed separately for the vertical section only.

These costs also include a conduit termination into the center and 5 feet of three-conductor wire sized to match the disconnect. Switch costs also include 600-volt Fusetrons.

SPACE FACTOR REQUIREMENTS	
SWITCH SIZE	SPACE FACTOR
30/3	1
60/3	1
100/3	1
200/3	2–1/2
400/3	4

COST OF M.C.C. 600–V BRANCH FEEDER CIRCUIT BREAKERS

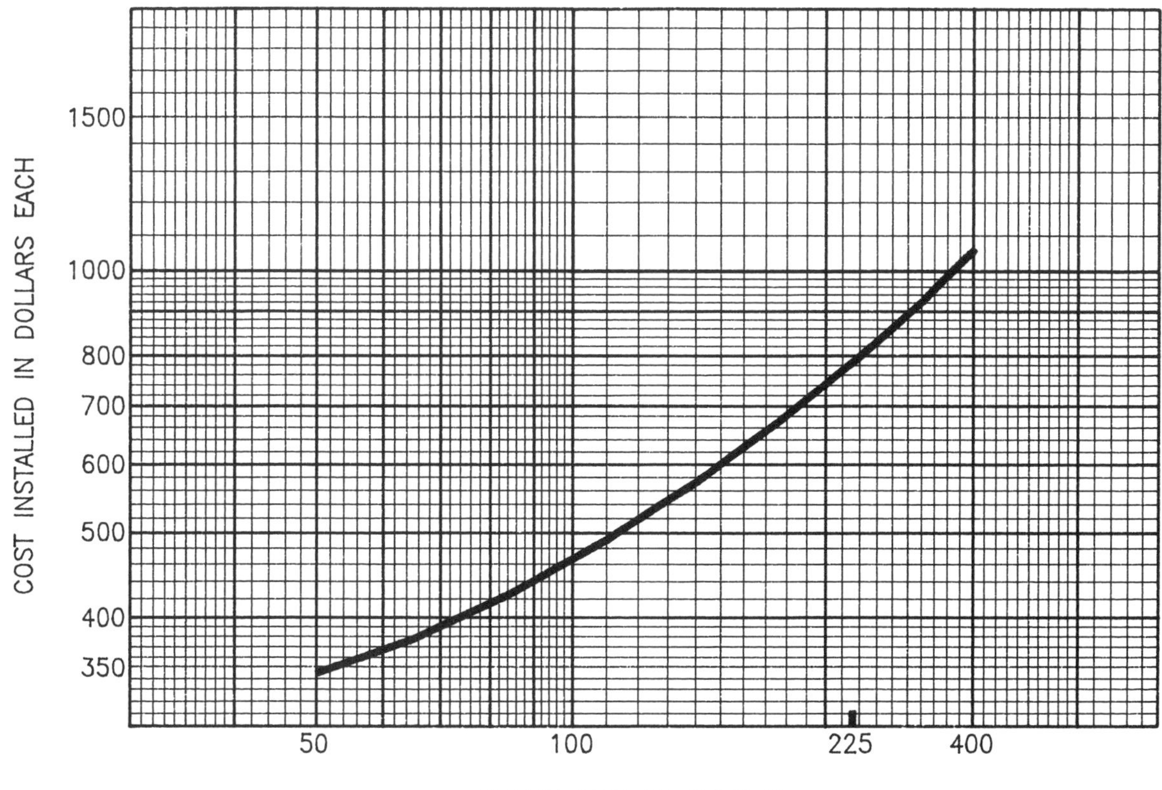

The costs shown for the circuit-breaker branch feeder disconnects consist of the published contractors' book price for the units only. Costs for the vertical section are not included with these costs; they are listed separately for the vertical section only.

These costs also include a conduit termination into the center and 5 feet of three-conductor wire sized to match the disconnect.

SPACE FACTOR REQUIREMENTS	
BREAKER SIZE	SPACE FACTOR
50/3	1
100/3	1
200/3	1–1/2
400/3	2

The costs shown for the full-voltage single-speed nonreversing starters are based upon the published contractors' book price. The control center components used in establishing these graphs are based upon the Square D Model 5 motor control centers.

Since Class 1, Type B wiring is the most popular, prices are based upon it. With independent wiring for each unit, the wires terminate at terminal blocks near the bottom of each unit. No intercontrol wiring is provided.

A space factor is approximately 12 inches in height.

Included: (material and labor)

1. *Motor starter with disconnect*
2. *Start-stop switch and pilot light in the cover*
3. *Two separate interlock switches, one N. O. and one N. C.*
4. *Control transformer*
5. *Overload relays in starter*
6. *Conduit terminal into section*
7. *Sufficient conductor of size required*

COST OF M.C.C. FULL–VOLTAGE NON–REVERSING STARTER – 1 SPEED

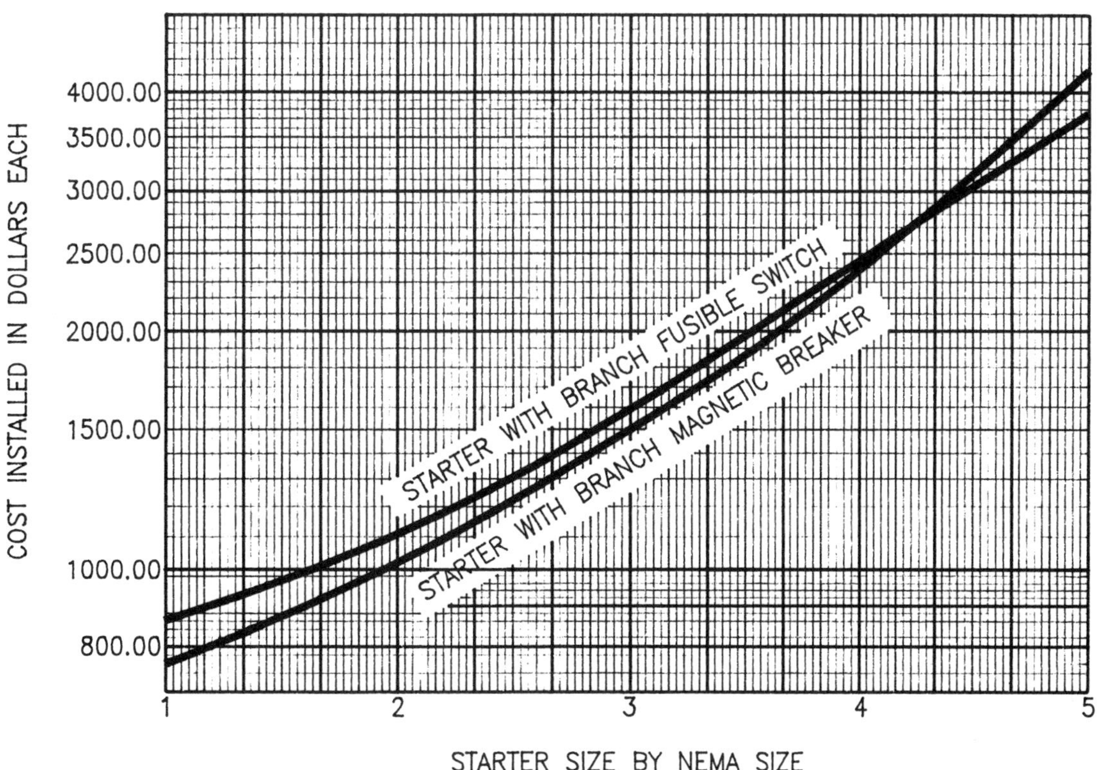

FULL–VOLTAGE STARTER (FVNR)					
NEMA SIZE	SPACE FACTOR		HORSEPOWER RANGE		
	CIRCUIT BREAKER	FUSIBLE SWITCH	200–VOLT MOTOR	230–VOLT MOTOR	460/575–VOLT MOTOR
1	1	1	0––7–1/2	0––7–1/2	0–10
2	1	1	8–10	8–15	11–25
3	1–1/2	1–1/2	11–20	16–25	26–50
4	2	3–1/2	21–40	26–50	51–100
5	4	5–1/2	41–75	51–100	101–200

The costs shown for the reduced-voltage autotransformer type with closed transition starters are based upon the published contractors' book price. The control center components used in establishing these graphs are based upon the Square D Model 5 motor control centers.

Since Class 1, Type B wiring is the most popular, prices are based upon it. With independent wiring for each unit, the wires terminate at terminal blocks near the bottom of each unit. No intercontrol wiring is provided.

A space factor is approximately 12 inches in height.

Included: (material and labor)

1. *Motor starter with circuit-breaker disconnect*
2. *Start-stop switch and pilot light in the cover*
3. *Two separate interlock switches, one N. O. and one N. C.*
4. *Control transformer*
5. *Overload relays in starter*
6. *Conduit terminal into section*
7. *Sufficient conductor of size required*

COST OF M.C.C. REDUCED VOLTAGE STARTER – AUTOTRANSFORMER TYPE CLOSED TRANSITION

COST INSTALLED IN DOLLARS EACH

10,000
8000
7000
6000
5000
4000
3500
3000
2500
2000
1500

3 4 5

STARTER SIZE BY NEMA SIZE

M.C.C. AUTOTRANSFORMER REDUCED VOLTAGE STARTER					
NEMA SIZE	SPACE FACTOR		HORSEPOWER RANGE		
	CIRCUIT BREAKER	FUSIBLE SWITCH	200–VOLT MOTOR	230–VOLT MOTOR	460/575–VOLT MOTOR
3	4	4–1/2	0–20	0–25	0–50
4	5	6	21–40	26–50	51–100
5	6	6	41–75	51–100	101–200

M.C.C. REDUCED VOLTAGE STARTER – AUTOTRANSFORMER TYPE – CLOSED TRANSITION

The costs shown for the reduced-voltage part-winding 2-step starters are based upon the published contractors' book price. The control center components used in establishing these graphs are based upon the Square D Model 5 motor control centers.

Since Class 1, Type B wiring is the most popular, prices are based upon it. With independent wiring for each unit, the wires terminate at terminal blocks near the bottom of each unit. No intercontrol wiring is provided.

A space factor is approximately 12 inches in height.

Included: (material and labor)

1. *Motor starter with circuit-breaker disconnect*
2. *Start-stop switch and pilot light in the cover*
3. *Two separate interlock switches, one N. O. and one N. C.*
4. *Control transformer*
5. *Overload relays in starter*
6. *Conduit terminal into section*
7. *Sufficient conductor of size required*

COST OF M.C.C. REDUCED VOLTAGE – PART WINDING – 2 STEP

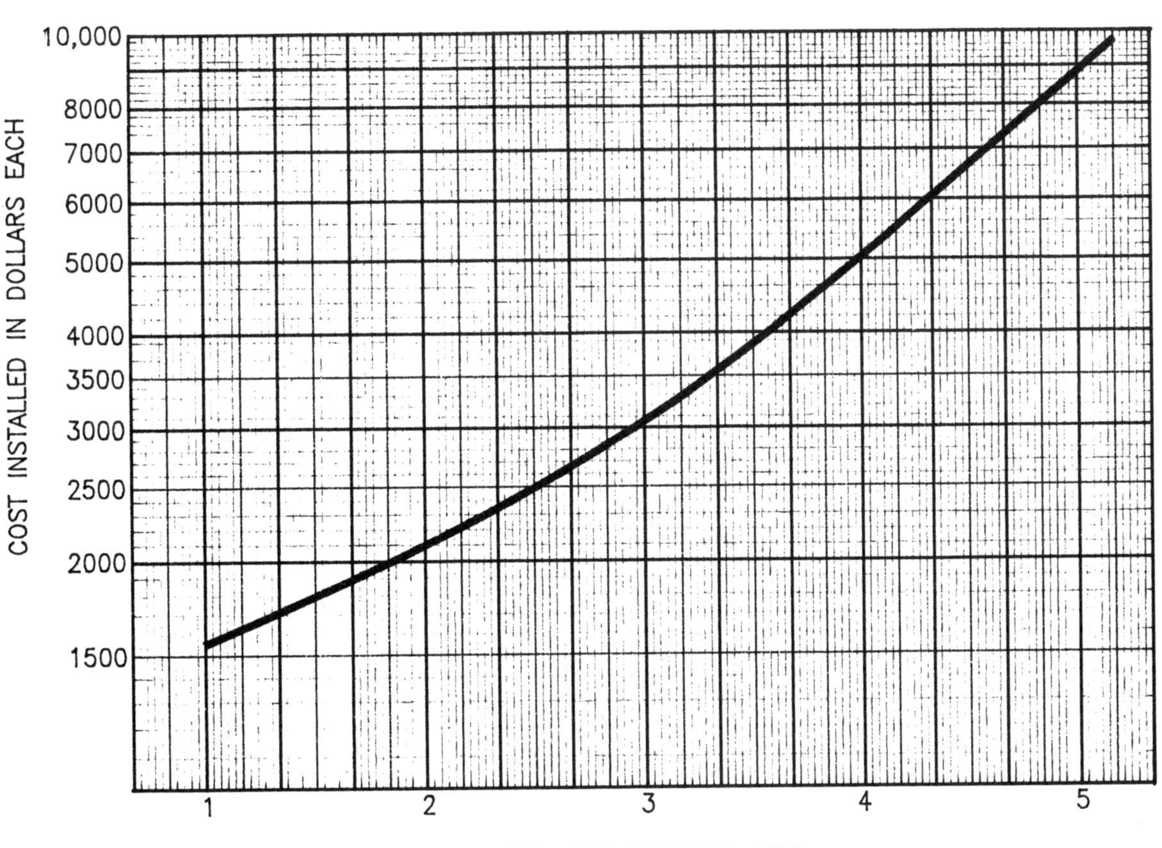

M.C.C. PART WINDING REDUCED VOLTAGE STARTER					
NEMA SIZE	SPACE FACTOR		HORSEPOWER RANGE		
	CIRCUIT BREAKER	FUSIBLE SWITCH	200–VOLT MOTOR	230–VOLT MOTOR	460/575–VOLT MOTOR
1–PW	2–1//2	2	0–10	0–10	0–15
2–PW	2–1/2	2–1/2	11–20	11–25	16–40
3–PW	3	4	21–40	26–50	41–75
4–PW	4–1/2	---	40–75	51–75	76–150
5–PW	7	---	76–125	76–150	151–300

DISTRIBUTION PANELBOARDS		
CONFIGURATION	SPACE REQUIREMENT	INSTALLED COST IN DOLLARS
1 PHASE 20 CIRCUIT	27"	309
1 PHASE 42 CIRCUIT	51"	769
3 PHASE 24 CIRCUIT	27"	478
3 PHASE 30 CIRCUIT	30"	507
3 PHASE 42 CIRCUIT	51"	829

DRY TYPE TRANSFORMERS			
TYPE AND SIZE		SPACE REQUIREMENT	INSTALLED COST IN DOLLARS
SINGLE PHASE 480/120/240V	5 KVA	30"	1102
	10 KVA	30"	1372
	15 KVA	36"	2548
	25 KVA	36"	2876
THREE PHASE 480/120/208V	9 KVA	30"	2192
	15 KVA	30"	2374
	30 KVA	36"	3399
	45 KVA	36"	4866

The costs shown for the distribution panelboards and dry-type transformers consist of the published contractors' book price for the units shown. Since it is assumed that the units are installed in a vertical section, they are not factory wired under the prices shown, and no labor is included for branch circuit wiring in the panelboards.

Transformers

DRY TYPE

OIL TYPE

COST OF GENERAL–PURPOSE DRY TRANSFORMERS

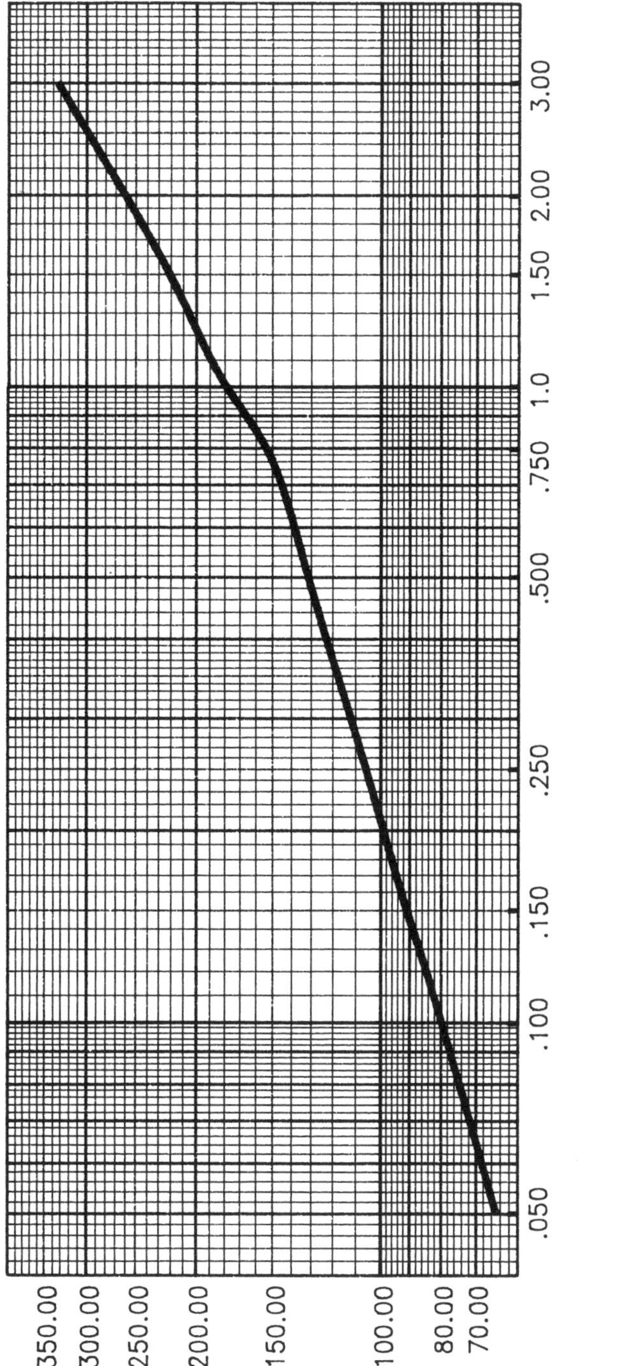

The costs shown for these single-phase dry transformers consist of the published contractors' book price as shown in the Square D Co. catalog. These costs include anchoring to a masonry wall with toggle bolts and installing the required conduit and wire terminals. These transformers are rated 240/480, 120/240, with no taps and are for indoor or outdoor use.

COST OF GENERAL–PURPOSE DRY TRANSFORMERS

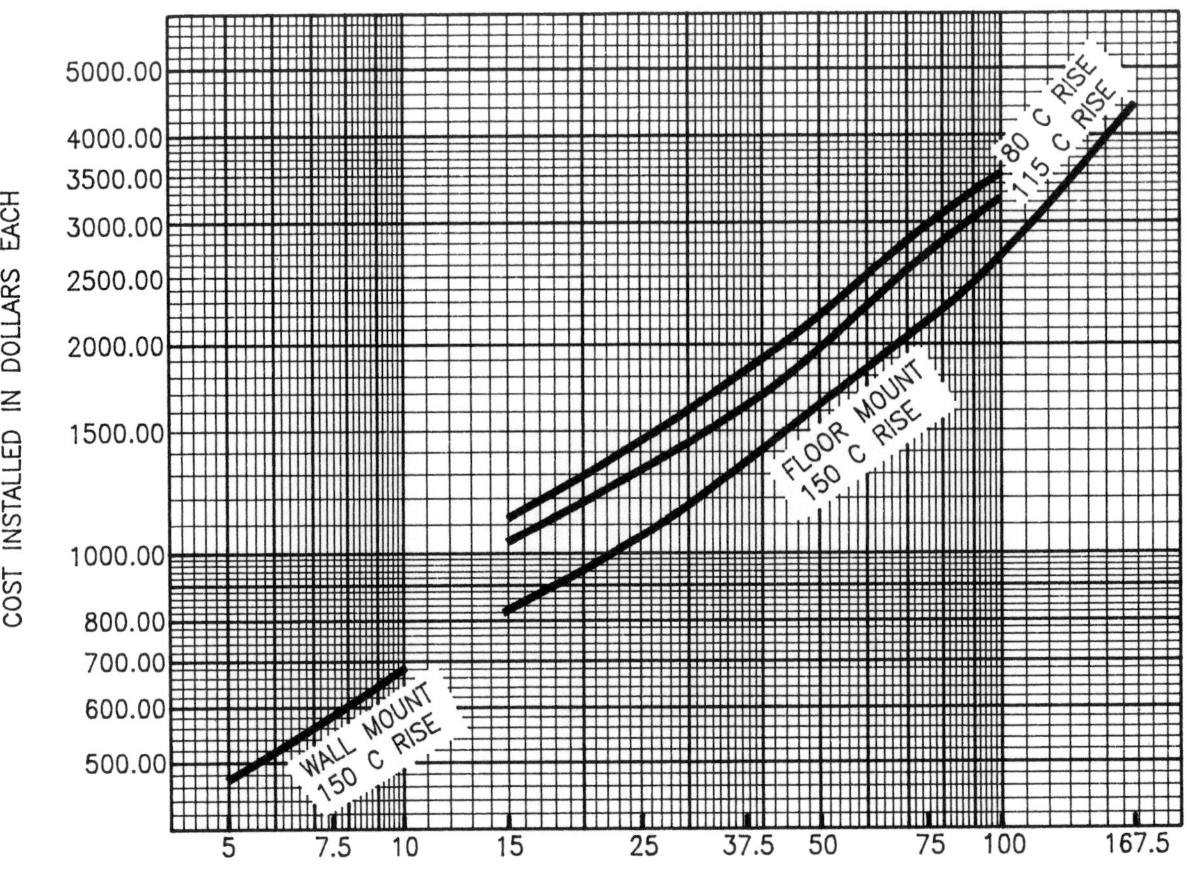

The costs shown for these single-phase dry transformers consist of the published contractors' book price as listed in the Square D Co. catalog. These costs include anchoring to a wall or floor as required and installing the required wire and conduit terminals. The transformers priced are as described below:

SINGLE-PHASE	*LIGHT & POWER*	*240 x 480—120/240*
.05–10 KVA	*Wall-mounted*	
15–167	*Floor-mounted*	*6—2 1/2% taps 2+ 4–*

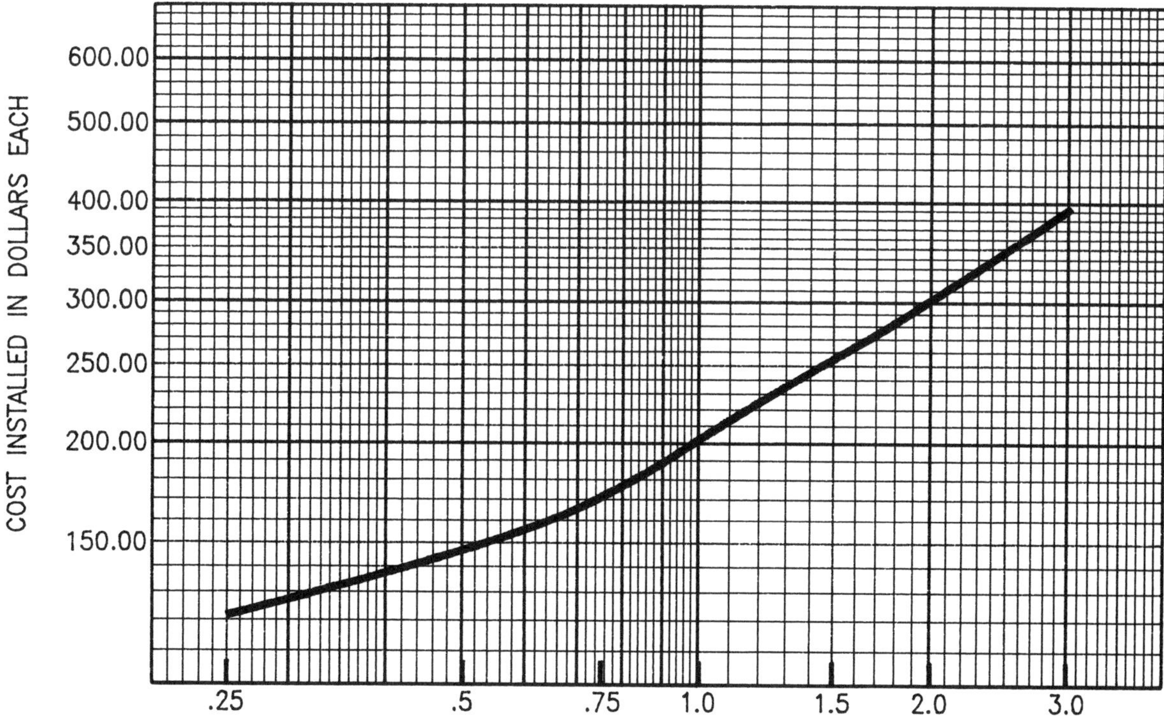

The costs shown for these single-phase dry-type buck-boost transformers consist of the published contractors' book price as shown in the Square D Co. catalog.These costs include anchoring to a masonry wall with toggle bolts and installing the required conduit and wire terminals. Transformer ratings are 120/240-12/24 or 120/240-16/32.

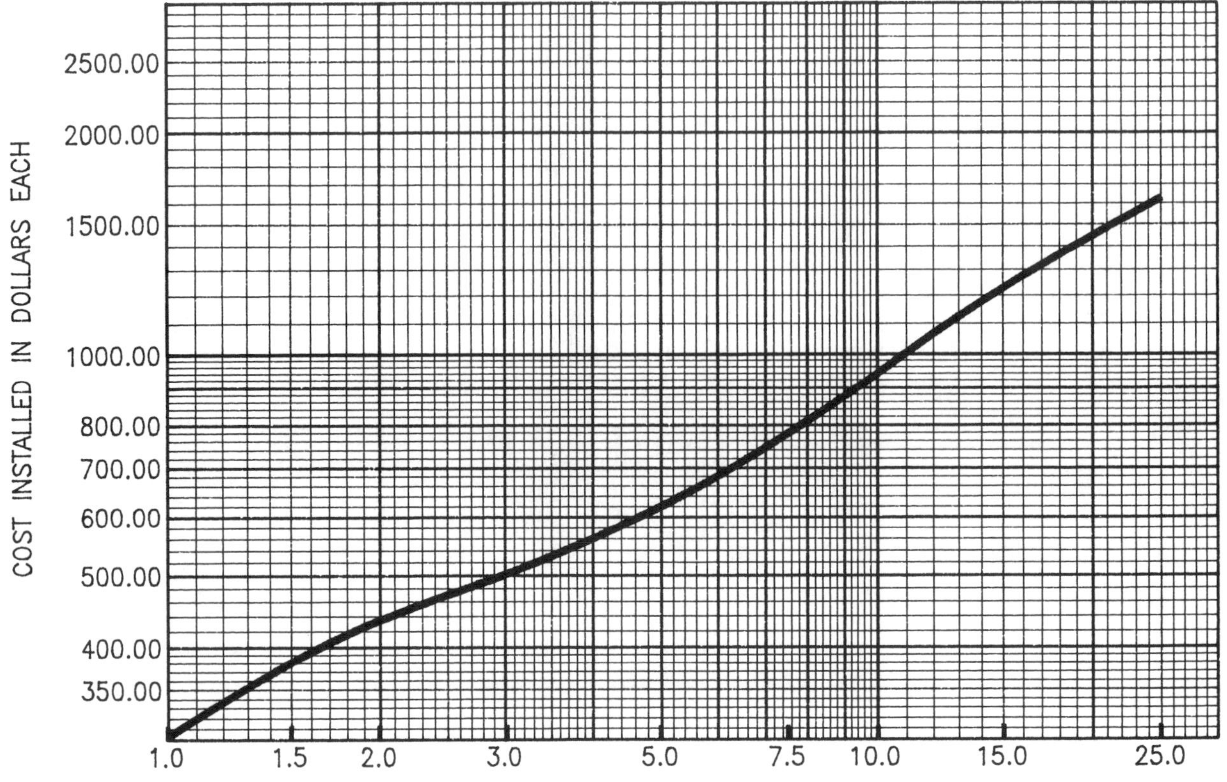

The costs shown for these isolating transformers consist of the published contractors' book price as shown in the Square D Co. catalog. These costs include anchoring to a wall or floor as required and installing the required conduit and wire terminals.

While any two-winding transformer is an isolating transformer, these particular transformers are designed to reduce the "electrical hash" that comes in through the utility distribution system. They are often used with electronic motor controls, x-ray machines, and computers.

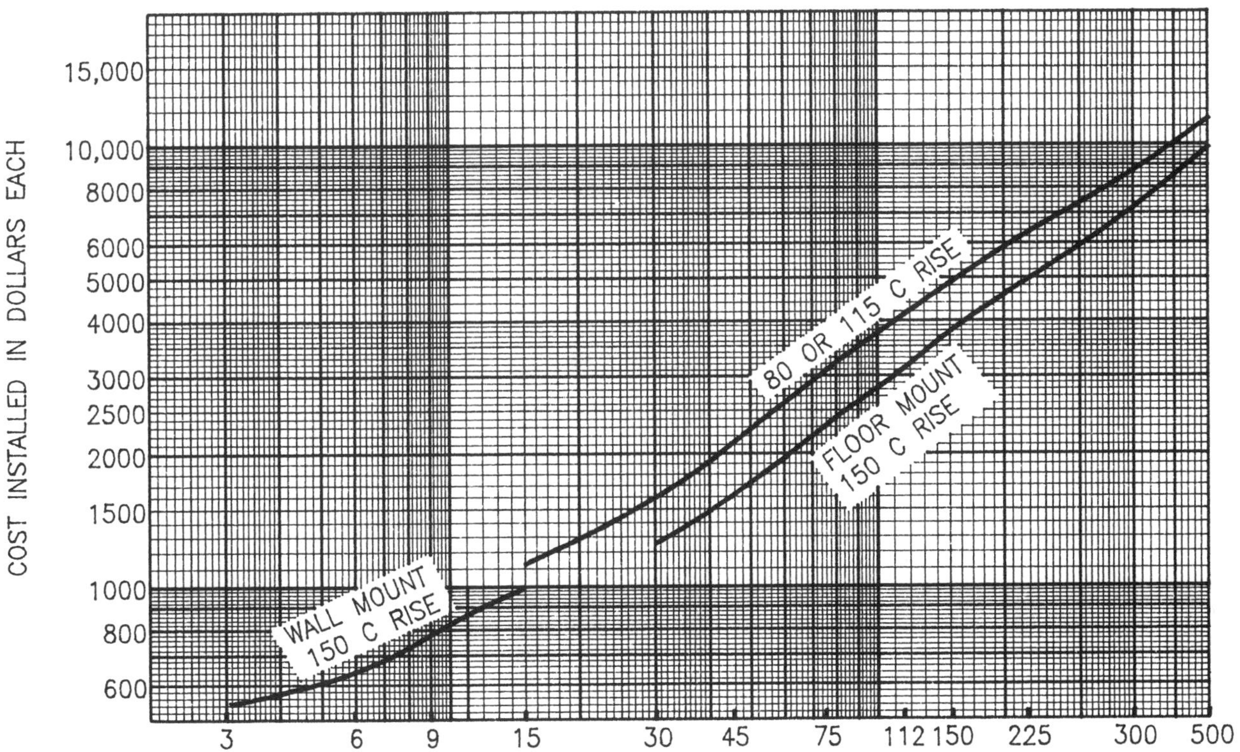

The costs shown for these three-phase dry transformers consist of the published contractors' book price as shown in the Square D Co. catalog. These costs include anchoring to a wall or floor as required and installing the required conduit and wire terminals. The transformers priced are as described below.

THREE—PHASE	*LIGHT & POWER*	*480-208Y/120*
3–15 kVA	*Wall-mounted 2—5%BN*	
30–500	*Floor Mt. 6—2 1/2% 2+ 4–*	

COST OF THREE-PHASE AUTOTRANSFORMER

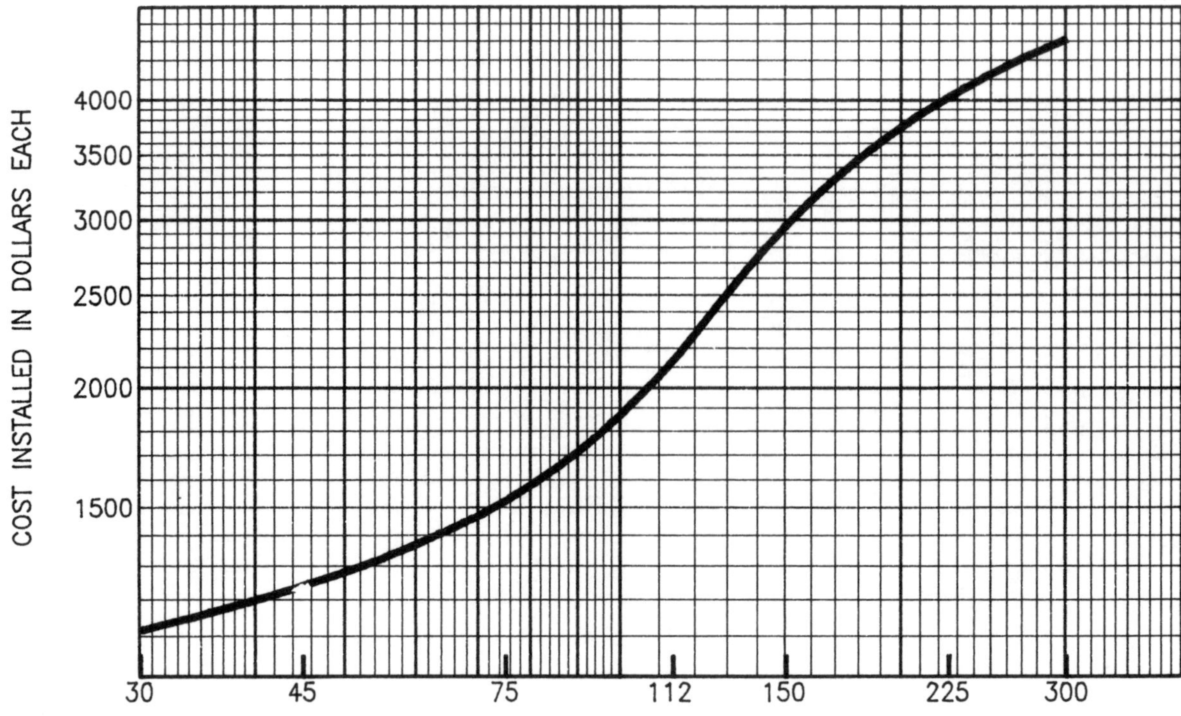

The costs shown for these three-phase autotransformers consist of the published contractors' book price as shown in the Square D Co. catalog.

Where they are not restricted by local ordinances or where isolation is not required by certain equipment, they are economical and quieter and have better voltage regulation.

The transformers are rated at 480Y/277 volts, three-phase, four wire to 208Y/120 and cannot be used on a 480-volt three-wire system.

COST OF ISOLATING–TYPE DRY TRANSFORMERS

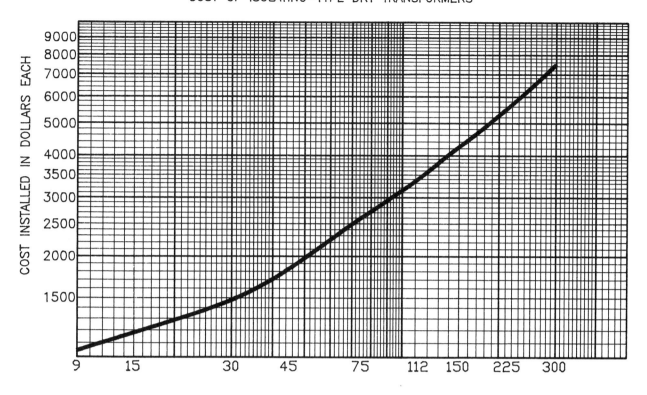

COST INSTALLED IN DOLLARS EACH

9000
8000
7000
6000
5000
4000
3500
3000
2500
2000
1500

9 15 30 45 75 112 150 225 300

TRANSFORMER SIZE IN KVA

The costs shown for these isolating transformers consist of the published contractors' book price as shown in the Square D Co. catalog. These costs include anchoring to a wall or floor as required and installing the required conduit and wire terminals.

While any two-winding transformer is an isolating transformer, these particular transformers are designed to reduce the "electrical hash" that comes in through the utility distribution system. They are often used with electronic motor controls, x-ray machines, and computers.

COST OF POLE MOUNTED TRANSFORMERS

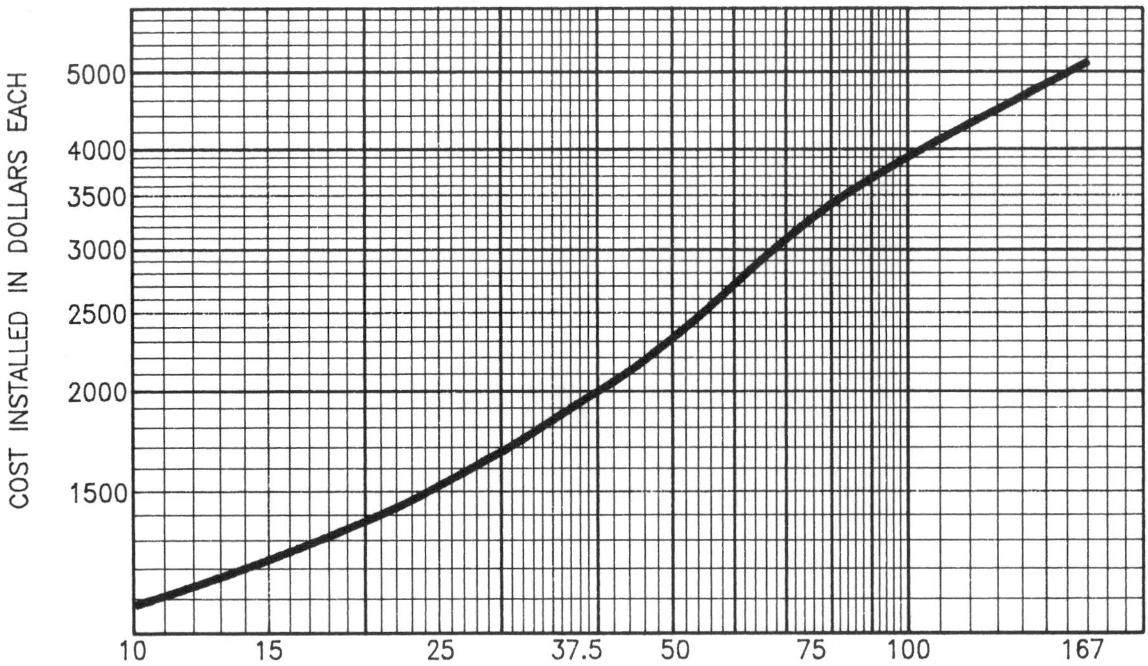

The costs shown for these pole-mounted transformers consist of the published contractors' book price and are as described below.

The pole-type transformers represented are two-bushing type. The voltages used were 7200/12470Y to 120/420 with four 2 1/2% taps below normal. Reference is General Electric type HSBA.

Installation costs include mounting the transformer and making high- and low-voltage connections.

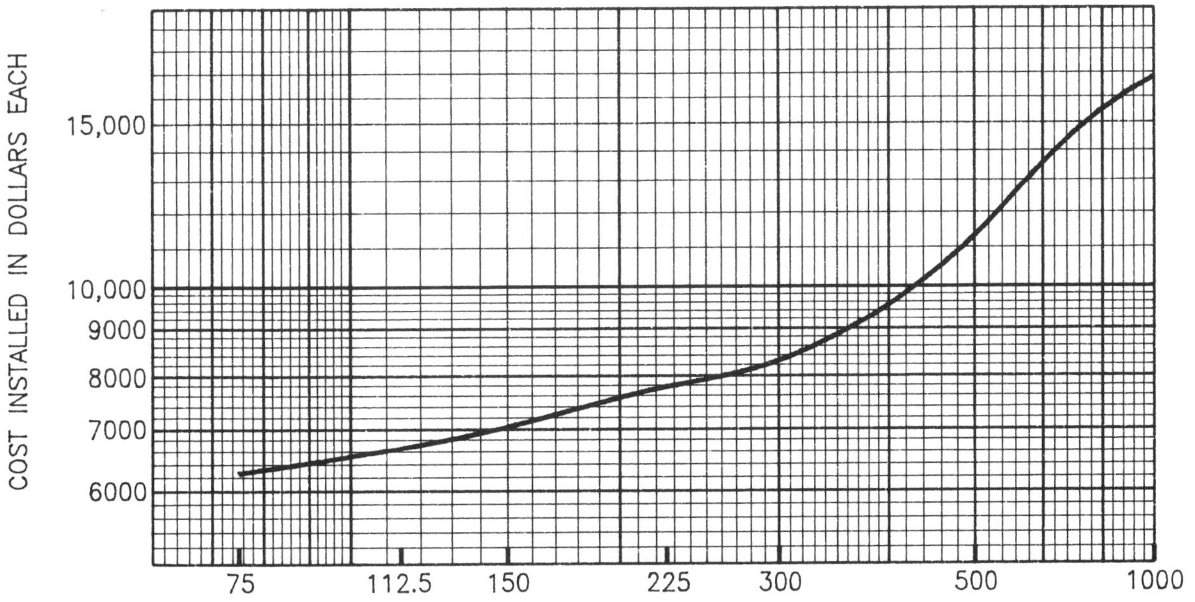

The costs shown for the pad-mounted transformers consist of the published contractors' book price and the items described below.

The pad-mounted transformers shown are considered to be single three-phase transformers of the sizes shown, with high-voltage terminations and secondary wire terminals sized to match the transformer ampacity. Also included is a 6-inch concrete base with rebar as a transformer foundation. The transformers referenced are GE Compads found in Catalog Section 5434, page 2, are rated 12470 Grd/7200 to 208 GrdY/120, and have four 2 1/2% taps below normal.

Auxiliary Systems

SOUND SYSTEM

EMERGENCY CALL SYSTEM FOR ELDERLY HOUSING

APARTMENT INTERCOM SYSTEM

MASTER TELEVISION ANTENNA SYSTEM

COST OF TELEPHONE CABINETS

4" DEEP FLUSH CABINETS	
SIZE	COST INSTALLED IN DOLLARS EACH
12" X 24"	172.00
18" X 30"	238.00
24" X 30"	291.00
30" X 30"	342.00
30 X 36"	396.00
36" X 48"	712.00
3/4" PLYWOOD BACKBOARD	
SIZE	COST INSTALLED IN DOLLARS EACH
4' X 8'	77.50
4' X 8'	51.00

The costs shown for the telephone cabinets consist of the published contractors' book price for cabinets of the sizes shown, which are related to frontal area and a 4-inch-deep cabinet. The plywood board is finished with black insulated varnish. It is further assumed that the cabinet is mounted flush in a masonry wall and has 1 1/4- to 2 1/2-inch GRC conduit terminal included. Terminal size depends upon cabinet size.

COST OF LIGHT COMMERCIAL SIGNALING EQUIPMENT

TYPE OF UNIT	MANUFACTURER	AMOUNT
TRANSFORMER	EDWARDS–NO.592 10 VA – 8, 16, 24V.	$43.00
TRANSFORMER	EDWARDS–NO.598 30VA – 8, 16, 24V.	52.50
TRANSFORMER	EDWARDS 50VA – NO.88–50, 12 24V 100VA – NO.88–100, 12, 24V 250VA – NO.88–250, 12,16,20,24V	 83.00 113.00 206.00
PUSHBUTTON	EDWARDS INTERIOR TO 48 VOLTS NO.695–11 & NO. 147 W/ S.S. PLATE EXTERIOR TO 48 VOLTS NO. 1786–C	 64.50 97.00

The costs shown for this light commercial signaling equipment consist of the published contractors' book price. The interior-type pushbutton 695-11 also includes a stainless steel plate upon which to mount the pushbutton. The 1786-C pushbutton has a threaded conduit entrance on the back plate.

TYPE OF UNIT	MANUFACTURER		AMOUNT
FLUSHCALL SERIES 662	EDWARDS CATALOGUE NO.		
	POWACALL TRANSFORMER	590&593	$69.00
	RINGACALL BELL	660	66.00
	BUZZACALL BUZZER	661	66.00
	TUCALL (BELL & BUZZER)	662	73.50
	MELOCALL	663	68.25
	TOGELPUSH (PUSHBUTTON)	664	60.50
BELL, BUZZER, OR COMBINATION	EDWARDS CATALOGUE NO.		
	6 VAC BELL	720	17.00
	6 VAC BUZZER	725	16.00
	6 VAC BELL/BUZZER	730	22.50
BELL	EDWARDS CATALOGUE NO.		
	8 VAC BELL	55–4"	34.25
BUZZER 15	EDWARDS CATALOGUE NO.		
	8 VAC BUZZER	#15–0AJ	27.00

The costs shown for these audible signals consist of the published contractors' book price for the units shown. The costs include labor and material for either flush or surface type of mounting.

TYPE OF UNIT	MANUFACTURER	AMOUNT
PUSHBUTTON	EDWARDS INTERIOR NO.850 WITH NO. 147 W/ S.S. PLATE	$74.50
PUSHBUTTON 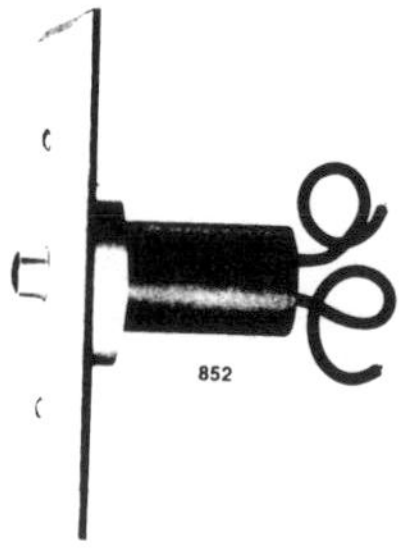 852	EDWARDS EXTERIOR NO. 852 WITH STAINLESS STEEL PLATE	83.00
PUSHBUTTON 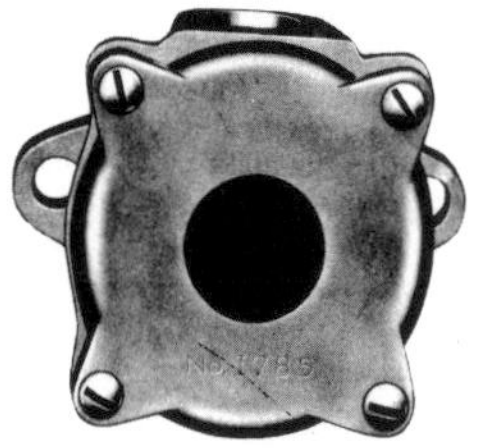 1785	EDWARDS OUTDOOR NO. 1785 WEATHERPROOF, FOR 1/2" CONDUIT MOUNTING	97.00
BELLS, BUZZERS 	EDWARDS BELLS NO. 340A–4N5 120V BUZZERS NO.340A–N5 120V	121.50 110.00

The costs shown for the light commercial high-voltage type of pushbutton consist of the published contractors' book price. The outdoor pushbutton (#1785) is provided with a 1/2 inch conduit entrance.

DESCRIPTION		COST INSTALLED IN DOLLARS EACH		
	BELLS, HORNS, SIRENS AND CHIMES	4" DIAMETER	6" DIAMETER	10" DIAMETER
A6 + 500 + NB	SINGLE STROKE BELLS			
	SURFACE MOUNTED	116.50	139.00	165.00
	FLUSH MOUNTED	168.00	190.50	——
	WEATHERPROOF	155.50	174.50	194.50
	VIBRATING BELLS			
	SURFACE MOUNTED	117.00	139.50	165.50
	FLUSH MOUNTED	139.50	191.00	——
	WEATHERPROOF	156.00	179.00	195.00
	CAST ALUMINUM GUARD	N/A	N/A	N/A
	FEDERAL NO. 350 & 450 GRILL MODEL HORNS	ALTERNATING CURRENT	DIRECT CURRENT	
	SURFACE MOUNTED	115.00	114.50	
	FLUSH MOUNTED	163.50	166.00	
	WEATHERPROOF	146.50	149.00	
	SEMI–FLUSH	131.50	134.00	
	FEDERAL NO.350 & 450 + PR SINGLE PROJECTOR HORNS			
	SURFACE MOUNTED	139.00	141.50	
	FLUSH MOUNTED	190.50	193.00	
	WEATHERPROOF	171.50	174.00	
	FEDERAL NO.350 & 450 + PR DOUBLE PROJECTOR HORNS			
	SURFACE MOUNTED	147.00	164.00	
	FLUSH MOUNTED	199.00	215.00	
	WEATHERPROOF	180.50	192.50	
	FEDERAL MODEL A SIREN	562.00		
	EDWARDS NO. 338 SINGLE STROKE CHIME	148.00		

The costs shown for these audible signals consist of the published contractors' book price and are as manufactured by Federal Sign and Signal Corp. The costs include labor and material for either flush or surface type installation.

11:24 39

CLOCKS		COST INSTALLED IN DOLLARS EACH					
		TYPE OF SYSTEM					
MOUNTING	CLOCK FACE	INDICATING ONLY NO CORRECTION		SYNCHRONOUS WIRED WITH INDIVIDUAL AUTOMATIC CORRECTION		ELECTRONIC WITH INDIVIDUAL AUTOMATIC CORRECTION	
		TYPE OF MOUNTING		TYPE OF MOUNTING		TYPE OF MOUNTING	
		INDIVIDUAL	IN TIME TONE UNITS	INDIVIDUAL	IN TIME TONE UNITS	INDIVIDUAL	IN TIME TONE UNITS
SURFACE MOUNTING	ROUND 9"	N.A.	N.A.	166.00	N.A.	N.A.	N.A.
	ROUND 12"	128.00		169.00		191.00	
	ROUND 15"	N.A.		180.00		N.A.	
	SQUARE 12"	145.00		219.00		256.00	
SEMI–FLUSH MOUNTING	ROUND 9"	N.A.	N.A.	180.00	N.A.	200.00	N.A.
	ROUND 12"	136.50	94.00	176.00	129.50	203.00	157.00
	ROUND 15"	N.A.	N.A.	194.00	N.A.	232.00	N.A.
	SQUARE 12"	153.50	111.00	190.00	143.00	256.00	185.00
WALL OR CEILING MOUNTED DBL DIAL	ROUND 12"	367.50	N.A.	444.00	N.A.	470.00	N.A.
	SQUARE 12"	423.00	N.A.	499.00	N.A.	575.50	N.A.
FLUSH EXECUTIVE SERIES	ROUND 12"	480.00	N.A.	532.00	N.A.	558.00	N.A.
	ROUND 15"	586.50	N.A.	586.50	N.A.	665.00	N.A.
	ROUND 18"	677.00	N.A.	729.00	N.A.	755.50	N.A.
CELESTRA DIGITAL	SURFACE MTD	624.00	N.A.	628.00	N.A.	661.00	N.A.
	SEMI–FLUSH	682.00	N.A.	686.00	N.A.	719.00	N.A.
	DOUBLE DIAL	1297.00	N.A.	1305.00	N.A.	1370.00	N.A.

The costs shown for these clocks consist of the published contractors' book price for the units described (6310 Series) and are as manufactured by the Simplex Time Recorder Co. Note that the 9- and 15-inch clocks are not available for mounting in the time-tone units.

Included: (material and labor)

1. *Clock with recessed clock receptacle and box in masonry wall for surface-mounted unit*
2. *Clock with special recessed back box and conduit terminals for semiflush mounting*
3. *Installing and connecting in time-tone units or special back box as required*

The costs shown for these time-tone units consist of the published contractors' book price and the labor for installation; however, they do not include costs for the clock or the speaker.

The master time control center, in addition to controlling the clocks, has the following features:

1. *6 local program control circuits*
2. *7-day programming*
3. *Automatic daylight saving time correction*
4. *Manual override switches*
5. *7-day battery standby*
6. *4 program schedules plus other features*

The master clock controller is for controlling clocks only.

This equipment is manufactured by Simplex Time Recorder Co.

COST OF CLOCK/PROGRAM SYSTEM ACCESSORIES

TYPE OF UNIT	ALL BY SIMPLEX	COST INSTALLED IN DOLLARS EACH
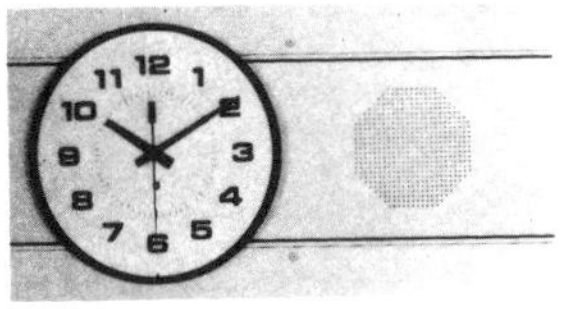 TYPE 6331-9002 SHOWN WITH ROUND CLOCK (NOT INCLUDED)	#6331–9002 TIME–TONE UNIT FOR ROUND OR SQUARE CLOCK	
	SURFACE MOUNTED	156.00
	SEMI–FLUSH MOUNTED	152.00
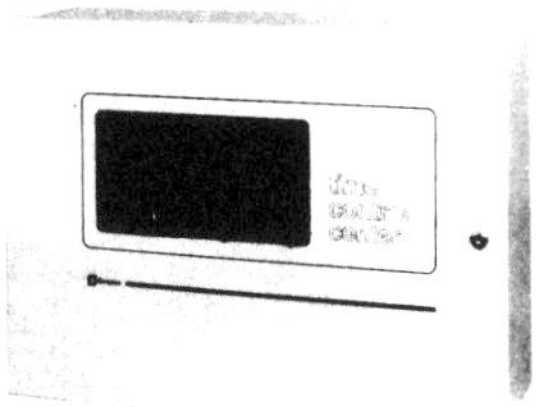 6400-9001 WALL MOUNTED TIME CONTROL CENTER	#6400–9001 TIME CONTROL CENTER FOR SYNCH. WIRED OR ELECTRONIC	
	SURFACE MOUNTED	2188.00
	RACK MOUNTED	2081.00
	#2351 MASTER CLOCK CONTROLLER	1458.00
————	CLOCK GUARDS	
	FOR 12" CLOCK	103.00
	FOR 15" CLOCK	118.00
————	#6850 STATIC FREQUENCY GENERATOR FOR ELECTRONIC SYS.	
	120/208V, TO 750KVA	2208.00
	277/480V, TO 750KVA	6624.00

COST OF HARDWIRED FIRE ALARM CONTROL PANEL

TYPE OF UNIT	DESCRIPTION	AMOUNT
	SIMPLEX #4001–9404 – HARDWIRED FOR FLUSH OR SURFACE MOUNTING. INCLUDES 4 ALARM ZONES 1 SIGNAL CIRCUIT LEAD CALCIUM BATTERY & CHARGER	$856.00
	SIMPLEX #4002–9404 INCLUDES 8 ALARM ZONES 2 SIGNAL CIRCUITS LEAD CALCIUM BATTERY & CHARGER	1956.00
	REMOTE ANNUNCIATOR (AT BLDG. ENTRANCE)	
	#4601–9101 FOR USE WITH THE 4001 PANEL	237.00
	#4602–9101 FOR USE WITH THE 4002 PANEL	509.00

The costs shown for these fire alarm control panels consist of the published contractors' book price and the labor for installation. The 4001 panel has the unique feature of allowing a system walk test that permits each initiating device to be tested without actuating the municipal connection.

TYPE OF UNIT	DESCRIPTION	AMOUNT
	#4100 MICROPROCESSOR BASED FLUSH OR SURFACE MOUNTING. INCLUDES 8 ALARM ZONES 2 SIGNAL CIRCUITS LEAD CALCIUM BATTERY & CHARGER AUXILIARY RELAY	$4110.00
	#4100-8001 ADDRESSABLE MICROPROCESSOR BASED INCLUDES 1 MAPNET MODULE 2 SIGNAL CIRCUITS LEAD CALCIUM BATTERY & CHARGER AUXILIARY RELAY	6370.00
	#4100-8201 ADDRESSABLE MICROPROCESSOR BASED WITH FIRE & VOICE COMMAND CENTER INCLUDES 1 MAPNET MODULE 2 SIGNAL CIRCUITS LEAD CALCIUM BATTERY & CHARGER AUXILIARY RELAY 100W AMPLIFIER & MICROPHONE 4 SPEAKER CIRCUITS	9375.00

The costs shown for these fire alarm control panels consist of the published contractors' book price and the labor for installation. One of the many features is that with generally only two wires, this system is capable of identifying the location of any initiating device.

COST OF FIRE ALARM SYSTEM DETECTORS

TYPE OF UNIT	DESCRIPTION	AMOUNT	
	ALL COMPONENTS BY SIMPLEX	WITH OUTLET	NO OUTLET
	CEILING MOUNTED PHOTOELECTRIC TYPE SMOKE DETECTOR		
	HARDWIRED TYPE	$139.50	$105.50
	ADDRESSSABLE TYPE	207.00	——
	CEILING MOUNTED IONIZATION TYPE SMOKE DETECTOR		
	HARDWIRED TYPE	136.00	102.50
	ADDRESSSABLE TYPE	205.00	——
	HEAT DETECTOR – FIXED TEMPERATURE + RATE OF RISE		
	HARDWIRED TYPE	66.00	35.50
	EXPLOSION PROOF TYPE	237.50	——
	ADDRESSSABLE TYPE	151.00	——

The costs shown for these fire detectors consist of the published contractors' book price as established by the Simplex Time Recorder Co. The costs include flush ceiling boxes and the labor for installation.

COST OF SIMPLEX FIRE ALARM COMPONENTS

TYPE OF UNIT	DESCRIPTION	AMOUNT
MAGNETIC DOOR HOLDER	FLUSH CEILING/WALL UNIT	$122.00
	WIRE GUARD FOR SPEAKER	41.00
	WIRE GUARD FOR SPEAKER	41.00
WATER FLOW SWITCH	FOR HARDWIRED (4001) SYSTEM	199.00
	FOR ADDRESSABLE (4100) SYSTEM	437.00
OS&Y VALVE SWITCH (TAMPER SWITCH)	FOR HARDWIRED (4001) SYSTEM	199.00
	FOR ADDRESSABLE (4100) SYSTEM	437.00

The costs shown for these components include back boxes or standard outlet boxes as required and the necessary labor for installation.

COST OF SIMPLEX FIRE ALARM COMPONENTS

TYPE OF UNIT	DESCRIPTION	AMOUNT
FIRE ALARM AUDIO/VISUAL SPEAKER	FLUSH CEILING/WALL UNIT	$122.00
	WIRE GUARD FOR SPEAKER	41.00
FIRE ALARM HORN W/ FLASHING LIGHT	STANDARD UNIT FOR 4001 OR 4100 BASED SYSTEMS	153.00
	UNIT MEETING "ADA" REQUIREMENTS	XXXX
EMERGENCY TELEPHONE REMOTE JACK 	FLUSH MOUNTED	66.50
EMERGENCY TELEPHONE 	WITH COIL CORD AND PLUG	65.00

The costs shown for these components include back boxes or standard outlet boxes as required and the necessary labor for installation.

COST OF FIRE ALARM COMPONENTS

TYPE OF UNIT	DESCRIPTION	AMOUNT
MANUAL STATION	ALL COMPONENTS BY SIMPLEX	
	HARDWIRED SEMI–FLUSH MOUNTED	
	1 N.O. CONTACT	$68.00
	2 N.O. CONTACT	79.00
	HARDWIRED SURFACE MOUNTED	
	1 N.O. CONTACT	77.00
	2 N.O. CONTACT	88.00
	SEMI–FLUSH ADDRESSABLE TYPE	150.50
MANUAL STATION GUARD		39.00
	DUCT MOUNTED PHOTOELECTRIC SMOKE DETECTOR WITH SAMPLING TUBES	
	HARDWIRED TYPE	288.00
	ADDRESSABLE TYPE	382.00
	REMOTE TEST STATION (FOR HDWRD)	101.50

The costs shown for these components include back boxes or standard outlet boxes as required and the necessary labor for installation.

COST OF HIGH–TEMPERATURE, PLENUM–RATED FIRE ALARM CABLE

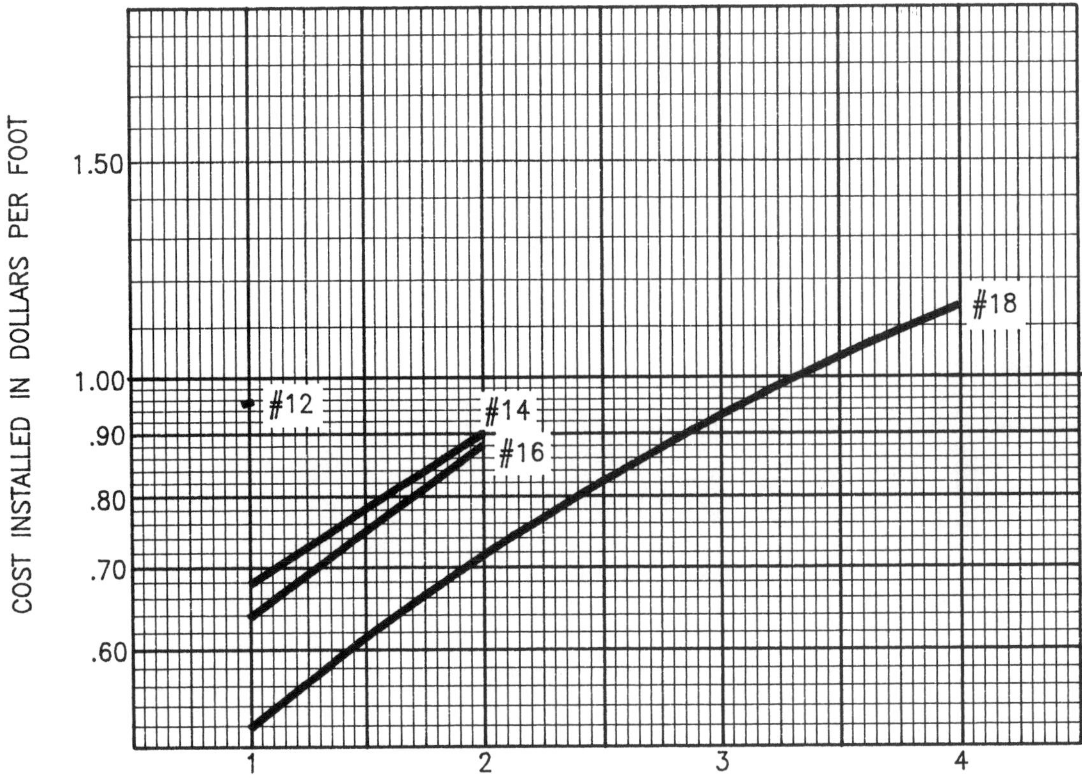

The costs shown for high-temperature cable for use in environmental air plenums, Teflon jacketed and rated at 150°C, consist of the published contractors' book price for the sizes shown and include labor for installation without conduit in accessible ceiling cavities.

COST OF AUTOMATIC FULL-FEATURE NURSE CALL SYSTEM COMPONENTS

TYPE OF UNIT	MANUFACTURER	AMOUNT
NURSE CONTROL STATION	RAULAND RESPONDER III 64 STATION	$2175.
STAFF STATION Staff Station	SS100	275.
DUTY STATION Duty Station	DS–210	303.
STAFF LOCATOR STATION	SRS–110	135.

The costs shown for these nurse call system components consist of the contractors' published book price and are based upon Rauland products. Included are the necessary installation labor for the equipment and a certain amount for supervision, final checkout, and training of operating personnel.

COST OF AUTOMATIC FULL–FEATURE NURSE CALL SYSTEM COMPONENTS

TYPE OF UNIT	MANUFACTURER	AMOUNT
CENTRAL EQUIPMENT CABINET	RAULAND RESPONDER III 64 STATION	$3991.
PATIENT BEDSIDE STATION Single Patient Station Dual Patient Station	WITHOUT PILLOW SPEAKERS BUT WITH CALL CORDS	
	SINGLE STATION	332.
	DOUBLE STATION	361.
EMERGENCY CALL STATION	PCS–113 PULL–CORD TYPE	131.
	PBS–113 PUSH BUTTON TYPE	132.

The costs shown for these nurse call system components consist of the contractors' published book price and are based upon Rauland products. Included are the necessary installation labor for the equipment and a certain amount for supervision, final checkout, and training of operating personnel.

TYPE OF UNIT	MANUFACTURER	AMOUNT
NURSE CONTROL STATION	RAULAND RESPONDER 3000 0–24 STATION DESK TYPE	$987.
PATIENT BEDSIDE STATION	BS–810 SINGLE STATION BS–820 DOUBLE STATION	148. 159.
DUTY/STAFF STATION	SS–300	141.
CENTRAL EQUIPMENT CABINET	NCS3000	3327.

The costs shown for these nurse call system components consist of the contractors' published book price and are based upon Rauland products. Included are the necessary installation labor for the equipment and a certain amount for supervision, final checkout, and training of operating personnel.

COST OF NURSE CALL SYSTEM COMPONENTS

TYPE OF UNIT	MANUFACTURER	AMOUNT
CORRIDOR DOME LIGHT	RAULAND	
	CL–7584 FOUR COLOR	$120.
	CL– 7582 TWO COLOR	113.
CABLE		
	2/C – #222	.61
	4/C – #241	.74
	4TSP – 3429	10.6
	12/C – #2010	1.36
	15/C – #2015	1.74

The costs shown for these nurse call system components consist of the contractors' published book price and are based upon Rauland products. Included in the dome light is the cost of the outlet box installed with conduit.

TYPE OF UNIT	MANUFACTURER	AMOUNT
COMPACT MASTER UNIT	RAULAND #DIR350LC BASIC UNIT WITH CHIME/LIGHT CALL-IN, 25 SELECTOR SWITCHES, 5 WATT I.C. AMPLIFIER, AMD 35 WATT PROGRAM AMPLIFIER IN 19" WIDE CABINET	$2489.
	ADD-ON OPTIONS	
	14" HIGH AUXILIARY HIGH CABINET	538
	ADDITIONAL 25 SELECTOR SWITCH BANK	1050.
	AM/FM TUNER & CASSETTE PLAYER	722.
	TIME-TINE GENERATOR	118.
CALL-IN SWITCH	#2304FA FLUSH PUSHBUTTON	62.
	#2307 FLUSH ROCKER/PRIVACY SWITCH	69.

This equipment is commonly used in small schools or other buildings where background music distribution, selective paging, and two-way intercommunication are required. This equipment is compatible with speakers and other accessories on the following pages. The costs shown include the published contractors' book price including outlet boxes where required. Included are the necessary installation labor for the equipment and a certain amount of supervision, final checkout, and training of operating personnel.

COST OF SOUND–REINFORCING SYSTEMS COMPONENTS

TYPE OF UNIT	MANUFACTURER	POWER	AMOUNT
TRUMPET REPRODUCER 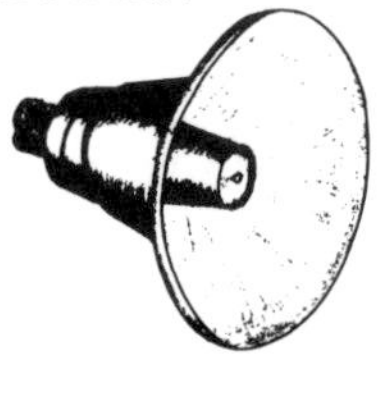	ATLAS MODEL #AP15T	15	$140.
WALL SPEAKER 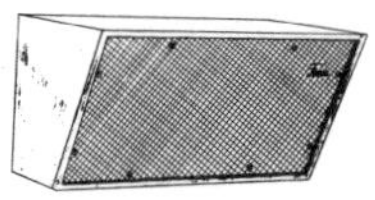 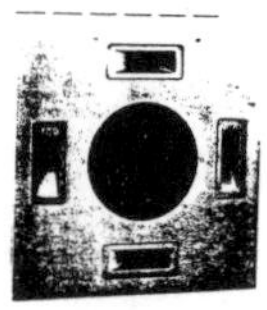 CEILING SPEAKER	FRASIER CAT #33 CAT #40	30 30	320. 594.
WIDE ANGLE TRUMPET 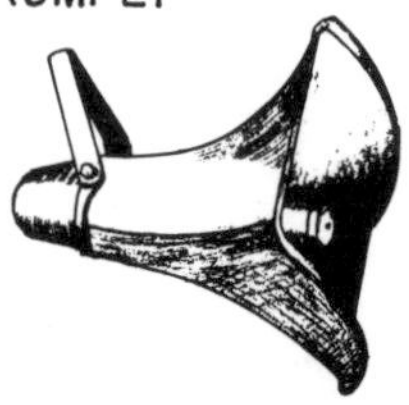	ATLAS #APC–30T 120 X 60 DEG. DISPER.	30	165.
FLUSH CEILING SPEAKER 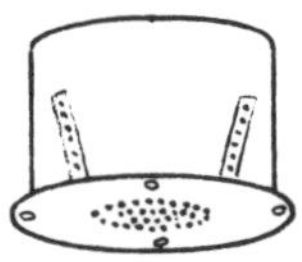	LOWELL 8" SPEAKER MTD. IN BACKBOX & RND GRILLE 12" W/ CONE TWEETER AND WOOFER (INCL. TRANS) 8" SPEAKER WITHOUT ENCLOSURE	15 15 15	93. 110. 37.
WIDE RANGE AUDITORIUM SPEAKER 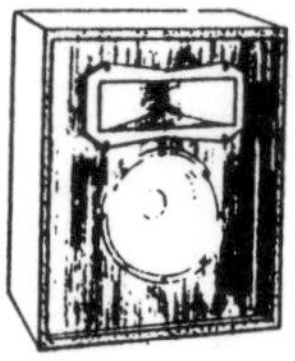	ELECTRO–VOICE #FR12–2 #FR15–2	100 200	668. 1102.
VOLUME CONTROLS 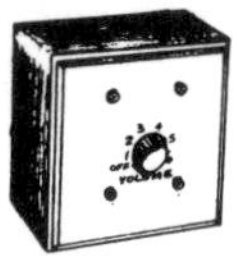	SOUNDOLIER – FLUSH MOUNTED #AT 10 10 WATT #AT–35 35 WATT		69. 71.

The costs shown for these sound system reinforcing components consist of the published contractors' book price and include outlet boxes where required. Included are the necessary installation labor for the equipment and a certain amount of supervision, final checkout, and training of personnel.

TYPE OF UNIT	MANUFACTURER	AMOUNT
MICROPHONE RECEPTACLE	SWITCHCRAFT #G3MS	$59.
	SOUNDOLIER #MRB-2-14N	143.
MIXERS	RAULAND #AP4601-8 FOR 8 MICROPHONES	1272.
P.A. AMPLIFIERS - 50 TO 15,000HZ 4 MIKE/AUXILIARY INPUTS	RAULAND	
	#1402 20 WATT	432.
	#1406 60 WATT	743.
	#1410 100 WATT	807.

The costs shown for these sound system reinforcing components consist of the published contractors' book price and include outlet boxes where required. Included are the necessary installation labor for the equipment and a certain amount of supervision, final checkout, and training of personnel.

TYPE OF UNIT	MANUFACTURER	AMOUNT
LAVALIERE MICROPHONE	ELECTRO–VOICE #C090	$235.
MICROPHONE	DYNAMIC SUPER CARDIOID ELECTRO–VOICE #N/D60	217.
	DESK MOUNTED MICROPHONE WITH 20' CORD – RAULAND #1295	122.

The costs shown for these sound system reinforcing components consist of the published contractors' book price. Included are the necessary installation labor for the equipment and a certain amount for supervision, final checkout, and training of personnel.

TYPE OF UNIT	MANUFACTURER	AMOUNT
ANTENNA KIT	BLONDER–TONGUE	$160.00
AM/FM TUNER WITH CASETTE PLAYER	AM/FM TUNER #MCX300	683.
WIRE AND CABLES	WEST PENN	
	#222 – ONE UNSHIELDED PAIR	.68
	#300 – THREE SHIELDED CONDUCTORS AND DRAIN IN COMMON JACKET	.79
	#292 – SHIELDED 20 GAGE MICRO– PHONE – CABLE WITH BRAID SHIELD	.85

The costs shown for these sound system reinforcing components consist of the published contractors' book price. Included are the necessary installation labor for the equipment and a certain amount for supervision, final checkout, and training of personnel. All cable is assumed to be pulled-in conduit.

COST OF HIGH–TEMPERATURE SIGNALING & POWER–LIMITED CABLE

	GAGE	NUMBER OF PAIRS OR CONDUCTORS	COST INSTALLED PER FOOT
NON–SHIELDED	22 SOLID	1 PR	$.41
	18 STRND	1 PR	.58
	18 SOLID	3/C	.65
	16 SOLID	1 PR	.70
OVER–ALL FOIL SHIELD	24 SOLID*	2 PR	.54
	24 SOLID	25 PR	1.75
	22 SOLID	1 PR	.49
	22 SOLID	2 PR	.49
	22 SOLID	3 PR	.61
	22 SOLID	4 PR	.77

* BRAIDED SHIELD WITH DRAIN WIRE

The costs shown for high-temperature signaling and power-limited cable consist of the published contractors' book price for Teflon-jacketed cable approved for use in environmental air plenums. Included is the labor for installation without conduit in accessible ceiling cavities.

TYPE OF UNIT	DESCRIPTION	AMOUNT
ROOM STATION FOR TOILET AND BEDROOM	JERON #2320	$46.50
APARTMENT DOOR RELEASE	JERON #8109	110.00
CORRIDOR LIGHT	JERON #8801	26.00
4" CORRIDOR BELL	JERON #8601	88.50
24VOLT TRANSFORMER	JERON #8815	66.50

The equipment shown here is of a design suggested by the Department of Housing and Urban Development, is frequently used in housing for the elderly, and is of an economical style. Costs shown include a back box where required and labor for installation of box and equipment.

TYPE OF UNIT	DESCRIPTION	AMOUNT
PHOTOELECTRIC SMOKE DETECTOR 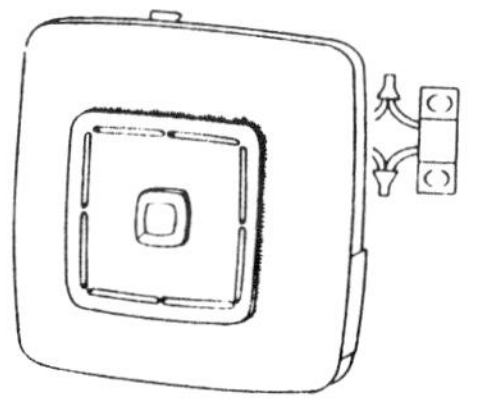	JERON #7100	$46.50
DUTY STATION FOR OFFICE 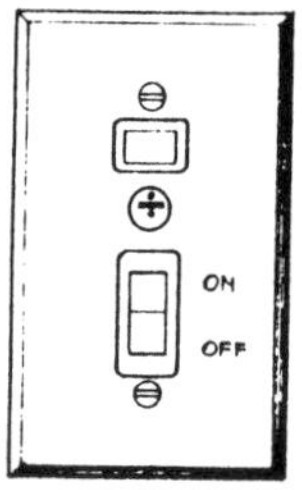	JERON #8817	110.00
EMERGENCY PHONE 	JERON #2047–1	26.00
MASTER ANNUNCIATOR BUZZER AND SILENCING SWITCH SIMILAR TO MASTER UNIT SHOWN ON THE APARTMENT CALL SYSTEM 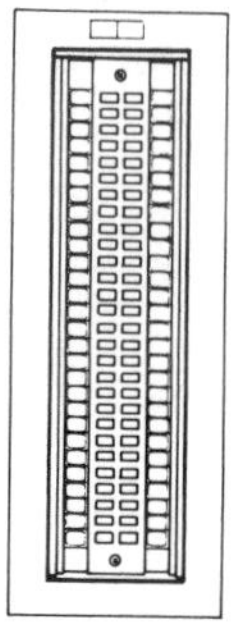	JERON #8815	
	10 BUTTON	357.50
	20 BUTTON	538.00
	30 BUTTON	708.00
	40 BUTTON	882.00

The equipment shown here is of a design suggested by the Department of Housing and Urban Development, is frequently used in housing for the elderly, and is of an economical style. Costs shown include a back box where required and labor for installation of box and equipment.

COST OF APARTMENT INTERCOM SYSTEM

TYPE OF UNIT	DESCRIPTION	AMOUNT
APARTMENT SPEAKER UNIT	#2001 (P.B. TALK CONTROL)	57.00
	#2005 (VOICE ACTUATED CONTROL)	54.50
APARTMENT DOOR RELEASE	JERON #8109	110.00
POWER SUPPLY TRANSFORMER	JERON #8010	26.00

The equipment shown here is of a design suggested by the Department of Housing and Urban Development, is frequently used in housing for the elderly, and is of an economical style. Costs shown include a back box where required and labor for installation of box and equipment.

COST OF APARTMENT INTERCOM SYSTEM

TYPE OF UNIT	DESCRIPTION	AMOUNT
COMBINATION MASTER UNIT AND ENTRANCE SPEAKER (PLAS. BUTTONS)	ASSY OF #3003 P.B. PANEL, #3301 PLASTIC BUTTONS, 2-40 LINE DIRECTORIES, 3 GANG FRAME, AND 3 GANG BACK BOX	$770.00
AMPLIFIER	JERON	
	#5010 (FOR P.B. TALK SYSTEM)	232.50
	#5020 (DUAL LOBBY APPLICATION)	347.00
	#5050 (VOICE ACTIVATED SYSTEM)	491.00

The equipment shown here is of a design suggested by the Department of Housing and Urban Development, is frequently used in housing for the elderly, and is of an economical style. Costs shown include a back box where required and labor for installation of box and equipment.

COST OF TV MASTER ANTENNA SYSTEM

TYPE OF UNIT	MANUFACTURER	AMOUNT
ROOF ANTENNA	COMMERCIAL GRADE BROAD BAND CHANNEL MASTER #CCS-1843 MTD ON 8' MAST WITH 3 GUYS	$263.
	COMMERCIAL GRADE SINGLE CHANNEL CHANNEL MASTER BTY SERIES ON 8' MAST WITH 3 GUYS	429.
	ADD FOR ADDITIONAL CHANNEL	333.
AMPLIFIER	MED. GAIN–33dB – BIDA #450030	658.
	HIGH GAIN–50dB BIDA #450–50	732.
	SINGLE CHANNEL – BIDA #HMCA–6	741.

The costs consist of the published contractors' book price for materials, including anchoring and fastening materials. Antennas are mounted on an 8-foot-high mast guyed in three directions. Amplifiers are mounted on a plywood board and include input and output coaxial cable connections to the next component.

COST OF TV MASTER ANTENNA SYSTEM

TYPE OF UNIT	MANUFACTURER	AMOUNT
WALL OUTLET 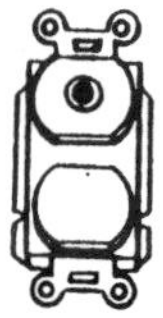	BLONDER TONGUE	
	3V–3182	$27.50
	CABLE TERMINATOR #BTF–TP	5.76
SIGNAL SPLITTER 	TWO WAY #CRS–2	23.50
	FOUR WAY #CRS–4	27.50
TRUNKLINE TAP 	#CRT–4A	48.50
CABLE 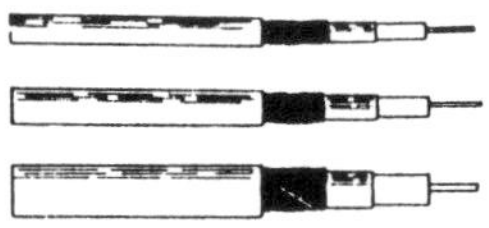	RG–59 (6dB/100' CH13)	1.07
	RG6 (3dB/100' CH13)	1.28
	RG11 (2.1 dB/100' CH13)	1.65

These costs consist of the published contractors' book price for materials and include an outlet box for the wall outlet. Coaxial cable is costed as pulled-in conduit.

WALL OUTLET, SIGNAL SPLITTER, TRUNKLINE TAP, AND CABLE

Electric Heating and Controls

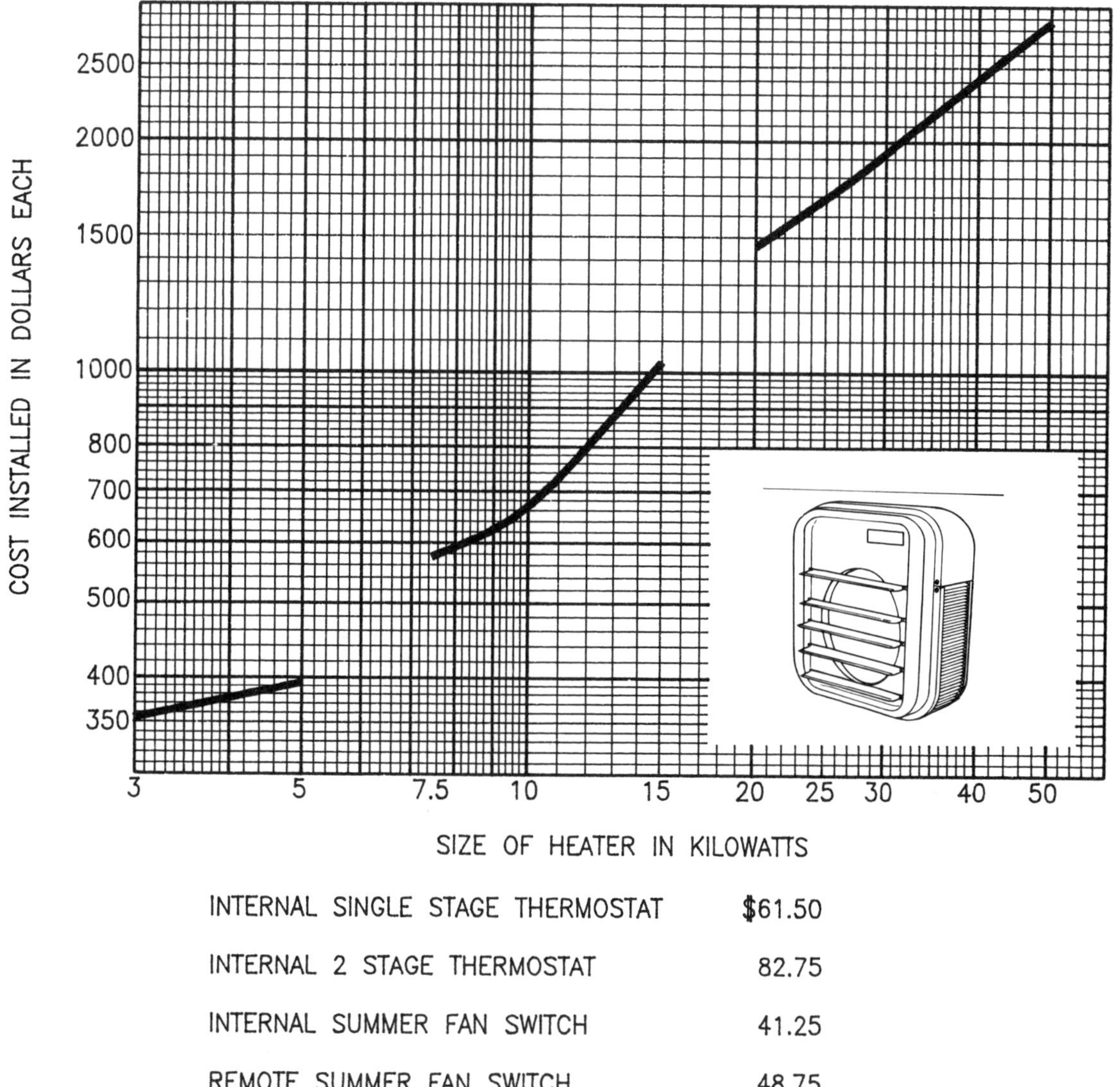

INTERNAL SINGLE STAGE THERMOSTAT	$61.50
INTERNAL 2 STAGE THERMOSTAT	82.75
INTERNAL SUMMER FAN SWITCH	41.25
REMOTE SUMMER FAN SWITCH	48.75

The costs shown for these units consist of the published contractors' book price and the labor for installation. This commercial-quality unit is manufactured by Marley Electric Heating Co. and is type MUH. Included is a universal wall/ceiling mounting bracket. No branch circuit wiring or controls are included.

COST OF INFRARED HEATERS

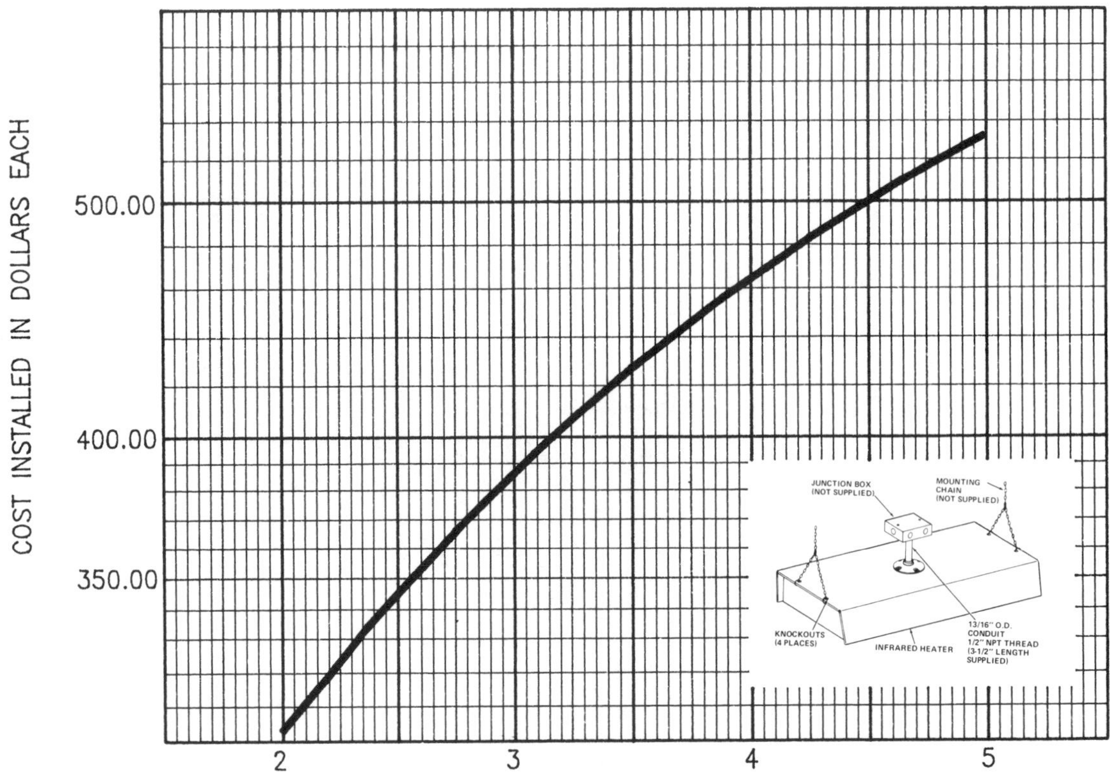

SIZE OF HEATER IN KILOWATTS

SURFACE MOUNTING KIT, 2 KW SIZE	$40.00
SURFACE MOUNTING KIT, 3 KW SIZE	49.50
SURFACE MOUNTING KIT, 4 KW SIZE	65.75

The costs shown for these units consist of the published contractors' book price for the units shown and the labor for installation. These commercial units, sometimes called "people heaters," are manufactured by Marley Electric Heating Co. and are its type RDO. They are UL-labeled for either indoor or outdoor use with the bottom of the unit installed no lower than 84 inches above the floor. Heating elements are included, but no branch wiring or controls.

COST OF RESIDENTIAL BASEBOARD HEATERS

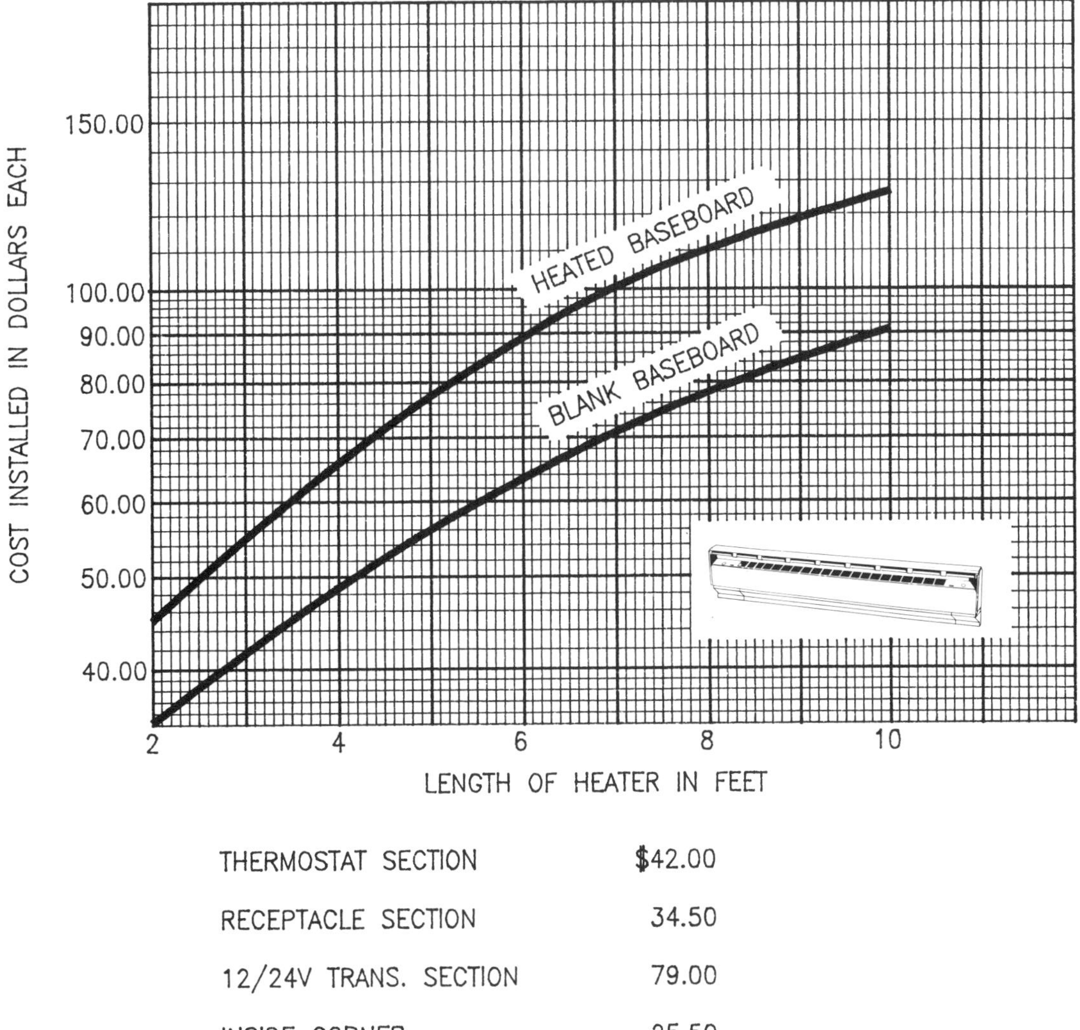

THERMOSTAT SECTION	$42.00
RECEPTACLE SECTION	34.50
12/24V TRANS. SECTION	79.00
INSIDE CORNER	25.50
LOAD TRANS. SWITCH	60.75

The costs shown for these units consist of the published contractors' book price for the units shown and the labor for installation. These residential units are manufactured by Marley Electric Heating Co. and are the QMK-2500 Series, rated at 250 watts per linear foot. No branch circuit wiring or controls are included.

COST OF COMMERCIAL BASEBOARD HEATERS

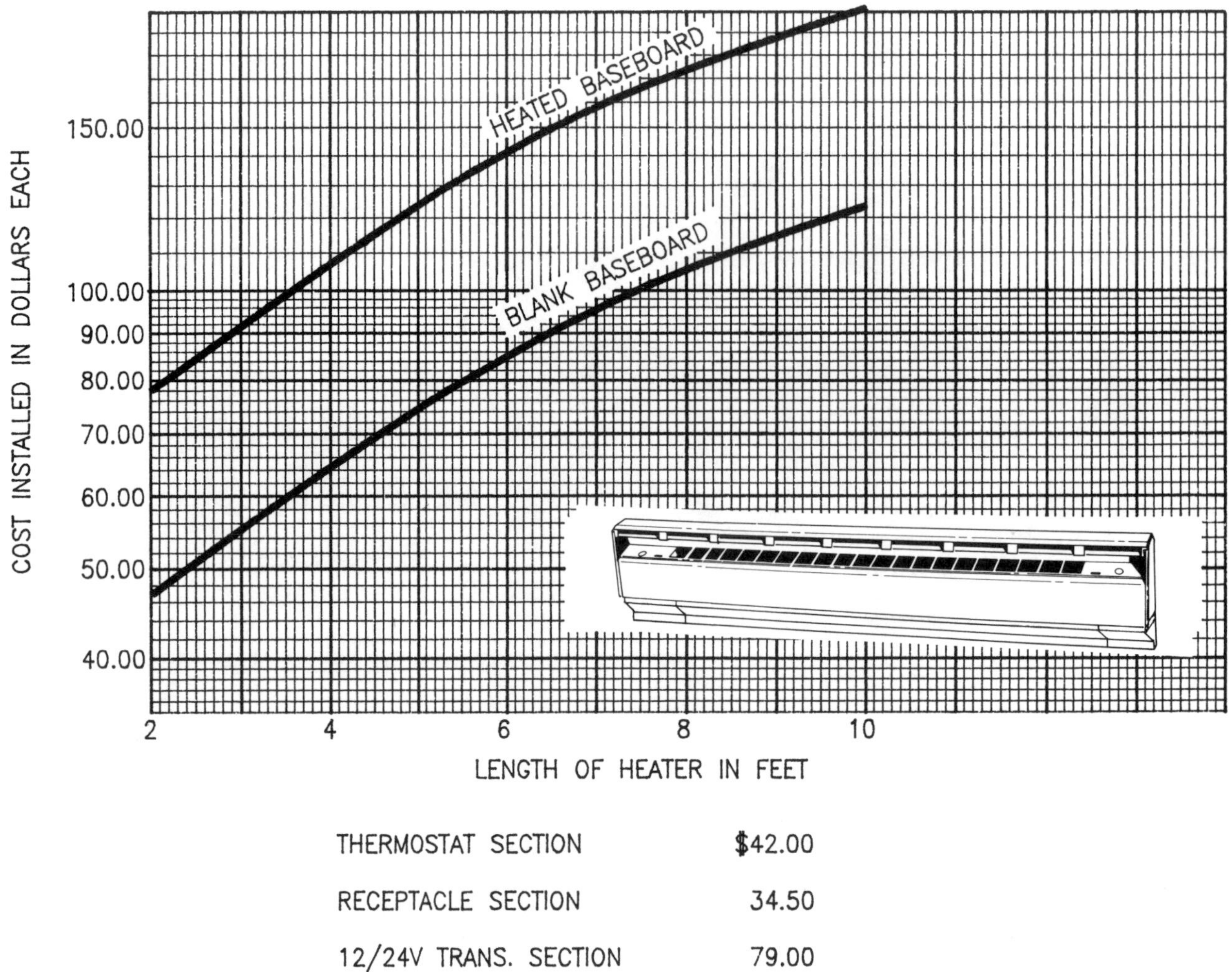

THERMOSTAT SECTION	$42.00
RECEPTACLE SECTION	34.50
12/24V TRANS. SECTION	79.00
INSIDE CORNER	25.50
LOAD TRANS. SWITCH	60.75

The costs shown for these units consist of the published contractors' book price for the units shown and the labor for installation. These commercial-grade units are manufactured by Marley Electric Heating Co. They are the QMKC Series, and are rated at 250 watts per linear foot. No branch circuit wiring or controls are included.

COST OF COMMERCIAL SILL-HEIGHT – DECORATIVE STYLE

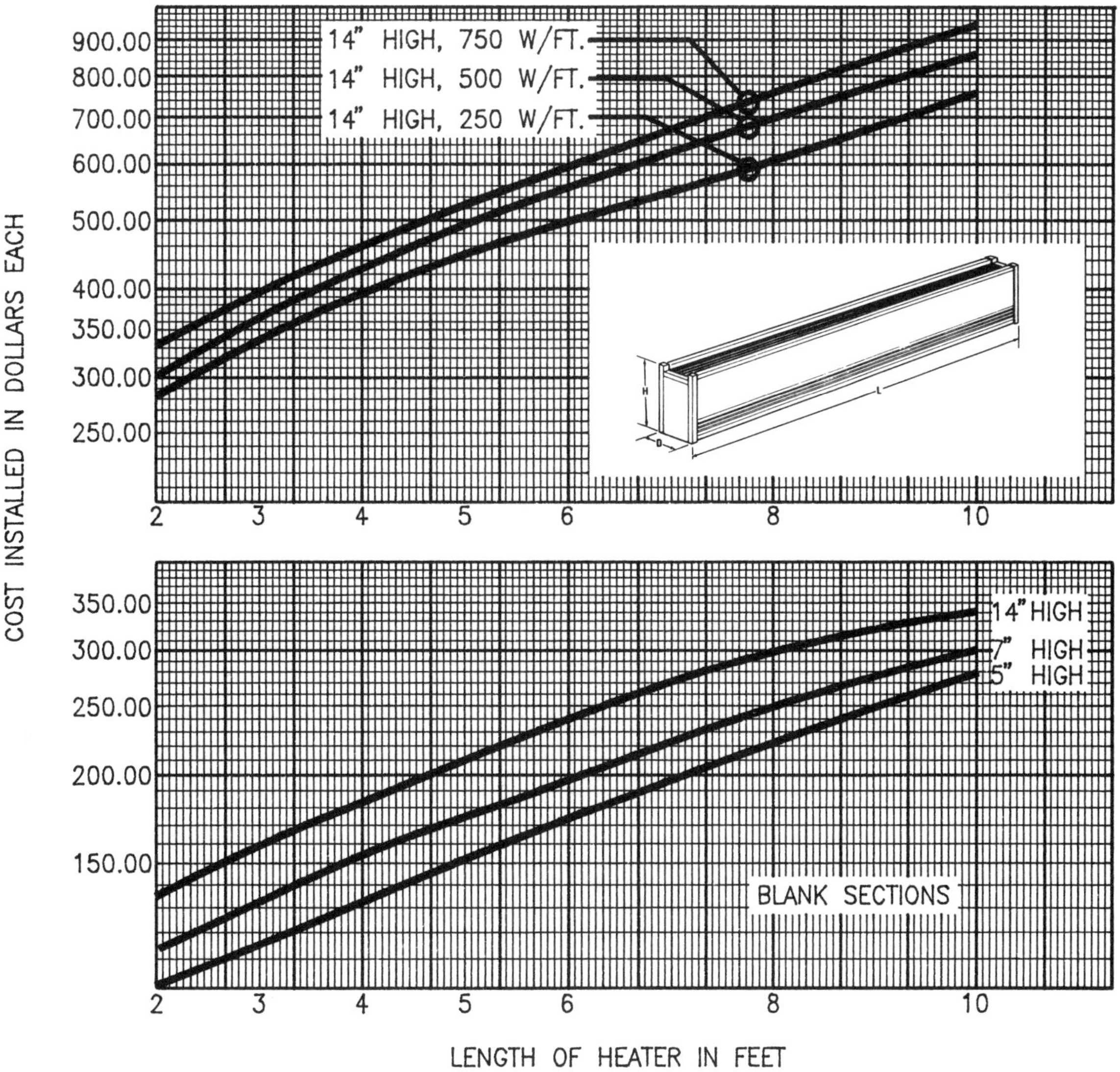

FILLER SECTIONS FOR 5, 7, OR 14"			
3" LONG	$29.00	12" LONG	$41.75
6" LONG	32.25	18" LONG	46.75
9" LONG	37.50		

The costs shown consist of the published contractors' book price for the units shown and the labor for installation. These commercial units are manufactured by Marley Electric Heating Co. and are the ADB Series, rated at various wattage densities per linear foot. These units are 14 inches high. No branch circuit wiring or controls are included.

COST OF SILL–HEIGHT CONVECTORS – DECORATIVE STYLE

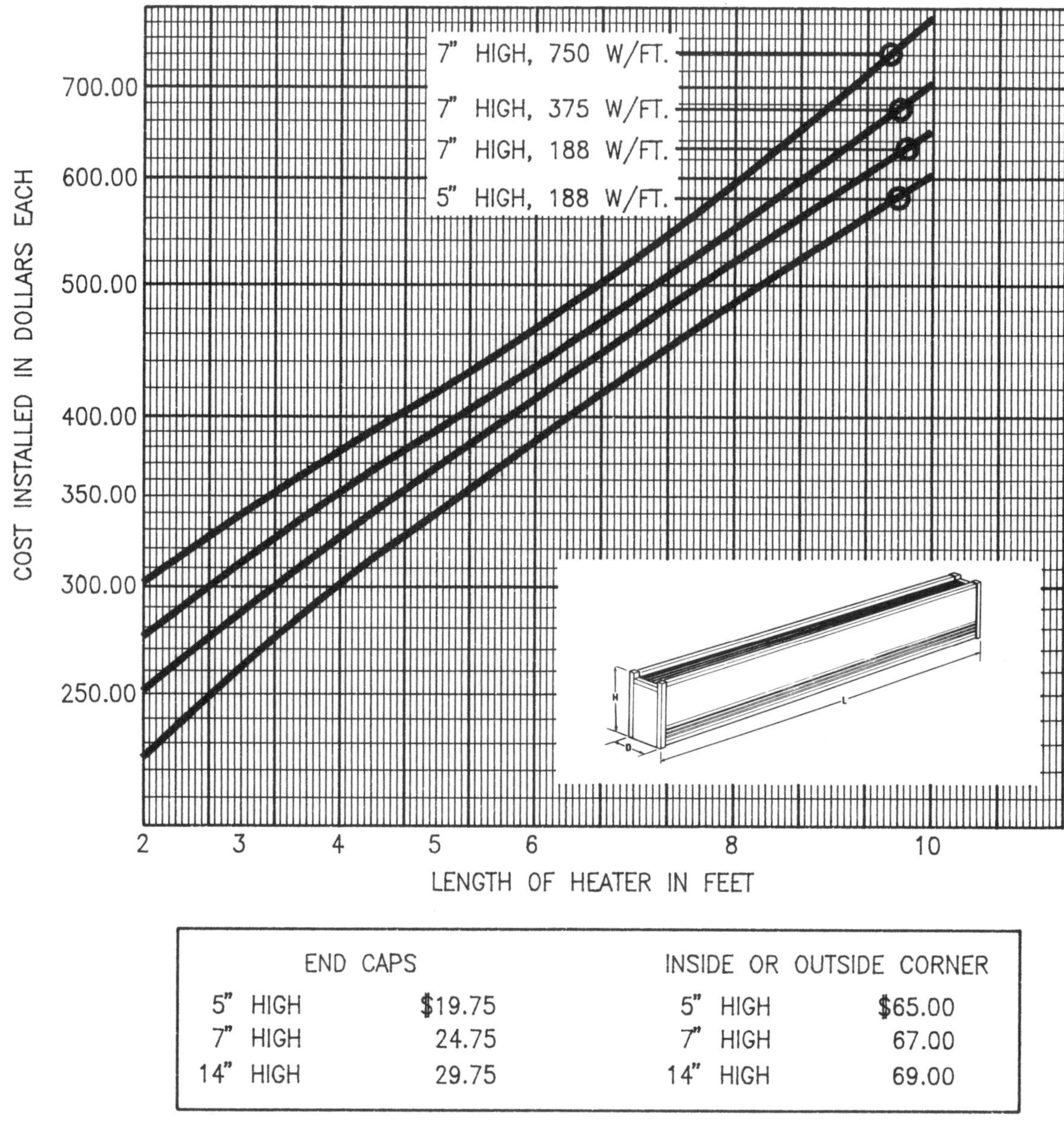

END CAPS		INSIDE OR OUTSIDE CORNER	
5" HIGH	$19.75	5" HIGH	$65.00
7" HIGH	24.75	7" HIGH	67.00
14" HIGH	29.75	14" HIGH	69.00

The costs shown consist of the published contractors' book price for the units shown and the labor for installation. These commercial units are manufactured by Marley Electric Heating Co. and are the ADB Series, rated at various wattage densities per linear foot. These units are 5 and 7 inches high. No branch circuit wiring or controls are included.

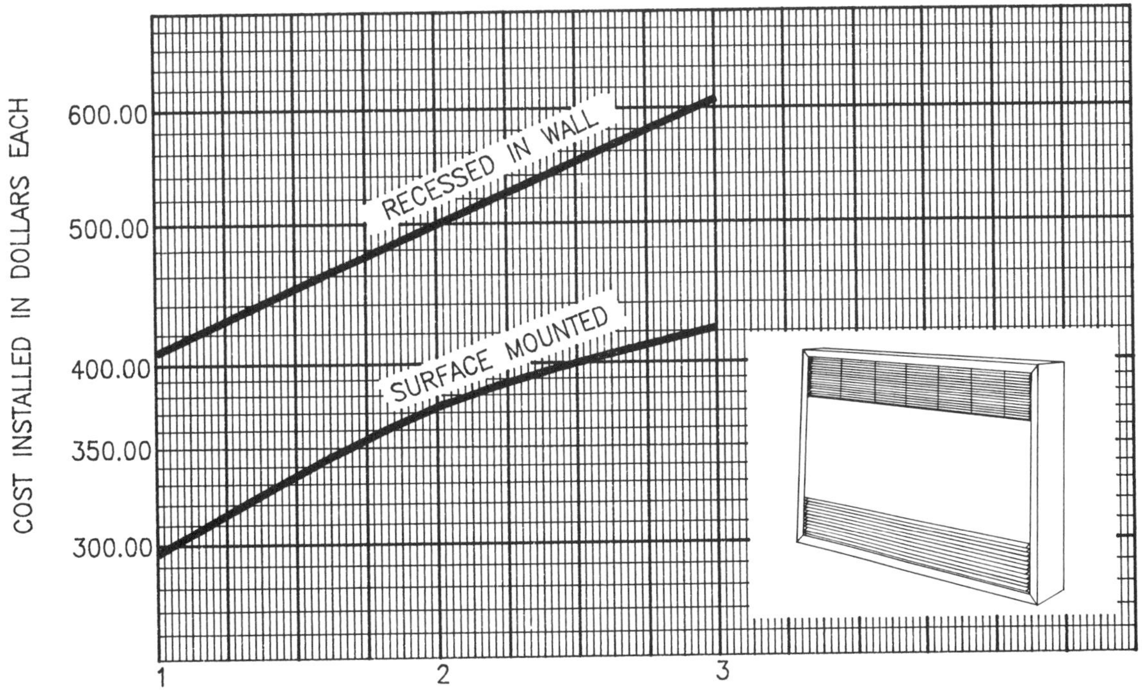

The costs shown for these units consist of the published contractors' book price for the units shown and the labor for installation. These commercial units are the KSF and KSR Series and are manufactured by Marley Electric Heating Co. The KSF is for surface mounting, while the KSR is for recessed mounting. These units have no fans. No branch circuit wiring or controls are included in the prices.

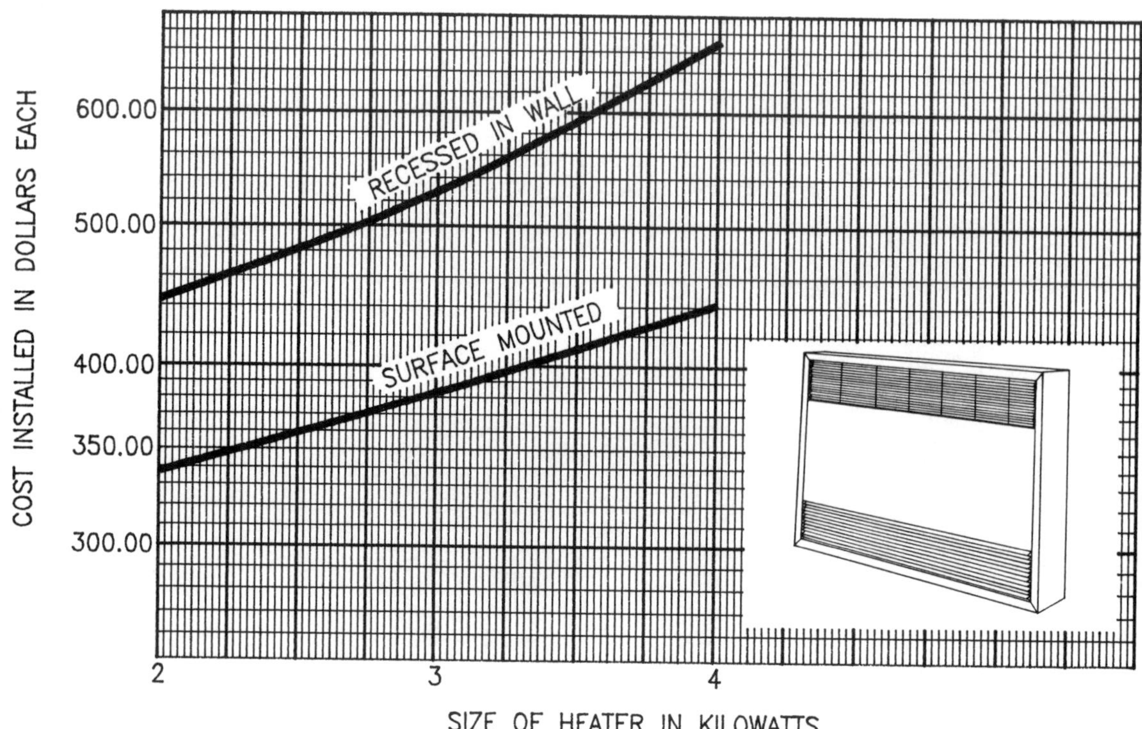

INTEGRAL THERMOSTAT	$43.00
INTERNAL REMOTE CONTROL RELAY	43.00
INTERNAL POWER DISC. SWITCH	43.00

The costs shown for these units consist of the published contractors' book price for the units shown and the labor for installation. These commercial units are the KSF and KSR Series and are manufactured by Marley Electric Heating Co. The KSF is for surface mounting, while the KSR is for recessed mounting. These units have no fans. No branch circuit wiring or controls are included in the prices.

COST OF WALL HEATERS WITH FAN

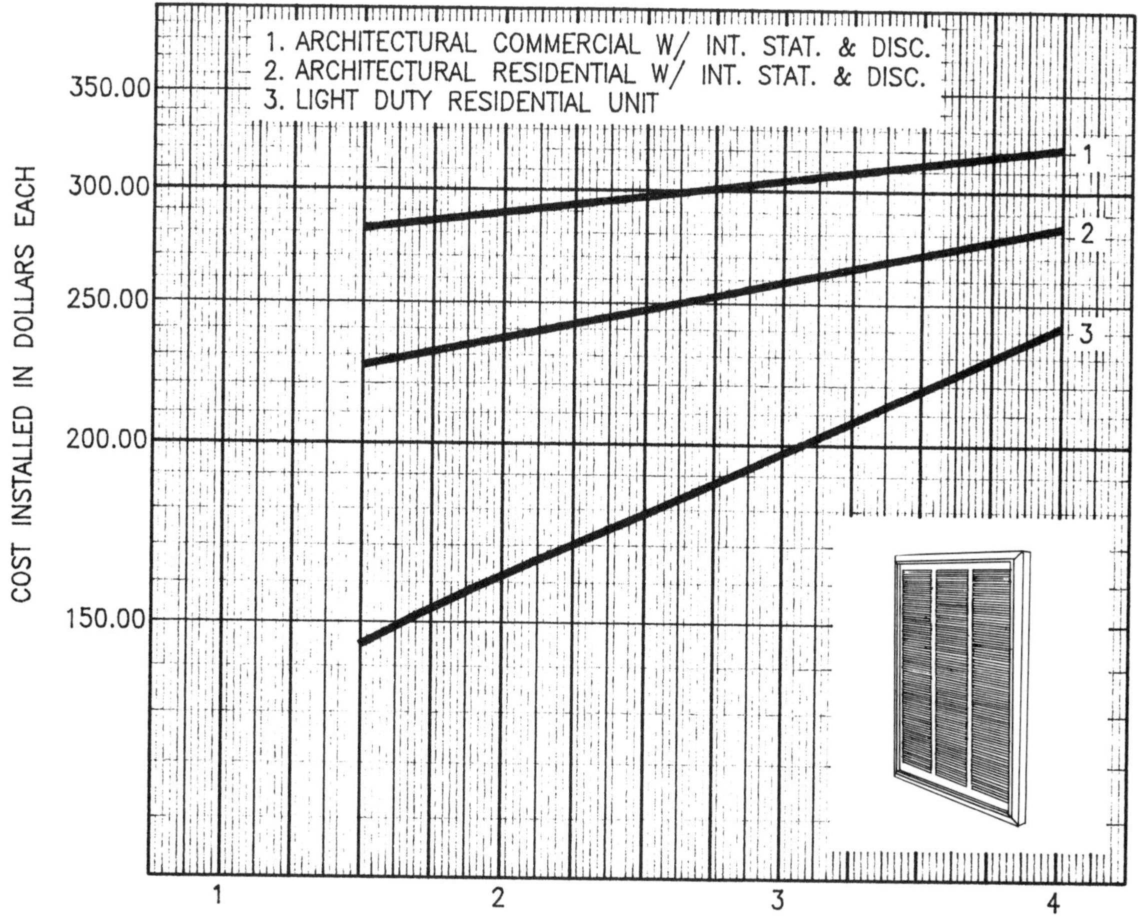

The costs shown for these units consist of the published contractors' book price for the units shown and the labor for installation. These units are manufactured by Marley Electric Heating Co. and are of the AWH and FWH Series. No branch circuit wiring or controls are included.

COST OF MISCELLANEOUS ELECTRIC HEATERS

TYPE OF UNIT		MANUFACTURER	WATTAGE	INSTALLED COST
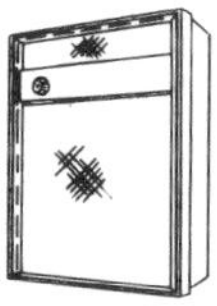	RECESSED BATHROOM HEATER WITH BUILT–IN THERMOSTAT & FAN	QMARK H5022	1250	$102.00
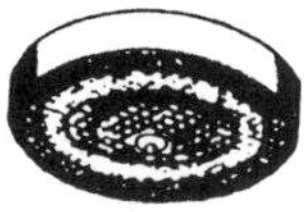	RADIANT CEILING HEATER 120 VOLTS	QMARK #QRC12	1250	95.00
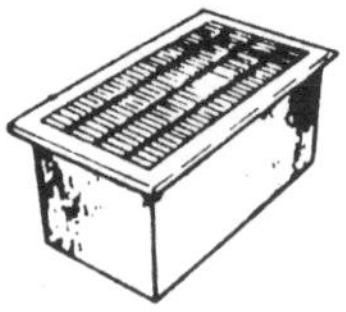	FAN FORCED AIR DROP–IN HEATER WITH COMB–INATION WATTAGE AT 120 VOLTS	QMARK #FDI–1415–4M #FDI–1415–7M	750 or 1500	230.50 270.75
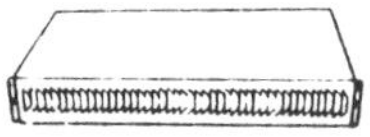	FAN FORCED KICK SPACE HEATER INTEGRAL STAT. KIT	QMARK #QTSI–A	450 THRU 1800	192.50 25.00
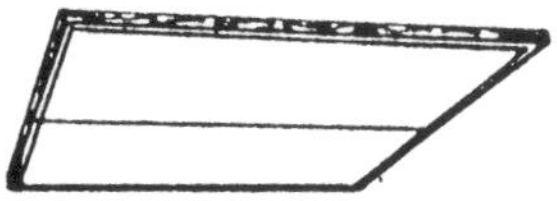	RADIANT CEILING PANEL WITH SURFACE MTG KIT WITH RECESSED KIT	QMARK #CP754–1	750	166.00 221.00 223.50

The costs shown for these units consist of the published contractors' book price for the units shown. Labor is included for installation, but no branch circuit wiring or controls are included. The catalog numbers are from Qmark, a division of Marley Electric Heating Co.

COST OF ROOF AND PIPE HEATING CABLE

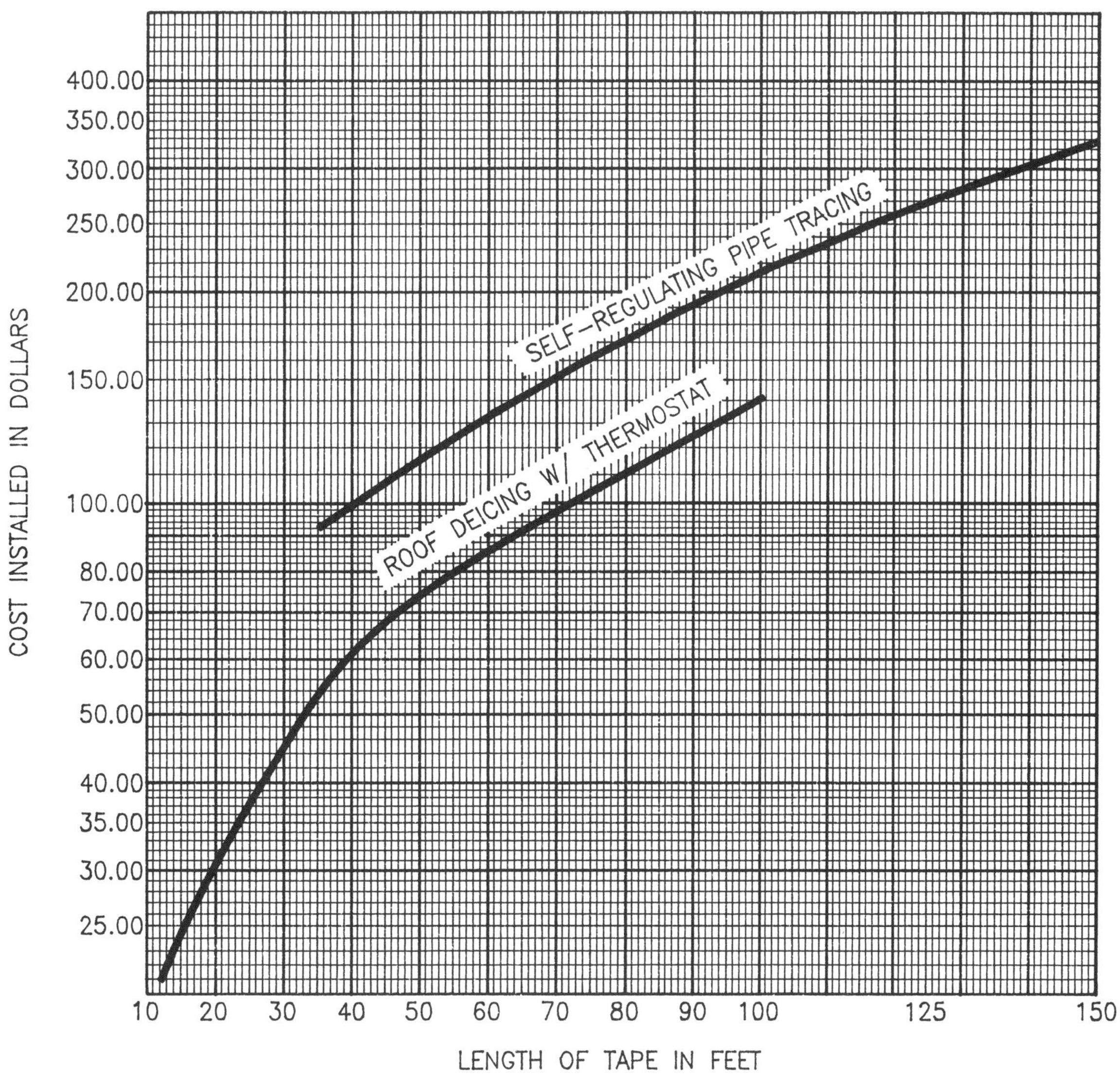

The costs shown for these units consist of the published contractors' book price and the labor for installation. These tapes are manufactured by Easy Heat Inc. Pipe tracing consumes about 1 1/2 feet of tape per foot of pipe protected. Both types are 120 volt. The pipe-heating cable has a built-in thermostat and is UL-listed.

COST OF INTERIOR CONCRETE–FLOOR–HEATING CABLE MATS

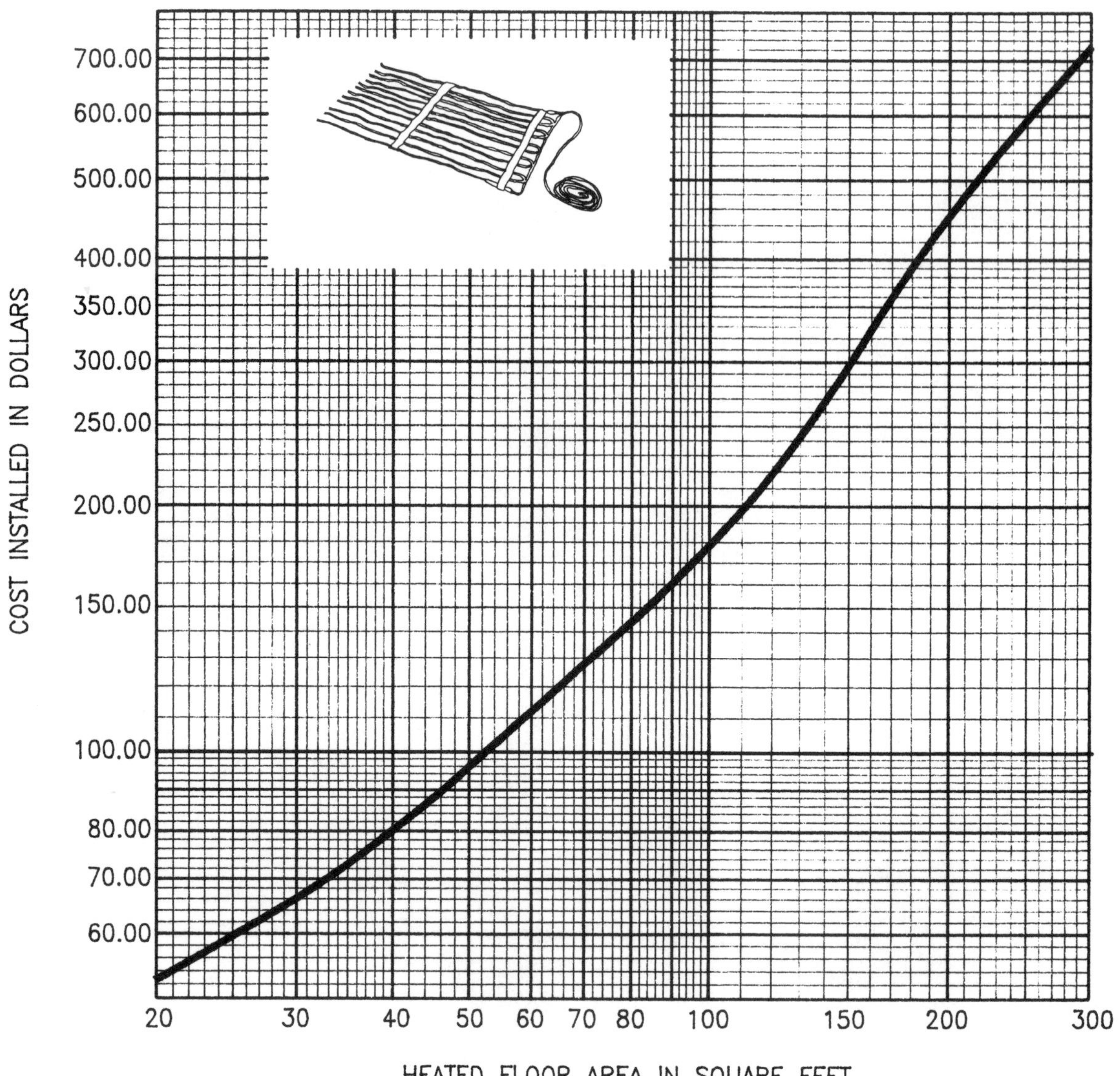

HEATED FLOOR AREA IN SQUARE FEET

The costs shown for these units consist of the published contractors' book price and the labor for installation. These mats are manufactured by Easy Heat Inc., are rated at 20 watts per square foot, and are for indoor use only. Mats are 16 inches wide. No branch circuit wiring or controls are included.

J-12

COST OF MAT-TYPE ASPHALT/CONCRETE SNOW-MELTING CABLE

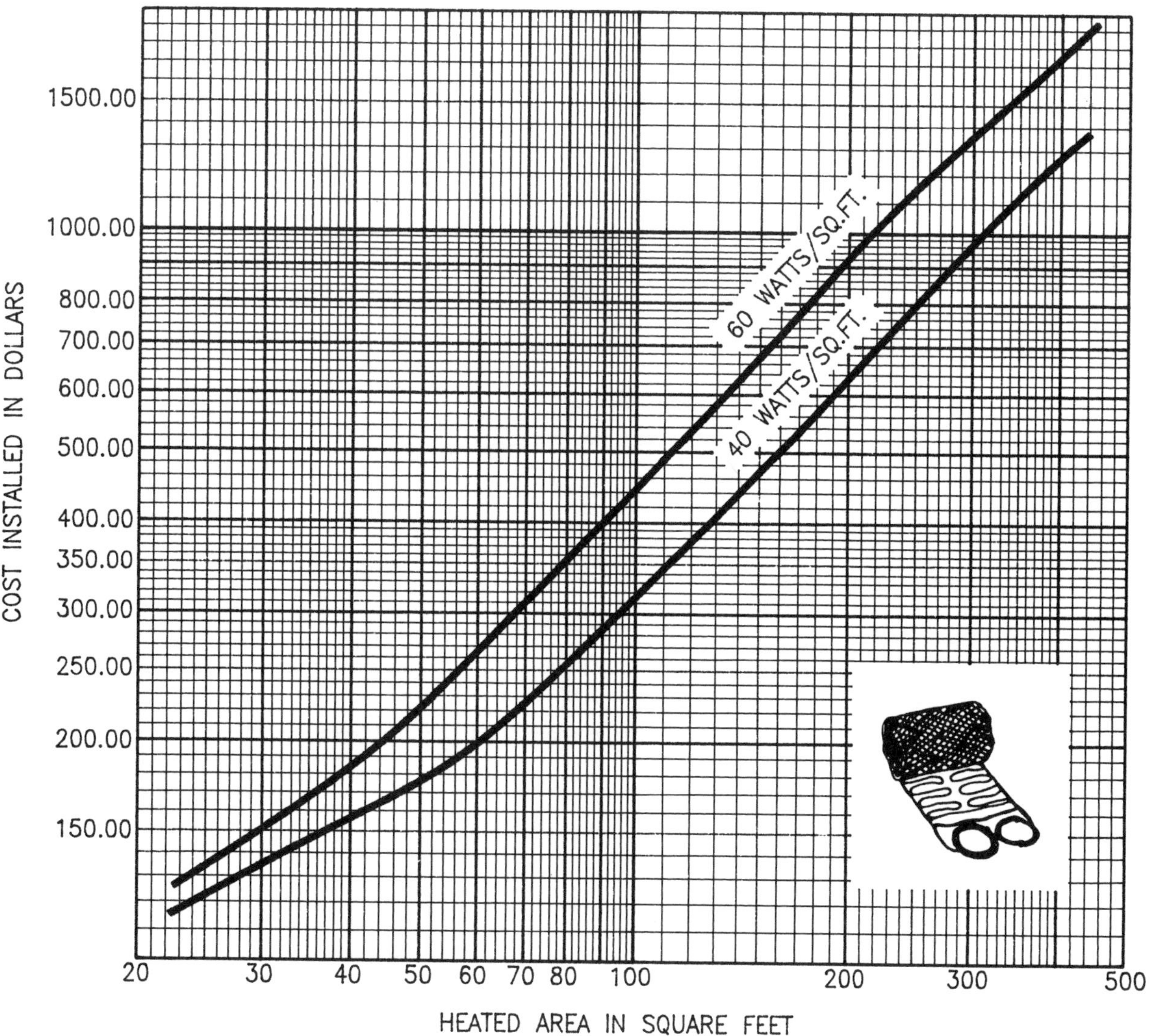

The costs shown consist of the published contractors' book price for the units shown and the labor for installation. The cable is made up into mats 18 inches wide; these mats come in wattage densities of 40 and 60 watts per square foot. They are manufactured by Easy Heat Inc. Branch circuit wiring and controls are not included.

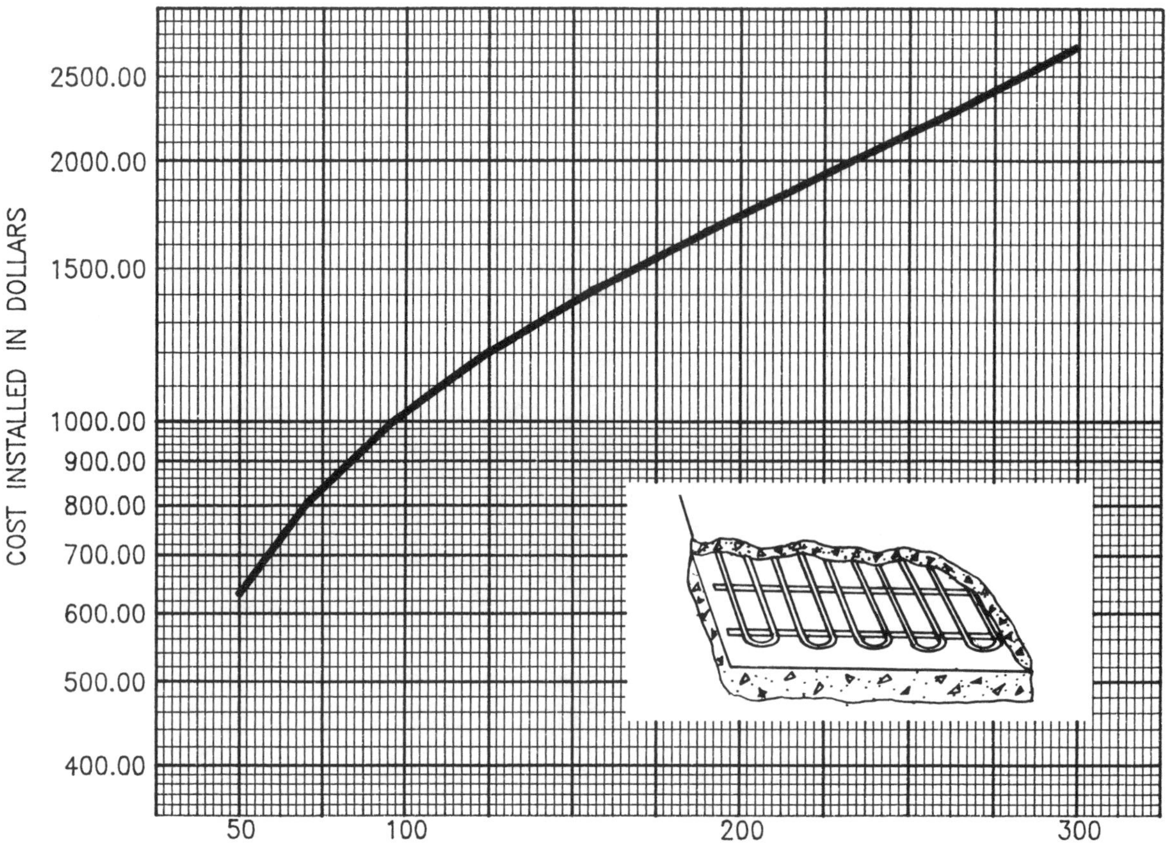

The costs shown for these cables consist of the published contractors' book price for the cables required and the labor for installation. These mineral-insulated heating cables are manufactured by Easy Heat Inc. The graph includes a 4- by 4-inch by #8 welded wire mesh and the fastening of the heating cable to it on a concrete base course for 2 to 2 1/2 inches of finish pour for the heated surface. The mesh will help keep the cables in place during the concrete pour. These costs do not include branch circuit wiring or controls.

DESCRIPTION		MANUFACTURER	INSTALLED COST
	SINGLE STAGE – SNAP ACTION DPST. 5KW RATED @ 240V.	QMARK #T-200	$66.00
	SINGLE STAGE – TAMPERPROOF SPST. 5KW RATED @ 240V.	QMARK MHT-4051E	134.75
	SINGLE STAGE – HEAVY DUTY SNAP-ACTION DPST. 5KW RATED @240V.	QMARK #T-87F	69.25
	TWO STAGE – MODULATING 5KW RATED @240V PER STAGE 35 – 90 DEGREE	QMARK #M7D	72.50
	SINGLE STAGE – EXPL. PROOF DPST. 5KW RATED @ 240V.	QMARK WR-80EP	347.25
	SINGLE STAGE WITH 10' CAPILLARY FOR FLOOR HEATING 5KW RATED @240V.	QMARK #FT-10-S	102.75

The costs shown for these units consist of the published contractors' book price for the units shown and the labor for installation. They also include a recessed junction box with conduit terminals for mounting each thermostat. No branch wiring is included. These units are manufactured by Qmark division of Marley Electric Heating Co.

DESCRIPTION		MANUFACTURER	INSTALLED COST
	LOW VOLTAGE THERMOSTAT SINGLE STAGE – SPST WITH ADJUSTABLE HEAT ANTICIOPATOR 30 VAC 50 TO 90 DEGREE	QMART #T87–F	$69.25

MISCELLANEOUS CONTROLLERS

	SINGLE SWITCH LOW VOLTAGE TRANSFORMER RELAY	QMART #WR–24A01G–8	67.00
	TWO SWITCH LOW VOLTAGE TRANSFORMER RELAY	QMART #WR–24A06G–3	86.75
	SNOW/ICE DETECTOR FOR ROOF & GUTTER	EASY HEAT #AS–6RG W/PROBE	688.00
	SNOW/ICE DETECTOR WITH AIR SENSING CONTROL	EASY HEAT #AS–6 W/PROBE	688.00
	SNOW/ICE DETECTOR WITH SLAB EMBEDDED SENSING CONTROL	EASY HEAT #SI–120U W/PROBE	973.75

The costs shown for these units consist of the published contractors' book price and the labor for installation. They also include a recessed junction box with conduit terminals for mounting the thermostat.

The snow and ice detector consists of a solid-state control box and sensors embedded in the slab which sense both temperature and moisture. Installation labor is included, but no branch circuit wiring. Equipment is manufactured by Easy Heat Inc.

Power Distribution Above 600 Volts

OVERHEAD

UNDERGROUND

INSTALLED COST IN DOLLARS						
DOUGLAS FIR OR LODGEPOLE PINE POLES						
POLE LENGTH	CLASS OF POLE 1	2	3	4	5	6
30	—	—	—	235.50	208.00	193.25
35	—	—	—	280.75	257.25	236.285
40	—	—	347.50	321.25	295.00	—
45	—	—	392.75	366.50	340.50	—
50	813.50	655.75	603.25	—	—	—

CLASS OF POLE DEFINITION						
POLE LENGTH IN FEET	CLASS OF POLE 1	2	3	4	5	6
	MINIMUM TOP CIRCUMFERENCE IN INCHES 27	25	23	21	19	17
	MINIMUM CIRCUMFERENCE AT 6' FROM BUTT IN INCHES					
30	37.5	35.0	32.5	30.0	28.0	26.0
35	40.0	37.5	35.0	32.0	30.0	27.5
40	42.0	39.5	37.0	34.0	31.5	29.0
45	44.0	41.5	38.5	36.0	33.0	30.5
50	46.0	43.0	40.0	37.5	34.5	32.0

The poles referred to here are distributed by Koppers Corporation, Inc., which has a plant in Denver, CO, and are fully pressure-treated.

The prices shown here include the cost of the poles in Denver (see page K-2 for the cost of trucking), clearing the site of the pole location in normal soil, digging the hole to the proper depth, setting the pole with proper equipment, and backfilling and tamping the earth around the pole after alignment. The associated labor is included.

COST OF POLE DELIVERY

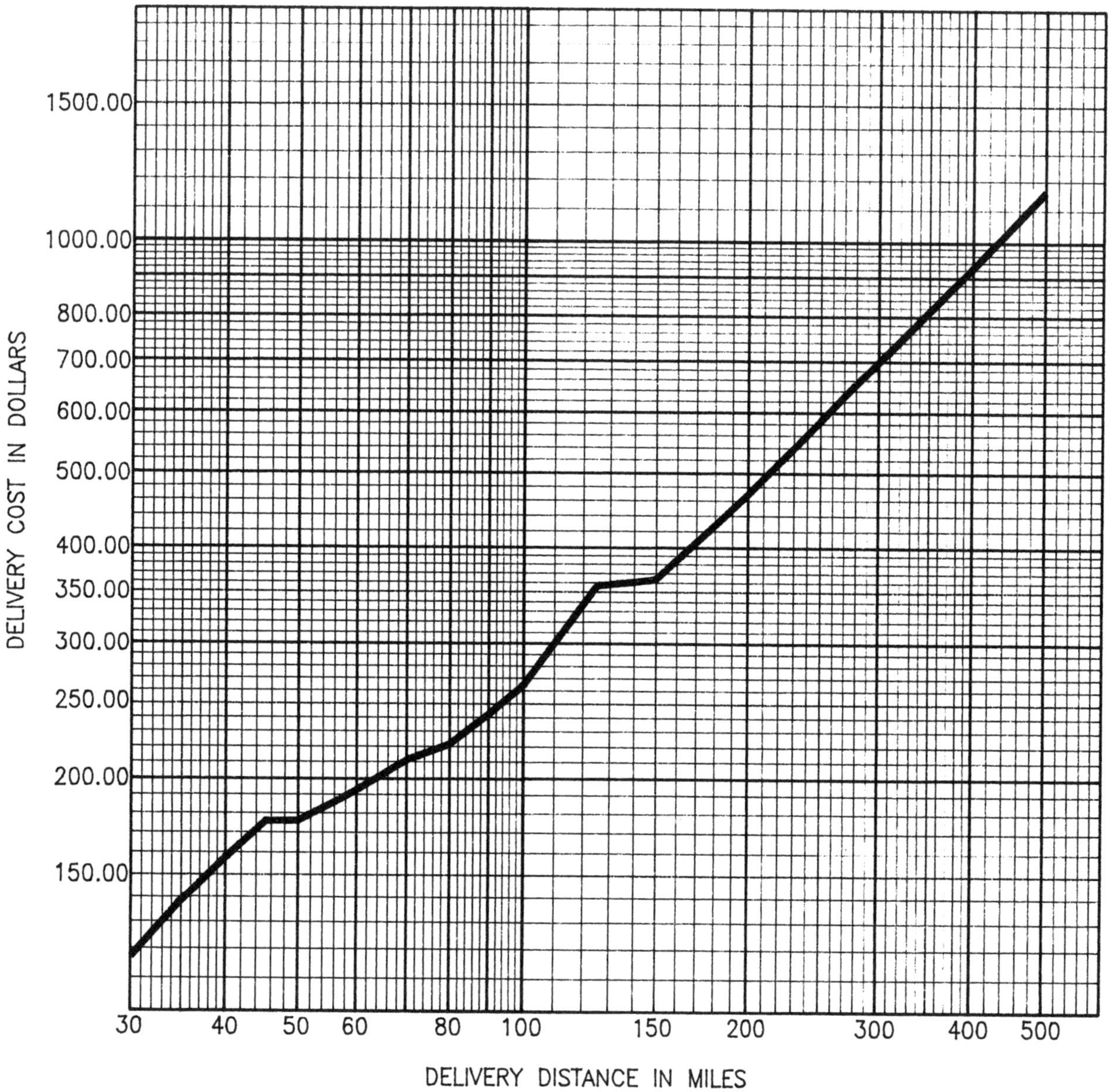

1500.00
1000.00
800.00
700.00
600.00
500.00
400.00
350.00
300.00
250.00
200.00
150.00

DELIVERY COST IN DOLLARS

30 40 50 60 80 100 150 200 300 400 500

DELIVERY DISTANCE IN MILES

Since the cost of pole delivery is somewhat dependent upon pole length, weight, and distance, the assumption has been made that the project involves one to five poles (delivery cost is the same for one or for five), not exceeding 30,000 pounds or longer than 45 feet (heavier and longer loads involve an additional rate). Poles 50 feet and longer are classified as transmission rather than distribution poles.

These costs represent "loaded distance" with 1 hour for loading and 1 hour for unloading. Presently additional time at either end costs about $45.00 per hour in the Denver area. The costs shown are for hauling within the state.

The costs shown for these poletop structures consist of the published contractors' book price for the various components making up a structure, the majority of which are Joslyn. The cost also includes the labor for the installation of the structure to the poletop at ground level before erecting the pole. The cost of the pole is not included.

COST OF POLETOP STRUCTURES

DESCRIPTION	INSTALLED COST
3-PHASE 4-WIRE 0-30° ANGLE — PLAN 5-30°	$271.00
PLAN 0-5°	156.00
THREE PHASE 4 WIRE SINGLE DEAD END	313.00
THREE PHASE 4 WIRE DOUBLE DEAD END	834.00
THREE PHASE 4 WIRE TAP AT 0–5 DEG. ANGLE (neutral)	520.00

COST OF POLE SUPPORTS

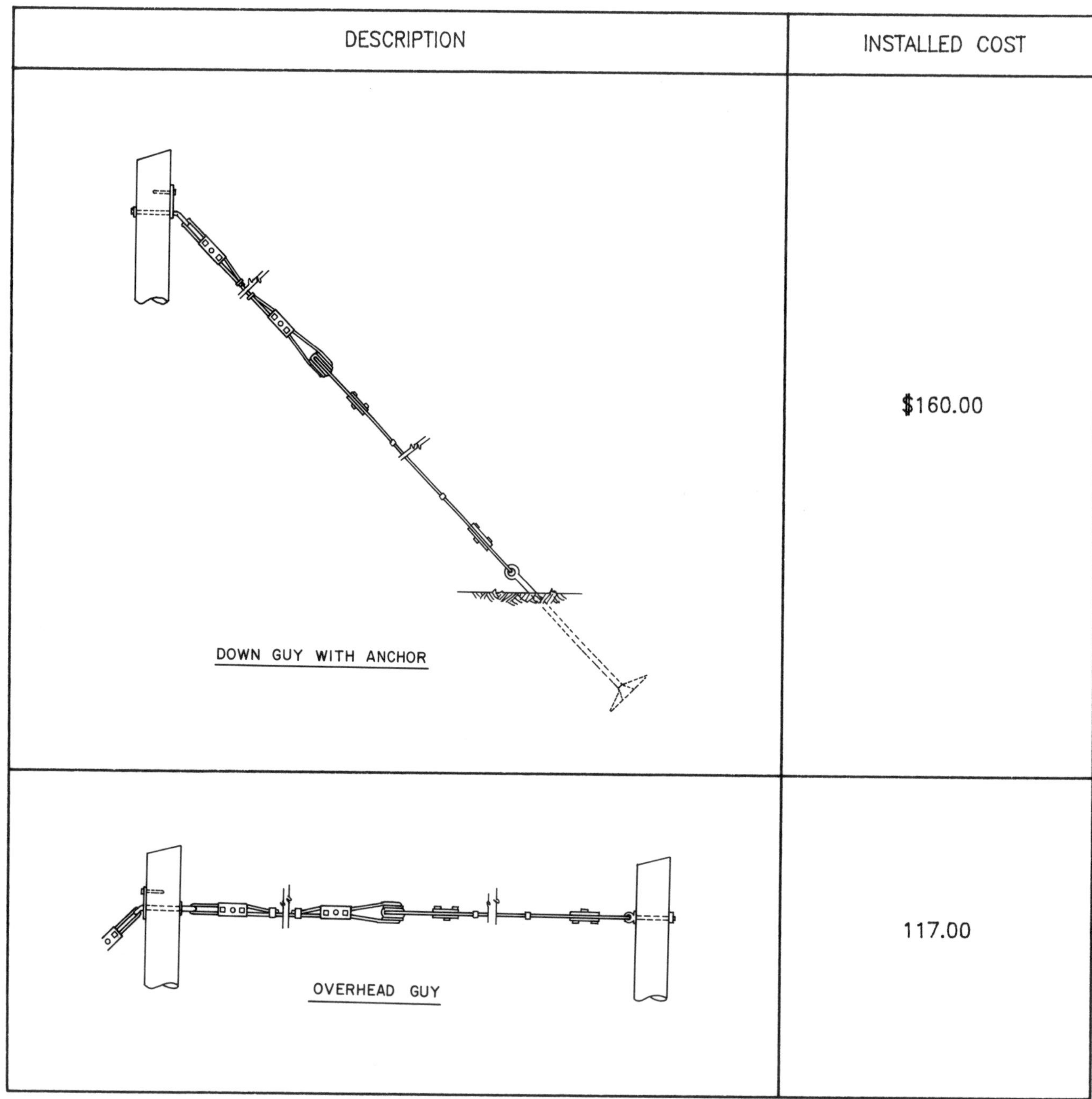

DESCRIPTION	INSTALLED COST
DOWN GUY WITH ANCHOR	$160.00
OVERHEAD GUY	117.00

The costs shown for the down guy consist of the published contractors' book price for the various components shown. Included are an eight-way expanding anchor and 8-foot anchor rod. Also included is an 8-foot plastic guy guard. Labor includes drilling the hole by hand, placing the anchor, backfilling and tamping as required, and assembling and fastening the guy.

DESCRIPTION	INSTALLED COST
 ALUMINUM SERVICE WEDGE CLAMP	$26.00
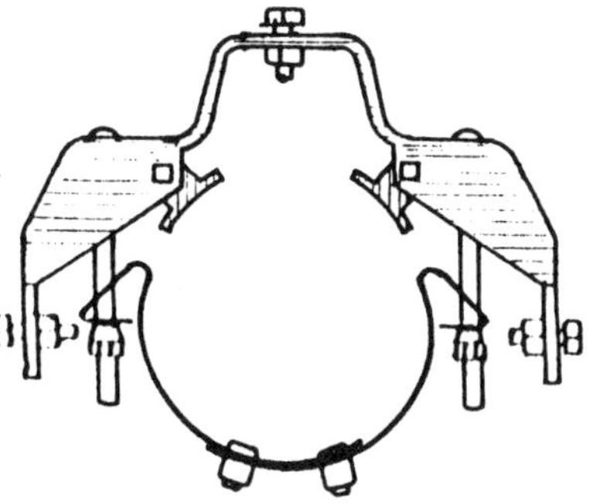 3 PHASE TRANSFORMER CLUSTER MOUNTING BRACKET	122.00
 INSULATED CLEVIS AND THRU BOLT	22.00
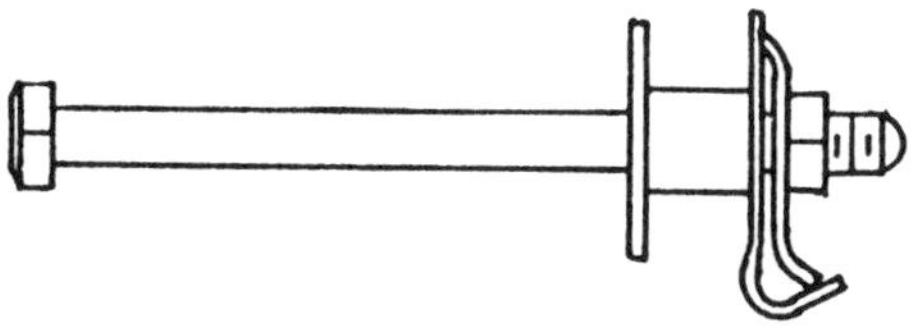 MESSENGER HANGER AND THRU BOLT	24.00

The costs shown consist of the published contractors' book price for the components shown and the labor for their installation.

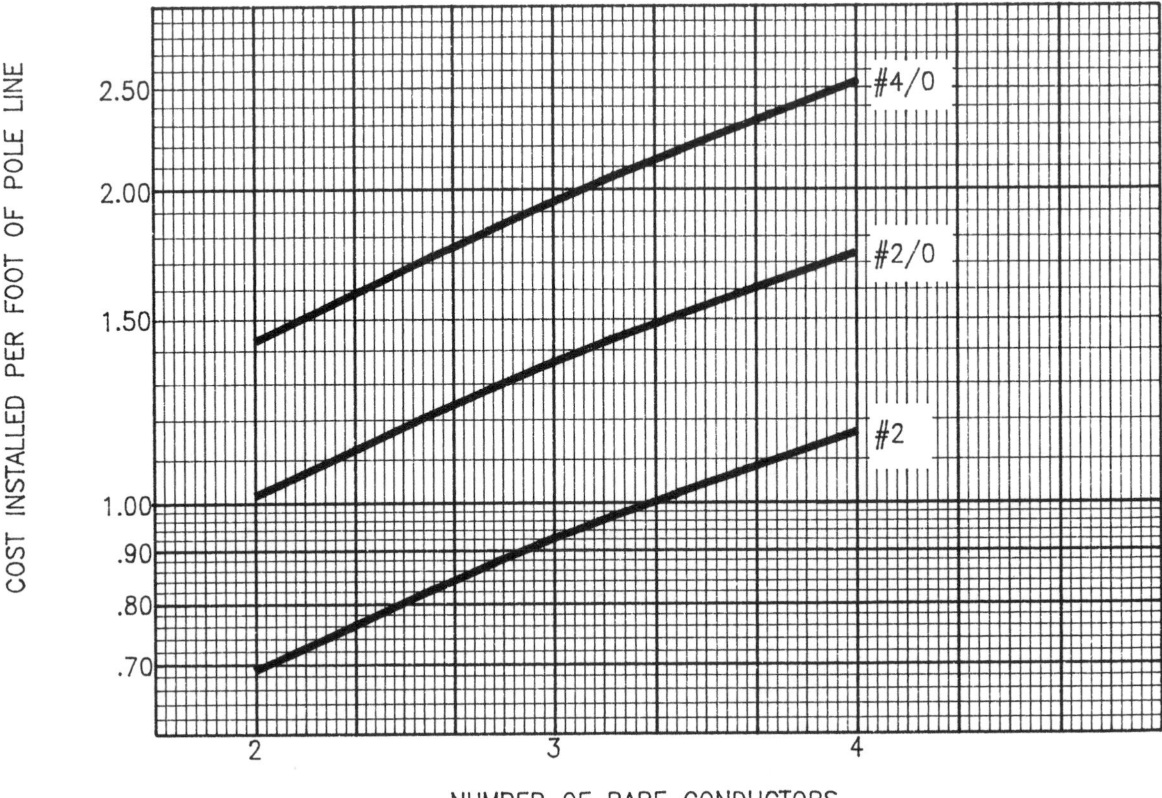

The costs shown for the ACSR bare conductor consist of the published contractors' book price and the labor for stringing, sagging, and tieing the conductors to the insulators.

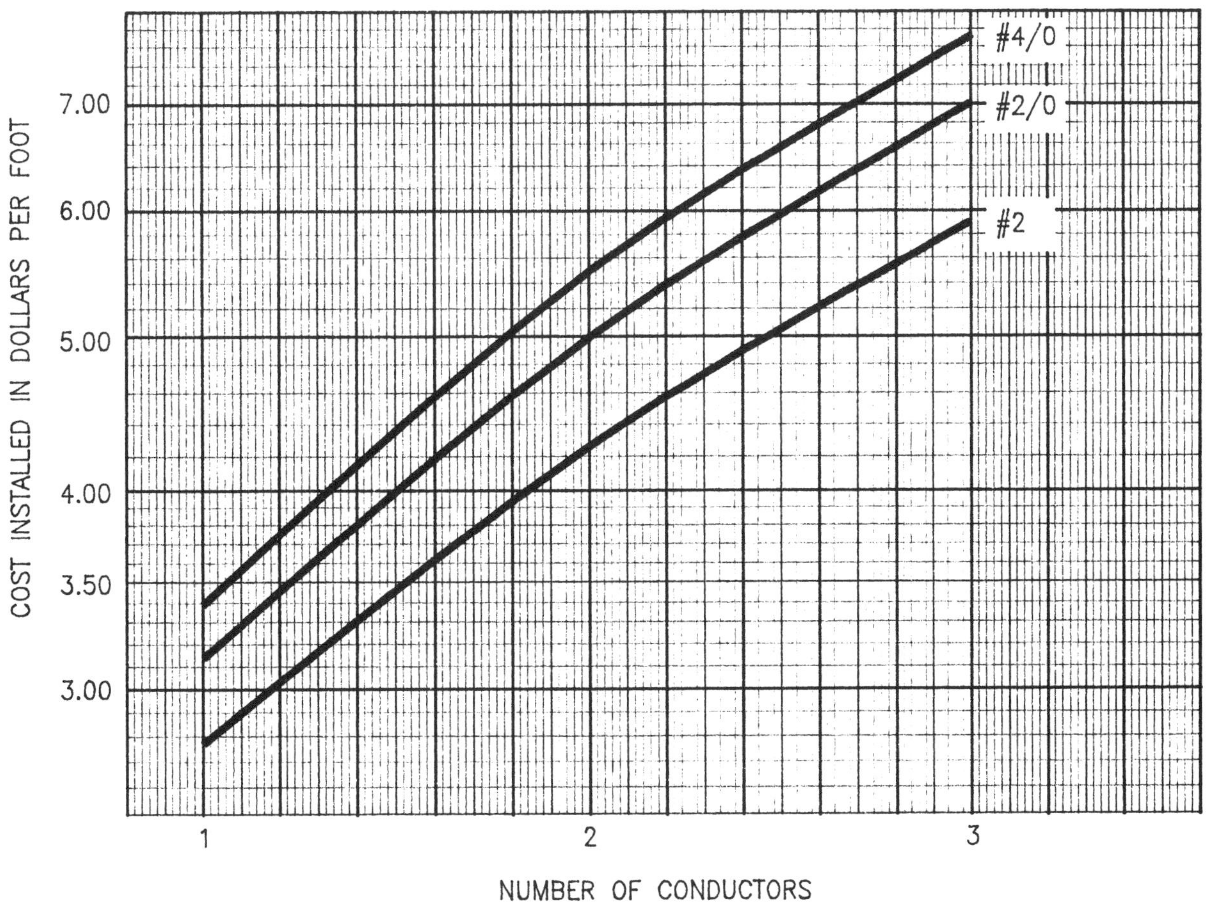

RATED 90 DEG. C.; COPPER CONCENTRIC NEUTRAL; .175" WALL THICKNESS FOR GROUNDED NEUTRAL AND EXTRUDED SEMI–CONDUCTING SHIELDING; SUITABLE FOR DIRECT BURIAL, CONDUIT, OR DUCT INSTALLATION.

The cost for the cable consists of the contractors' price for the size and type shown, purchased in 5000-foot quantity. Adjust price as required by length. The labor is also provided for installation in an open trench or pulled into conduit.

TYPE OF UNIT	MANUFACTURER	RATING	INSTALLED COST
FUSED CUTOUTS 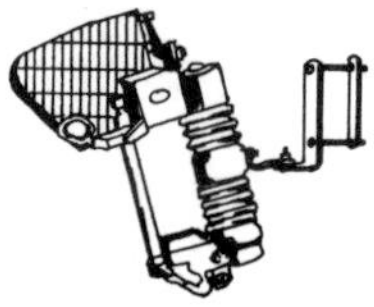	G.E. LOAD BREAK 7.8/13.8 KV	100 AMP	$172.00
LIGHTNING ARRESTER 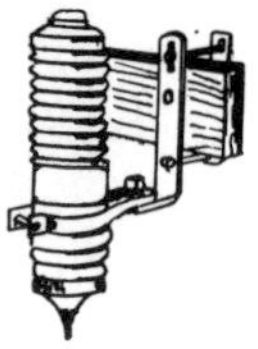	G. E. METAL OXIDE	9 KV 27 KV	57.00
EXTERIOR POLE TERMINATION 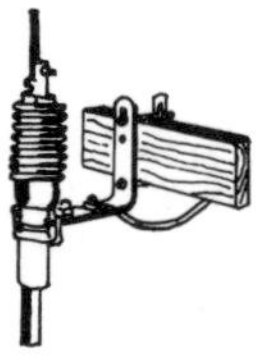	BLACKBURN TYPE P & PBB BRACKET	#2 – #4/0 25 KV	57.00
INTERIOR TERMINATION STRESS RELIEF CONE 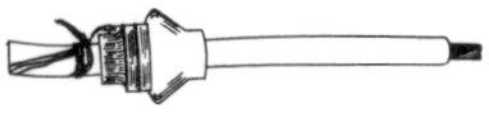	BLACKBURN TYPE SKD	15 KV	48.00
PRIMARY ELBOW TERMINATOR 	G. E. WITH TEST POINT	L – N 8.3 KV #2,1/0 & 4/0	38.00

The costs for these items consist of the published contractors' book price for the items illustrated. Material and labor are provided for mounting and terminating the cable as required.

Miscellaneous

COST OF JUNCTION BOXES

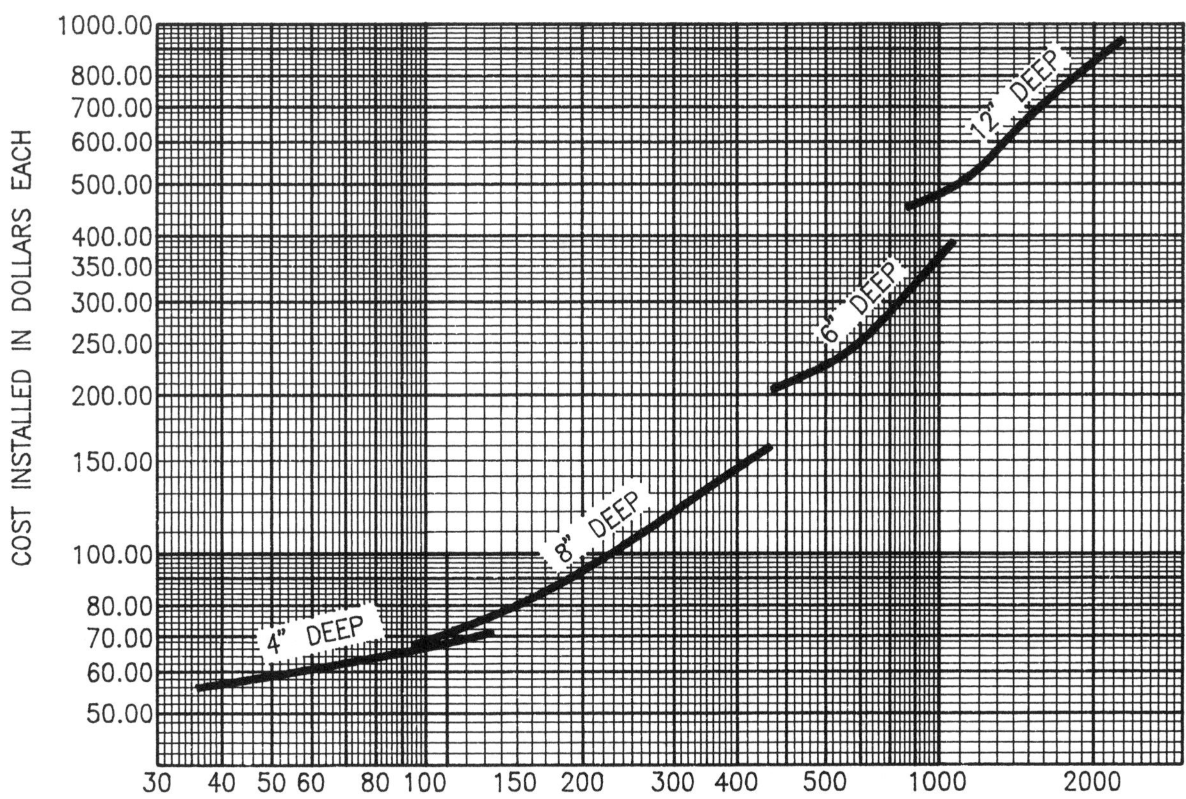

The costs shown for the junction boxes consist of the contractors' published book price. The boxes are assumed to be surface-mounted on masonry. Included are the fastening devices; however, no conduit terminals or holes are provided.

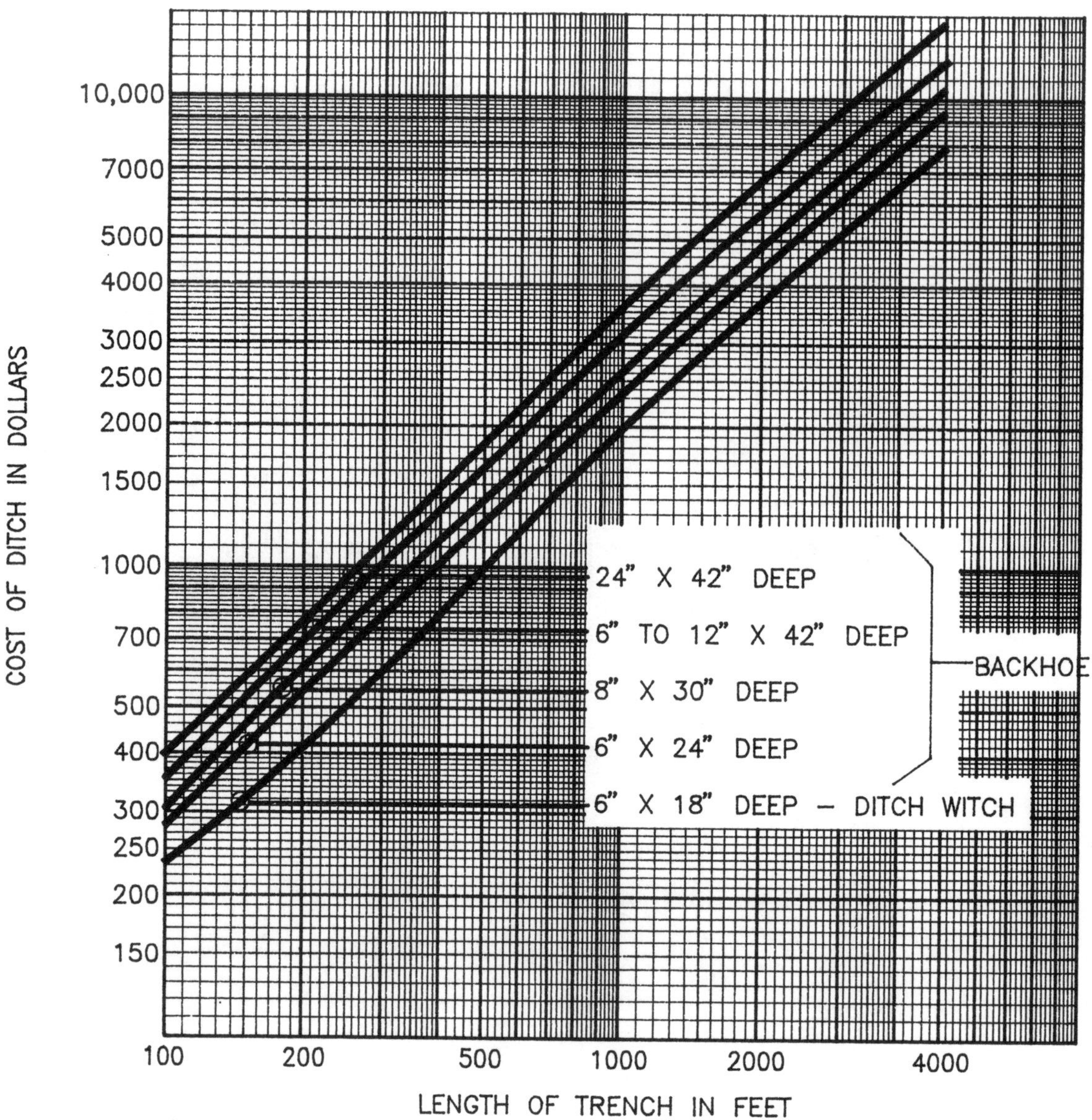

The costs shown for trenching and backfilling are based upon the size of the trench shown on the graph. Normal, average dirt-digging conditions are assumed. The estimator must use job factors for more difficult digging conditions or ditch sizes different from those shown. Generally speaking, the cost is influenced by the volume of the dirt that has to be removed.

Backfill: Where no specific density except that which can be obtained by the equipment wheel rolling over the ditch is required, add 50% to the trenching cost. For backfill requiring 90 to 95% machine compaction, as you might find under parking areas or roads, double the trenching costs.

COST OF DRILLING HOLE IN DOLLARS

DRILL FOR CONDUIT SIZE	WALL THICKNESS				
	8"	12"	16"	20"	24"
1/2"	17.25	21.00	24.75	28.75	32.50
1"	23.00	28.00	33.00	37.75	42.75
1-1/2"	23.00	28.00	33.00	37.75	42.75
2"	53.50	61.00	68.75	76.50	84.00
2-1/2"	53.50	61.00	68.75	76.50	84.00
3"	53.50	61.00	68.75	76.50	84.00
3-1/2"	68.75	80.25	91.75	99.25	110.75
4"	68.75	80.25	91.75	99.25	110.75

The costs shown for drilling holes in masonry are based upon the use of a diamond-core drill and include wear and tear on the drill.

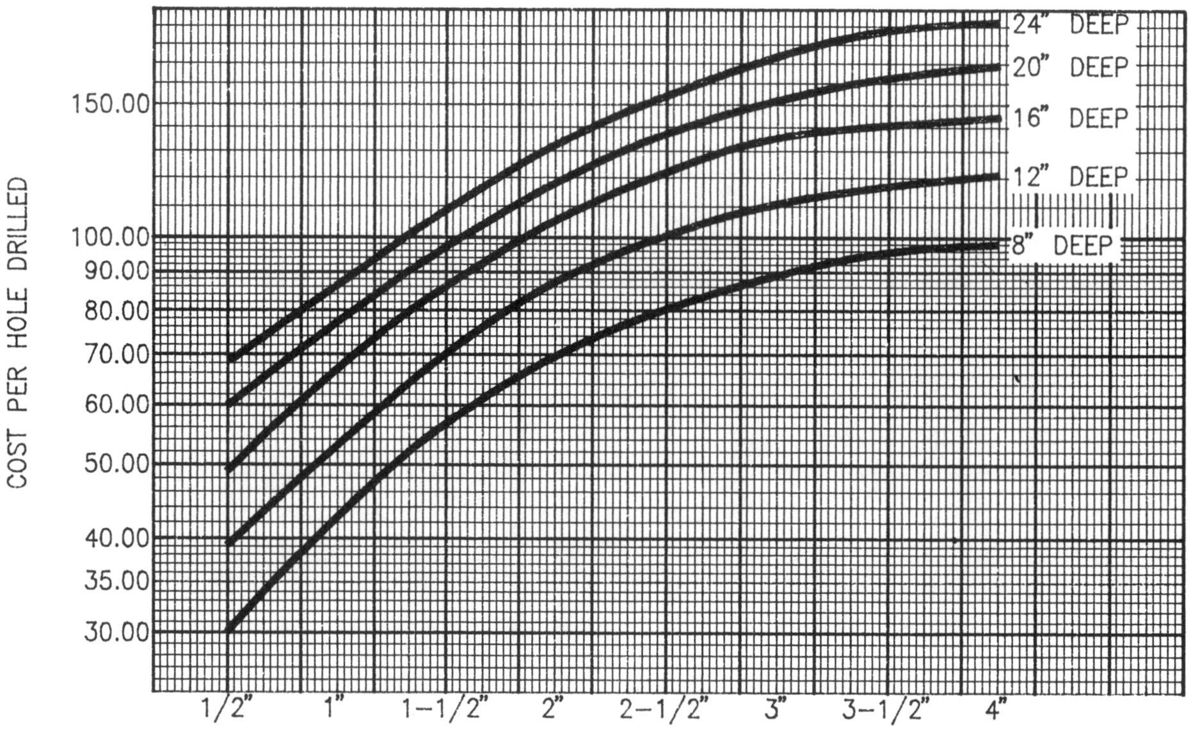

The costs shown for drilling holes in reinforced concrete are based upon the use of a diamond-core drill and include wear and tear on the drill bit.

COST OF CUTTING HOLES IN STEEL PANEL

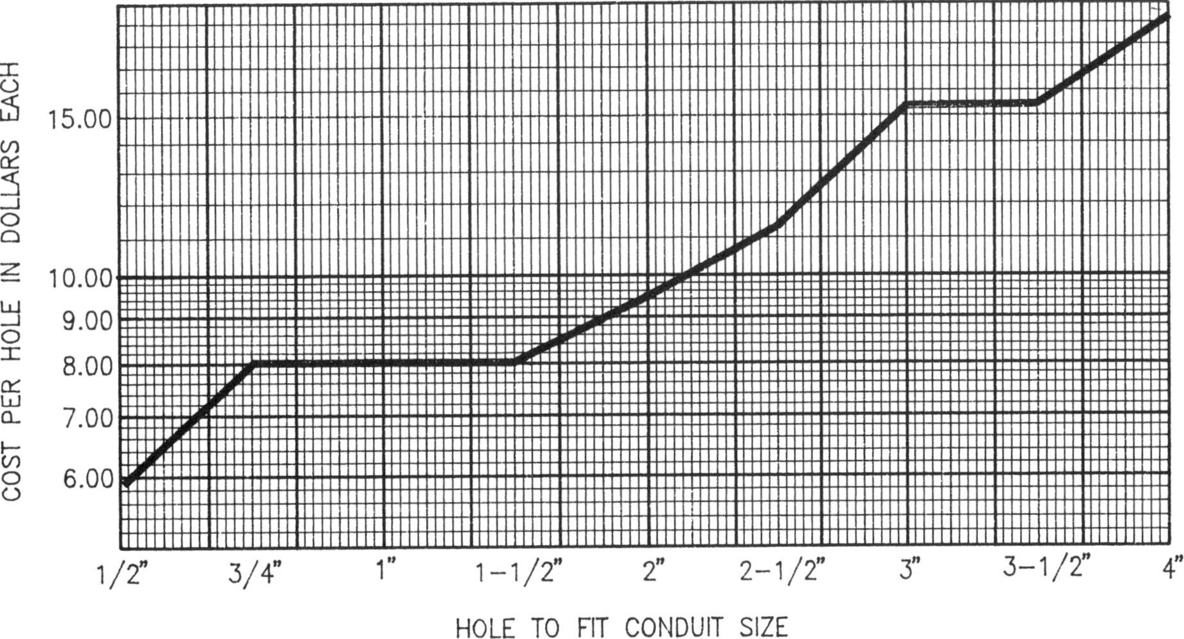

The costs shown here represent the costs of punching a hole in steel using a hydraulic punch. If a hole saw is to be used, add 20%.

COST OF CUTTING CHANNELS

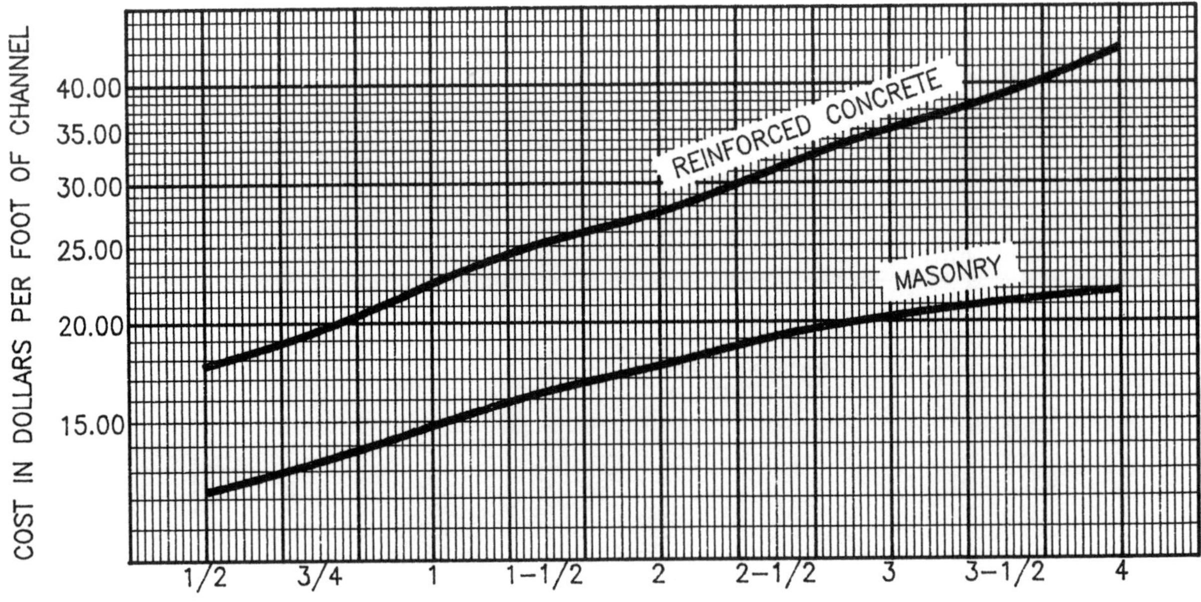

The costs shown for channeling in masonry or concrete are based upon two cuts with a power masonry saw, and an electric hammer for chipping out the trench is assumed to be available. The depth of the cut is based upon about 5/8 inch of cover over the conduit. Dry-mix cement and labor for its installation are included in the costs shown. Also included are the wear and tear on the masonry blades.

COST OF CUTTING ASPHALT PAVEMENT

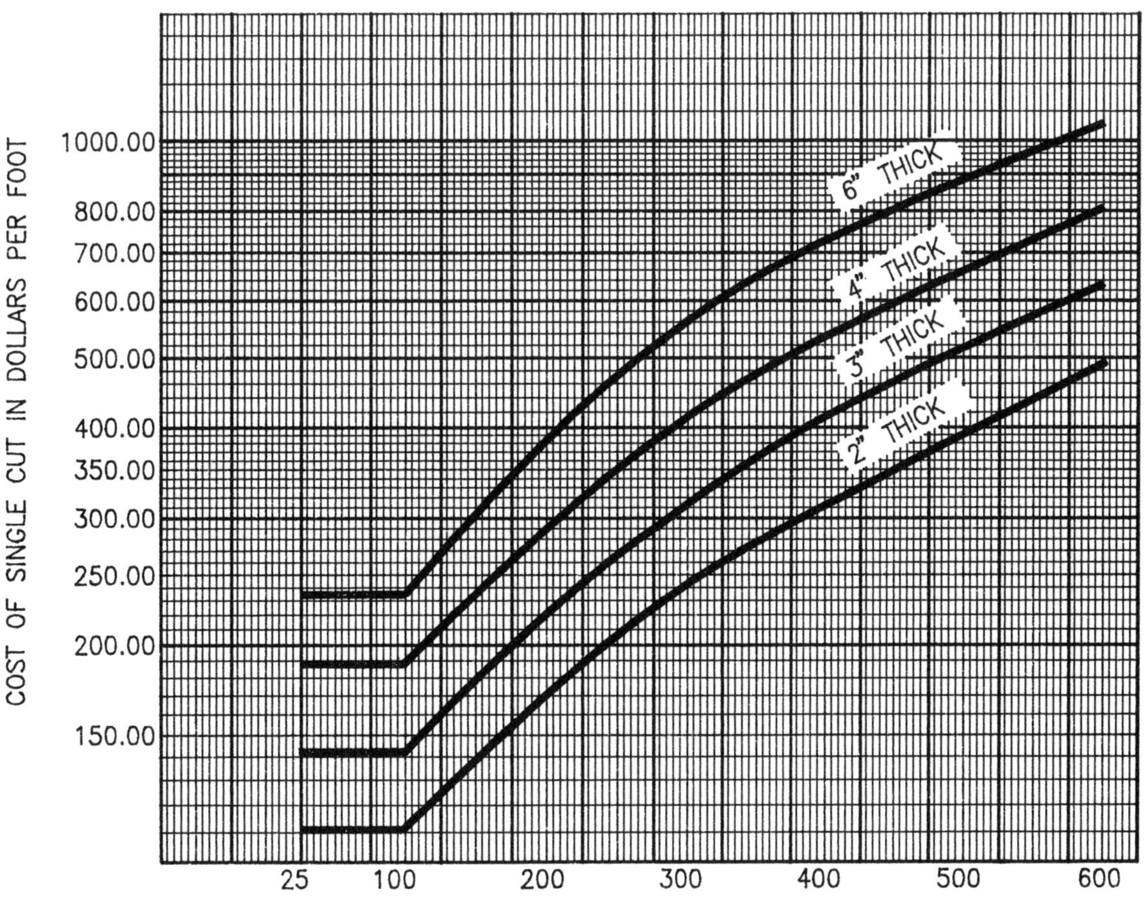

The costs shown for cutting asphalt pavement are based upon a single cut with a power masonry saw. The depth of cut as required to cut through the thickness of the asphalt is indicated on the graph. Bear in mind that you must add for handling debris and asphalt replacement as job conditions dictate.

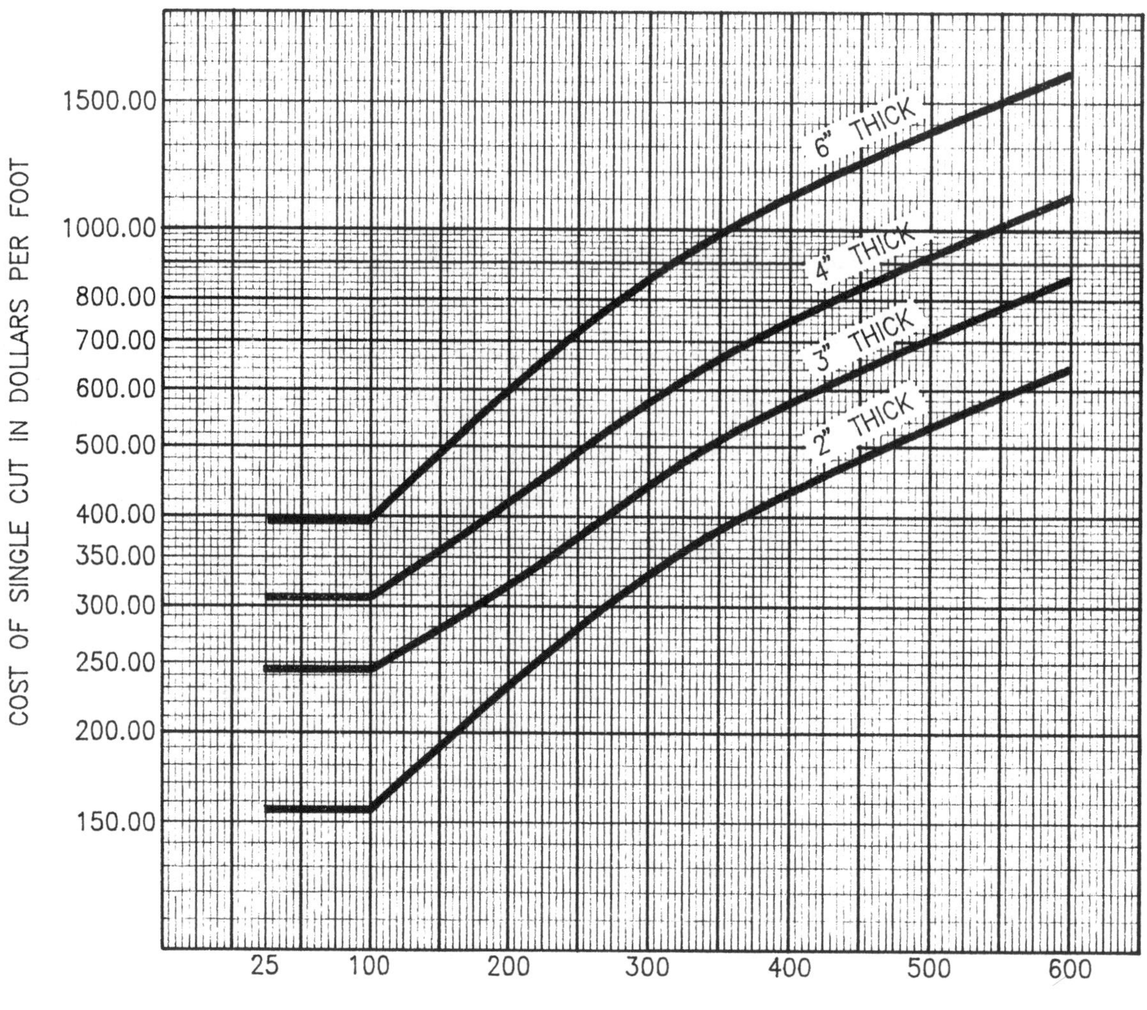

The costs shown for cutting concrete are based upon a single cut with a power masonry saw. Bear in mind that you must add for handling debris and concrete replacement as job conditions dictate.

DESCRIPTION		FASTENED TO DRYWALL	FASTENED TO HOLLOW MASONRY	FASTENED TO CONCRETE
TOGGLE BOLTS	1/8" X 3"	1.65	$2.25	
	3/16" X 4"	1.95	2.45	
	1/4" X 4"	2.36	2.90	
HOLLOW WALL ANCHOR	TO 3/16"	1.90		
	OVER 1/4"	2.35		
FIBER OR PLASTIC ANCHOR	#8 X 1"	.80	1.30	1.80
	#10 X 1"	1.10	1.60	2.10
	#14 X 1-1/4"	1.80	2.30	2.80
EXPANSION SHIELD & BOLT	1/4"		3.45	4.90
	5/16"		3.95	5.25
	3/8"		4.40	5.75
LEAD ANCHOR & LAG SCREW	5/16"		2.50	3.00
	3/8"		3.40	3.90
	1/2"		4.45	4.95

The costs shown for these anchors consist of the published contractors' book price and the labor for installing on the surfaces indicated.

DESCRIPTION		FASTENED TO DRYWALL	FASTENED TO HOLLOW MASONRY	FASTENED TO CONCRETE
HAMMER DRIVE ANCHOR				
	3/16 X 7/8"			$1.50
	1/4 X 1"			1.80
	1/4 X 1–1/2"			2.25
STUD ANCHOR & NUT				
	1/4 X 2–1/4"			3.75
	3/8 X 2–3/4"			4.60
	1/2 X 3–3/4			5.85
SELF–DRILL ANCHOR & BOLT				
	1/4"			3.60
	5/16"			4.45
	3/8"			5.35
SELF–TAPPING SCREWS IN METAL				
	#8 X 1"	$1.44		
	#10 X 1"	2.14		
	#12 X 1"	2.85		

The costs shown here include the fastening devices plus the labor to make the installation to the surfaces shown.

Appendix

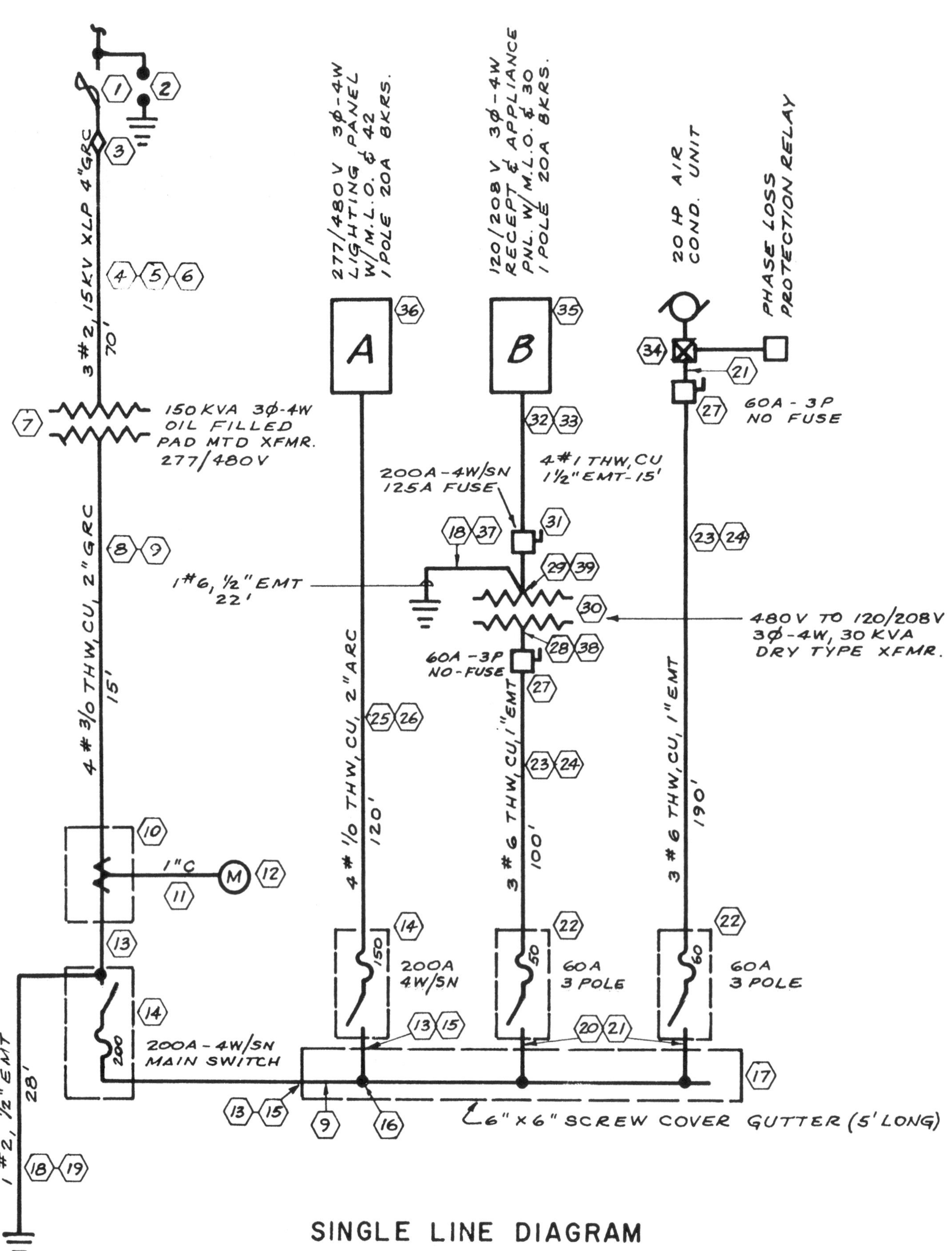

SINGLE LINE DIAGRAM

EXAMPLE NO. 1

REEP

PRICING SHEET

JOB EXAMPLE NO. 1 SHEET NO. 1

WORK SINGLE LINE DIAGRAM OF 2

PRICED BY G.V.K. DATE 2 JUNE 1992

DESCRIPTION	KEY	REMARKS OR DEVIATIONS	REF PAGE	QTY.	UNIT PRICE		MULT	EXTENDED PRICE	
100a 15 KV FUSED CUTOUT	1	ON POLE	K-8	3	172	00	*	$516	00
9 KV LIGHTINING ARRESTER	2	"	K-8	3	57	00		171	00
EXT. 15 KV CABLE TERMINATION	3	"	K-8	3	57	00		171	00
4" PVC COATED GRC	4	INCL. 20' UP POLE	E-1	90'	23	00		2070	00
3#2 15 KV XLPE CABLE	5	PULLED IN	K-7	105'	5	92		621	60
12" W. x 42" D. TRENCH	6		L-2	70'	--	--		250	00
150 KVA 3 PHASE PAD MTD. TRANSFORMER	7	INCL. PAD	H-9	1	--	--		7000	00
2" GRC	8		E-1	15'	5	40		81	00
4#3/0 THW, CU	9		E-8	24'	8	80		211	20
200a-4W INDOOR C.T. CABINET	10		C-2	1	--	--		690	00
1" GRC	11		E-1	15'	2	85		42	75
OUTDOOR METER HOUSING	12		C-2	1	--	--		229	00
2" NIPPLE ASSEMBLY	13		E-5	3	29	00		87	00
200a-4W/SN FUSIBLE DISC. SWITCH	14	277/480V	B-17	2	820	00		1640	00
CUT 2" HOLE IN GUTTER	15		L-5	2	9	50		19	00
FEEDER TAPS – #3/0 CONDUCTOR	16		E-15	10	27	80		278	00
6" x 6" SCREW GUTTER	17		C-7	5'	--	--		112	00
1/2" EMT	18		F-7	50'	1	59		79	50
1#2 BARE COPPER	19		D-2	30'	2	25		67	50
CUT 1" HOLE IN GUTTER	20		L-5	2	8	00		16	00
1" NIPPLE ASSEMBLY	21		E-5	3	14	00		42	00
60a-3P FUSIBLE DISC. SWITCH	22	600V.	B-18	2	270	00		540	00
1" EMT	23		E-1	290'	2	20		638	00
3#6 THE, CU	24		E-8	290'	2	08		603	20
2" ALUM. RIGID CONDUIT	25		E-1	120'	4	00		480	00
4#4/0 THW, CU	26		E-8	120'	10	70		1284	00
60a-3P NO-FUSE DISC. SWITCH	27	600V.	B-19	2	132	00		262	00
1" CONDUIT TERMINAL (EMT)	28		E-2	1	--	--		8	00
2" CONDUIT TERMINAL (EMT)	29		E-2	1	--	--		23	00
30 KVA – INDOOR DRY TYPE TRANSFORMER	30	150 DEG. C	H-5	1	--	--		1250	00
200a-4W/SN FUSIBLE DISC. SWITCH	31		B-16	1	--	--		540	00
1-1/2" EMT	32		E-1	15'	3	10		46	50
4#1 THW, CU	33		E-8	15'	6	20		93	00
INSTALL 20 HP STARTER	34	3 WIRE + 10% FOR NEUT.	G-19	1	--	--	↓	160	00
SHEET TOTAL								$20,272	25

* MULTIPLIER APPLIED ON SUMMARY SHEET

REEP

PRICING SHEET

JOB EXAMPLE NO. 1 SHEET NO. 2

WORK SINGLE LINE DIAGRAM OF 2

PRICED BY G.V.K. DATE 2 JUNE 1992

DESCRIPTION	KEY	REMARKS OR DEVIATIONS	REF PAGE	QTY.	UNIT PRICE		MULT	EXTENDED PRICE	
PANEL "B" 208V, 30 CCT. 3PH MLO	35		B–11	1	—	—	*	$1060	00
PANEL "A" 277/480V 42 CCT. MLO	36		B–13	1	—	—		1490	00
1#6 BARE COPPER GROUND	37		D–2	25	1	40		35	00
APPLIANCE CONNECTION – 60a	38	3 WIRE	F–25	1	—	—		33	00
APPLIANCE CONNECTION – 125a	39	3 WIRE + 10% FOR NEUT	F–25	1	—	—		67	60
SHEET TOTAL								$2655	60

* MULTIPLIER APPLIED ON SUMMARY SHEET

REEP

SUMMARY SHEET

JOB *EXAMPLE NO. 1 – SINGLE LINE DIAGRAM* DATE *2 JUNE '92*

LOCATION

ARCHITECT ORIGINAL PRICE

ENCLOSED AREA $/sq. ft. CHANGE ORDER

CONNECTED LOAD (W/sq ft) DIVERSIFIED DEMAND (W/sq ft)

ALTERNATES

DESCRIPTION OF THE WORK *SERVICE EQUIPMENT, POWER DISTRIBUTION AND PANELBOARDS*

REMARKS

PRICING SHEET TOTALS	SHEET NUMBER	DESCRIPTION	AMOUNT	
	1	*SINGLE LINE DIAGRAM*	$ *20,272*	*25*
	2	*SINGLE LINE DIAGRAM*	*2655*	*60*
	TOTAL SUMMARIZED PRICE		*22,927*	*85*
	PRICE ADJUSTMENT MULTIPLIER		X *1*	*37*
	ADJUSTED SELL PRICE		*31,411*	*15*

SUBCONTRACT ITEMS	DESCRIPTION	AMOUNT	
	TOTAL OF SUBCONTRACT ITEMS		
	PROFIT MULTIPLIER	X	
	ADJUSTED TOTAL		

TOTAL JOB PRICE → $ *31,412* *50*

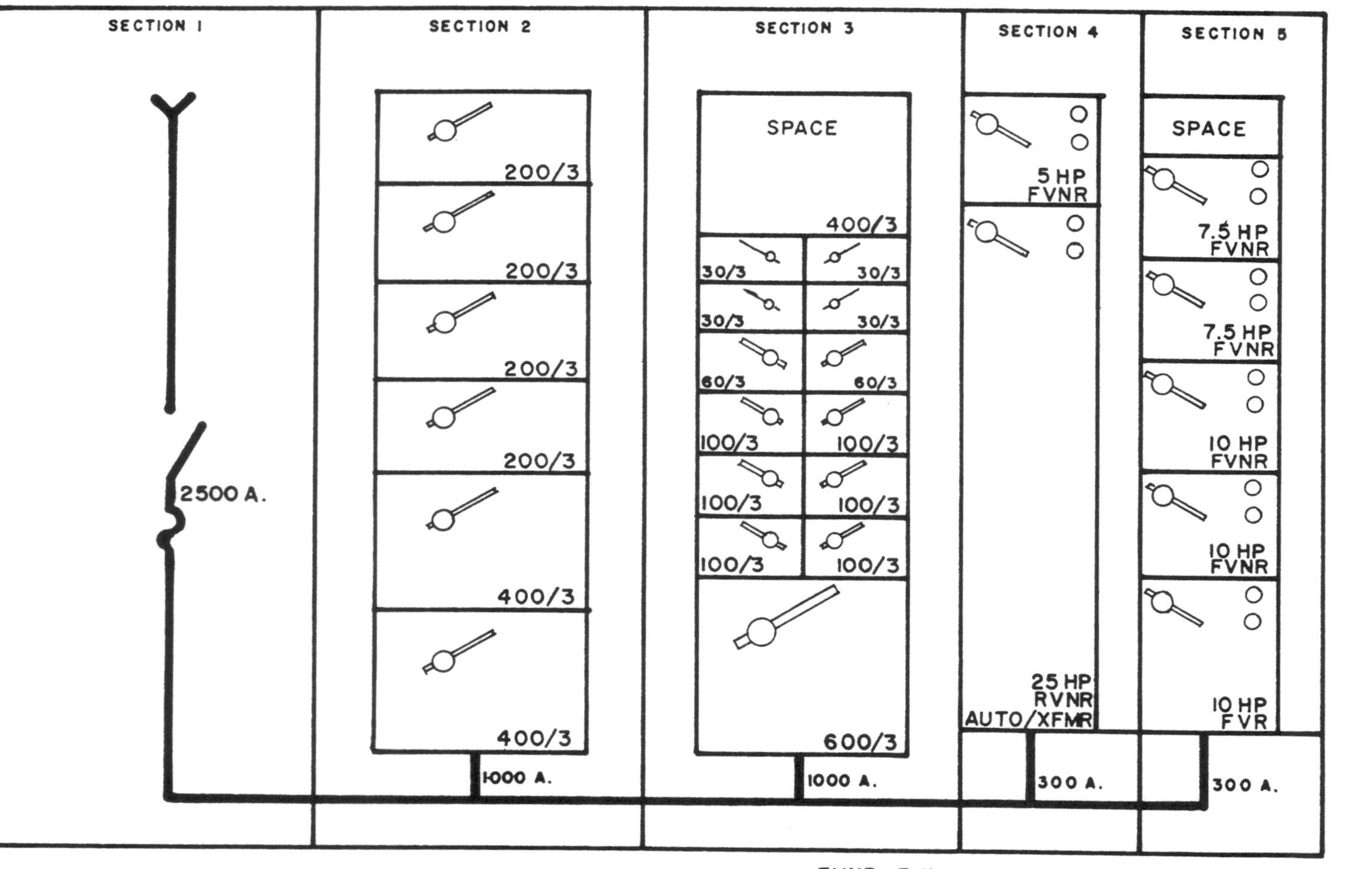

FVNR-Full Voltage Non-Reversing
RVNR-Reduced Voltage Non-Reversing
FVR -Full Voltage Reversing

120/208 VOLT MAIN DISTRIBUTION PANEL & MOTOR CONTROL CENTER

EXAMPLE NO. 2

REEP

PRICING SHEET

JOB EXAMPLE NO. 2 SHEET NO. 1

WORK 120/208V. MAIN DISTR. PANEL & MOTOR CONTROL CNTR. OF 1

PRICED BY G.V.K. DATE 6 JUNE 1992

DESCRIPTION	REF PAGE	REMARKS OR DEVIATIONS	QTY.	UNIT PRICE		MULT	EXTENDED PRICE	
2500a BOLTED PRESSURE SWITCH	B-1		1	—	—		13000	00
COST OF CBT. SECTIONS #2 & #3	B-1		2	4300	00		8600	00
600a BRANCH SWITCH UNIT	B-5		1	—	—		2050	00
400a BRANCH SWITCH UNIT	B-5		2	1480	00		2960	00
200a BRANCH SWITCH UNIT	B-5		4	720	00		2880	00
100a TWIN BRANCH UNIT	B-5		3	521	00		1563	00
60a TWIN BRANCH UNIT	B-5		1	—	—		360	00
30a BRANCH UNIT	B-5		2	321	00		642	00
COST OF MCC UNIT CBT. SECTIONS #4 & #5	G-29		2	2100	00		4200	00
5 HP FULL VOLTAGE NON-REV. STARTER	G-32		1	—	—		780	00
7-1/2 HP FULL VOLTAGE NON-REV. STARTER	G-32		2	780	00		1560	00
10 HP FULL VOLTAGE NON-REV. STARTER	G-32		2	1020	00		2040	00
25 HP AUTO-XFMR RED. VOLT. STARTER	G-33		1	—	—		2850	00
		UNADJUSTED TOTAL					43,485	00
		MULTIPLIER					X 1	37
		SHEET TOTAL					59,574	00

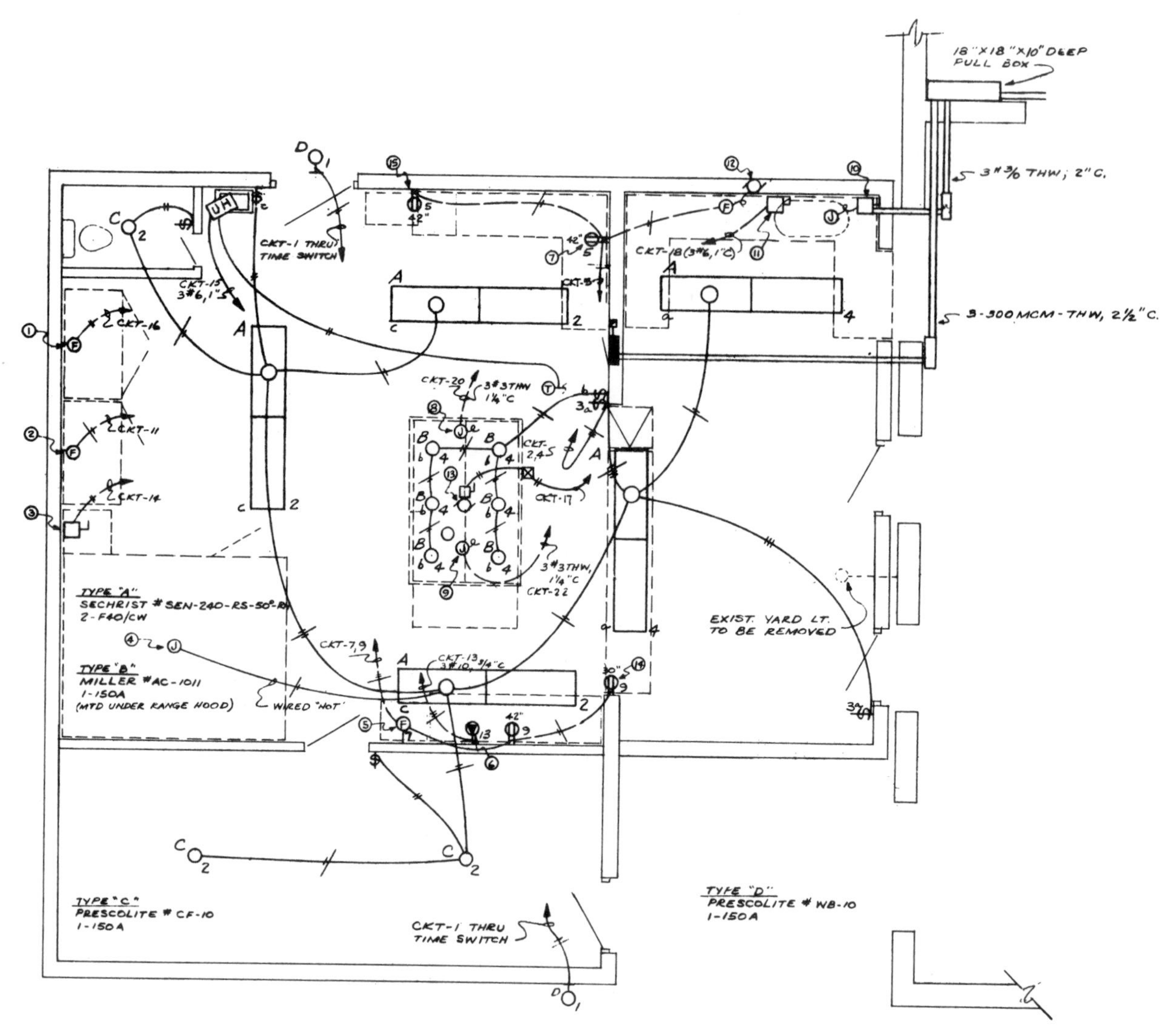

ELECTRICAL PLAN

SCALE: ¼"=1'-0"

KITCHEN EQUIPMENT SCHEDULE

MARK	DESIGNATION	HP OR KW	VOLTS	CONTRACTOR TO FURNISH
①	REACH IN FREEZER	¾ HP	240	BUSS #STY FUSEHOLDER & SWITCH W/ FLEX CONNECTION 12" UP.
②	REACH IN REFRIGERATOR	⅓ HP	120	BUSS #SSU FUSEHOLDER & FLEX CONN. 12" UP
③	WALK-IN REFRIGERATOR	1 HP	240	30a, 2P DISC. SWITCH & FLEX CONN. 36" UP.
④	LTG OUTLET FOR REFRIG.	.1 KW	120	J BOX 7' UP.
⑤	MIXER	½ HP	120	BUSS SSU FUSEHOLDER & FLEX CONN. 12" UP
⑥	FUTURE TOASTER	5 KW	240	30a, 250V REC. 42" UP.
⑦	GEN. USE RECEPTACLE	.2 KW.	120	REC. MTD. 42" UP.
⑧	GRIDDLE & OVEN	22 KW.	240	J. BOX & FLEX. CONNECTION 6" UP
⑨	GRIDDLE & OVEN	22 KW	240	J. BOX & FLEX CONNECTION 6" UP
⑩	BOOSTER HEATER	36 KW.	240	RELOCATED 200a 2P DISC. SW, & FLEX. CONNECTION 12" UP
⑪	DISHWASHER	10 KW.	240	60a, 2P NO FUSE DISCONNECT SWITCH & FLEX CONNECTION 12" UP
⑫	EXHAUST FAN	1/20 HP	120	BUSS #SSU & FLEX CONNECTION 7' UP.
⑬	EXHAUST FAN	¾ HP	240	30a, 2P NO-FUSE RAINTITE DISC. SWITCH & MANUAL MOT. STARTER
⑭	REC. FOR FUT. HOT PANS	.7 KW	120	REC. 30" UP
⑮	PEELER	¼ HP	120	REC. 42" UP.

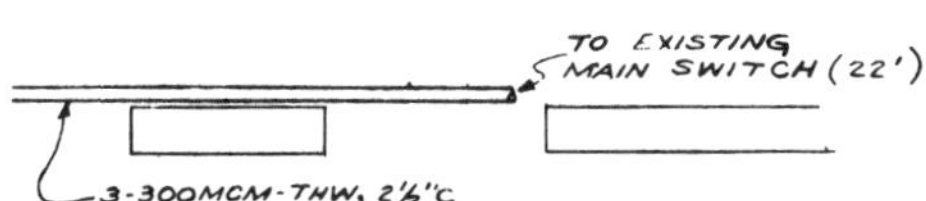

SCHEDULE FOR PANEL "A"						
120/240 VOLTS 1 PHASE 3 WIRE						
FLUSH MTG. MAINS MLO						
NOTES SQ. D #NQOB-42-3L (OR EQUAL)						
LOAD	CKT. NO.	BKR.	φ	BKR.	CKT. NO.	LOAD
EXT. LTG	1	20/1	A	20/1	2	LTG
SPARE	3		B		4	↓
PEELER & REC.	5		A		6	SPARE
MIXER	7		B		8	SPARE
REC.	9		A		10	SPARE
REFRIG.	11	↓	B	↓	12	SPARE
TOASTER	13	30/2	A	20/2	14	WALK-IN REFRIG.
↓	↓	↓	B	↓	↓	↓
UNIT HTR.	15	50/2	A	20/2	16	FREEZER
↓	↓	↓	B	↓	↓	↓
EXH. FAN	17	20/2	A	70/2	18	DISHWSH'R
↓	↓	↓	B	↓	↓	↓
SPARE	19	30/2	A	100/2	20	GRIDDLE
↓	↓	↓	B	↓	↓	↓
—	—	—	A	100/2	22	GRIDDLE
—	—	—	B	↓	↓	↓
SPACE	—	—	—	—	—	SPACE
	—	—	—	—	—	
	—	—	—	—	—	
	—	—	—	—	—	
↓	—	—	—	—	—	↓

SYMBOL LIST

SYMBOL	DESCRIPTION
	FLUORESCENT OR INCANDESCENT FIXTURE - UPPER CASE LETTER DENOTES TYPE, NO. DENOTES CIRCUIT NO; LOWER CASE LETTER, CONTROLLING SWITCH
	15A, 1P SWITCH. MTG. HT. + 48" ABOVE FLOOR. ARROW HART #1101-I & IVORY PLATE
	15A, 3 WAY SWITCH. MTG. HT. + 48" ABOVE FLOOR. A.H. #1103-I & IVORY PLATE
	15A, DUPLEX CONVENIENCE OUTLET MTG. HT. AS SHOWN ON PLAN. A.H. #5651-I & IV. PL.
	30A, 250V REC - ARROW HART #9344-I & IVORY PLATE.
	BUSS FUSEHOLDER OF TYPE INDICATED ON EQUIPMENT SCHEDULE
	JUNCTION BOX.
	UNIT HEATER - CHROMALOX #LUH-100, 240V, 1φ WITH #CR 350 CONTACTOR.
	THERMOSTAT - CHROMALOX #MHT 498 A. MTD. 5'-0" UP.
	TIMESWITCH - TORK #TZ 120L FL-5
	MANUAL MOTOR STARTER MTD. ON HOOD
	BRANCH CIRCUIT CONDUIT RUN CONCEALED ABOVE CEILING OR IN FLOOR
	BRANCH CIRCUIT CONDUIT RUN CONCEALED IN FLOOR.

KITCHEN ADDITION
CAMP ALEXANDER
ELEVEN-MILE RESERVOIR PARK COUNTY, COLORADO

CONSULTING ENGINEER

JOB NO:
DATE:
SCALE
DRAWN:
CHECKED:
APPROVED:
APPROVED:

SHEET E-1 OF

REEP

PRICING SHEET

JOB EXAMPLE NO. 3 SHEET NO. 1

WORK CAMP ALEXANDER OF 2

PRICED BY G.V.K. DATE 6 JUNE 1992

DESCRIPTION	REF PAGE	REMARKS OR DEVIATIONS	QTY.	UNIT PRICE		MULT	EXTENDED PRICE	
TYPE A LIGHTING FIXTURE	A–6		10	105	00	*	1050	00
TYPE B "	A–18		6	106	00		639	00
TYPE C "	A–16		3	71	00		213	00
TYPE D "	A–16		2	71	00		142	00
120/240 1PH/3W BRANCH PANEL, 42 CCT.	B–10		1	—	—		1300	00
30/2, NO FUSE DISC. SWITCH	B–19		1	—	—		100	00
60/2, "	B–19		1	—	—		130	00
30/2, NO FUSE RAINTITE DISC. SWITCH	B–19		1	—	—		135	00
2–1/2" GRC CONDUIT	E–1		70'	7	00		490	00
2" GRC CONDUIT	E–1		15'	5	30		79	50
1–1/4" GRC CONDUIT	E–1		35'	3	20		112	50
1" GRC CONDUIT	E–1		45'	2	70		121	00
2–1/2" "LB" CONDULET	E–3		1	—	—		160	00
2" "LB" CONDULET	E–3		1	—	—		100	00
3–300MCM THW WIRE	E–8		73'	12	00		876	00
3#3/0 THW WIRE	E–8		21,	7	20		151	00
3#3 THW WIRE	E–8		40,	3	10		124	00
3#6 THW WIRE	E–8		50,	2	05		102	50
300 MCM TERMINALS IN PULL BOX	E–15		6	41	00		246	50
2#12, 1/2" EMT	F–2		395,	2	30		908	50
3#12, 1/2" EMT	F–2		80,	2	50		200	00
4#12, 1/2" EMT	F–2		10,	2	70		27	00
3#10, 1/2" EMT	F–2		30,	2	65		79	50
CEILING FIXTURE OUTLETS & J–BOXES	F–19		10	31	95		607	05
WALL FIXTURE OUTLETS	F–19		2	27	35		519	65
15a DUPLEX RECEPTACLES	F–20		4	37	55		751	00
SINGLE POLE WALL SWITCH	F–23		4	42	85		171	40
3 WAY WALL SWITCH	F–23		2	48	50		97	20
2 WIRE THERMOSTAT	J–15		1	—	—		66	00
TIME SWITCH W/ASTRO DIAL	G–4		1	—	—		368	00
30a, 250V. RECEPTACLE	F–20		1	—	—		63	15
BUSS FUSE HOLDER & FLEX CONNECTION	G–18		4	89	50		358	00
3/4HP MANUAL MOTOR STARTER	G–18		1	—	—		89	50
			SHEET TOTAL				$7925	90

* MULTIPLIER APPLIED ON SUMMARY SHEET

REEP

PRICING SHEET

JOB EXAMPLE NO. 3 SHEET NO. 2

WORK CAMP ALEXANDER OF 2

PRICED BY G.V.K. DATE 6 JUNE 1992

DESCRIPTION	REF PAGE	REMARKS OR DEVIATIONS	QTY.	UNIT PRICE		MULT	EXTENDED PRICE	
200a–2W APPLIANCE CONNECTION	F–25		1	–	–	*	80	00
100a–2W APPLIANCE CONNECTION	F–25		4	42	00		168	00
60a–2W APPLIANCE CONNECTION	F–25		1	–	–		28	00
18" X 18" X 10" PULL BOX	L–1		1	–	–		125	00
6" X 6" X 4" PULL BOX	L–1		2	56	00		112	00
CUT 2–1/2" HOLES IN P.B. & EXIST. SWITCH	L–5		3	11	00		33	00
CUT 2" HOLE IN PULL BOX	L–5		1	–	–		9	50
RELOCATE EXISTING SWITCH	B–14		1	–	–		115	00
10KW HEATER	J–1		1	–	–		660	00
SHEET TOTAL							$1330	50

* MULTIPLIER APPLIED ON SUMMARY SHEET

REEP

SUMMARY SHEET

JOB *EXAMPLE NO. 3 – CAMP ALEXANDER* DATE *6 JUNE '92*

LOCATION ______

ARCHITECT ______ ORIGINAL PRICE ______

ENCLOSED AREA ______ $/sq. ft. ______ CHANGE ORDER ______

CONNECTED LOAD (W/sq ft) ______ DIVERSIFIED DEMAND (W/sq ft) ______

ALTERNATES ______

DESCRIPTION OF THE WORK *INTERIOR ELECTRICAL – COMPLETE*

REMARKS ______

PRICING SHEET TOTALS

SHEET NUMBER	DESCRIPTION	AMOUNT	
1	*INTERIOR ELECTRICAL*	$ 7925	90
2	*INTERIOR ELECTRICAL*	1330	50
	TOTAL SUMMARIZED PRICE	9256	40
	PRICE ADJUSTMENT MULTIPLIER	X 1	37
	ADJUSTED SELL PRICE	$12,681	27

SUBCONTRACT ITEMS

DESCRIPTION	AMOUNT	
TOTAL OF SUBCONTRACT ITEMS		
PROFIT MULTIPLIER	X	
ADJUSTED TOTAL		

TOTAL JOB PRICE → $ 12,681 27

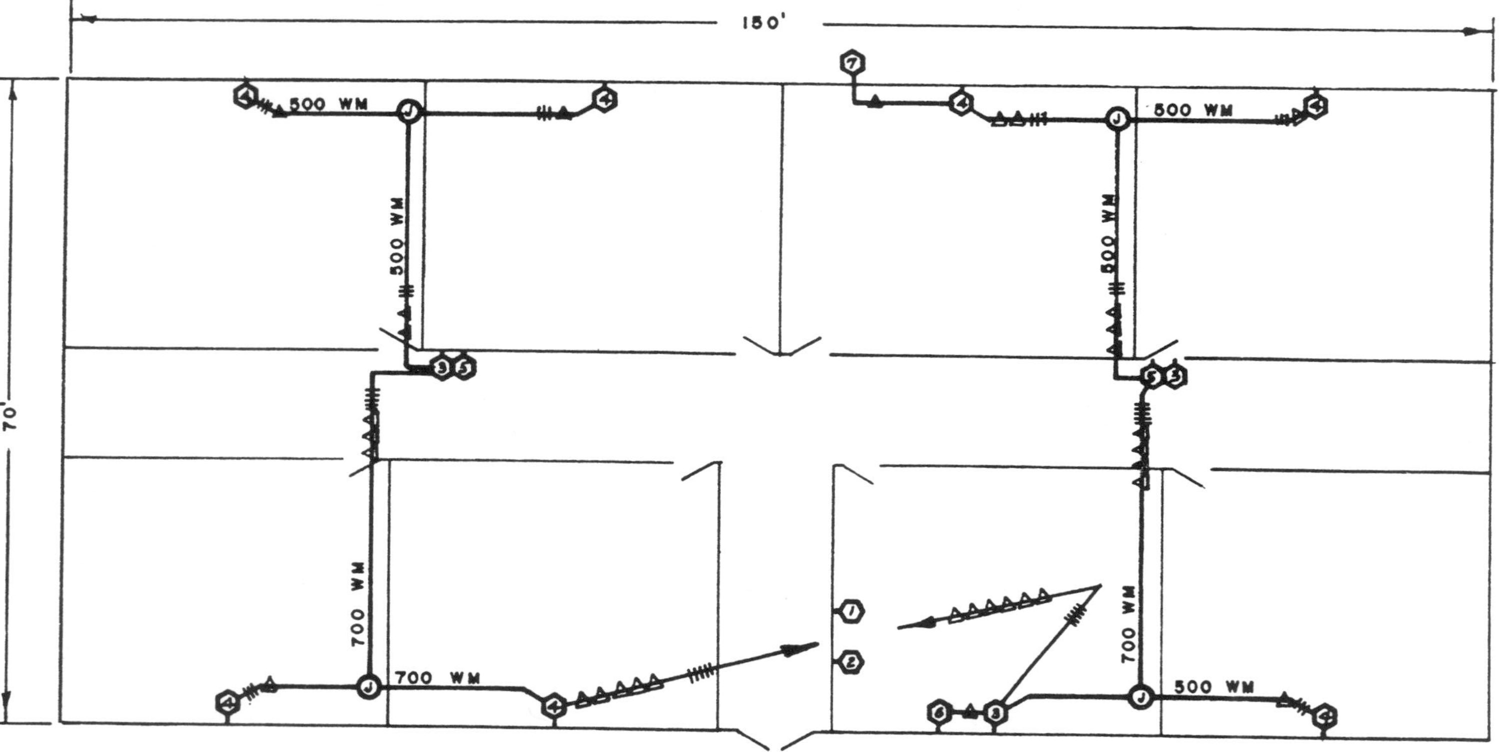

INSTALLATION OF CLOCK & SOUND SYSTEM IN EXISTING OLDER SCHOOL

EXAMPLE NO. 4

1. SYNCHRONOUS MASTER CLOCK with program control & daylight savings feature
2. COMPACT COMMUNICATION CENTER
3. SPEAKER, surface type
4. TIME-TONE UNIT wy 12"sq. corrected clock & 8" speaker
5. PROGRAM BELL - 6"
6. VOLUME CONTROL
7. EXTERIOR HORN - 15w

—‖‖‖ △△△— WIREMOLD in size indicated with 3-14 & sound cables indicated by triangles

REEP

PRICING SHEET

JOB EXAMPLE NO.4 SHEET NO. 1

WORK CLOCK & SOUND SYSTEMS IN EXISTING SCHOOL OF 1

PRICED BY G.V.K. DATE 9 JUNE 1992

DESCRIPTION	KEY	REMARKS OR DEVIATIONS	REF PAGE	QTY.	UNIT PRICE		MULT	EXTENDED PRICE	
SYNCH. WIRED MASTERED CLOCK	1	SURF. MTD.	I–7	1	2188	00	1.37	$2998	—
COMPACT COMMUNICATION CENTER	2		I–19	1	2489	00	1.37	3410	—
DESK MIKE	—		I–22	1	122	00	1.37	167	—
SURFACE MOUNTED SPEAKER	3		I–20	3	594	00	1.37	2441	—
EXTERIOR HORN	7		I–20	1	165	00	1.37	226	—
TIMETONE UNIT FOR 12" CLOCK	4	SURF. MTD.	I–7	7	156	00	1.37	1496	—
12" SYNCH. WIRED CLOCK	4		I–6	7	129	50	1.37	1064	—
8" SPEAKER & TRANSFORMER	4		I–20	7	37	00	1.37	355	—
6" PROGRAM BELL	5		I–5	2	139	50	1.37	382	—
SURFACE MTD. VOLUME CONTROL	6		I–20	1	69	00	1.37	95	—
WIREMOLD J–BOX	—		F–30	4	20	50	1.37	112	—
500 WIREMOLD	—		F–29	190,	3	15	1.37	820	—
700 WIREMOLD	—		F–29	180'	3	28	1.37	809	—
3#14 PULLED IN	—		F–11	240'		75	1.37	247	—
5#14 PULLED IN	—		F–11	200'	1	00	1.37	274	—
2/C #20 SPEAKER CABLE PULLED IN	—		I–23	799'		68	1.37	1095	—
DRILL 1" HOLE IN MASONRY WALL	—		L–3	10	23	00	1.37	315	—
				SHEET TOTAL				$16,306	—

REEP

PRICING SHEET

JOB ______________________________ SHEET NO. __________

WORK ______________________________ OF __________

PRICED BY DATE

DESCRIPTION	REMARKS OR DEVIATIONS	QTY.	UNIT PRICE	MULT	EXTENDED PRICE
		SHEET TOTAL			

REEP

PRICING SHEET FOR ITEMS NOT INCLUDED IN REEP

JOB ______________________ SHEET NO. __________

WORK ______________________ OF __________

PRICED BY DATE

DESCRIPTION	QTY.	UNIT LABOR		EXTENDED HOURS		UNIT MAT'L		EXTENDED PRICE	
TOTAL LABOR HOURS & MATERIAL DOLLARS						——		$	
LABOR RATE PER HOUR INCLUDING BENEFITS				x					
TOTAL LABOR DOLLARS				$					
OVERHEAD & D.J.E. MULTIPLIER				x 2	.14				
TOTAL LABOR, OVERHEAD & D.J.E DOLLARS				$		→			
TOTAL GROSS COST								$	
NET PROFIT								x 1	05
SHEET TOTAL								$	

REEP

SUMMARY SHEET

JOB ______________________________ DATE __________

LOCATION ______________________________

ARCHITECT ______________________________ ORIGINAL PRICE __________

ENCLOSED AREA ______________ $/sq. ft.______________ CHANGE ORDER __________

CONNECTED LOAD (W/sq ft) ______________ DIVERSIFIED DEMAND (W/sq ft) ______________

ALTERNATES ______________________________

____

DESCRIPTION OF THE WORK ______________________________

____

____

REMARKS ______________________________

PRICING SHEET TOTALS	SHEET NUMBER	DESCRIPTION	AMOUNT	
			$	
	TOTAL SUMMARIZED PRICE			
	PRICE ADJUSTMENT MULTIPLIER		X	
	ADJUSTED SELL PRICE			

SUBCONTRACT ITEMS	DESCRIPTION	AMOUNT		
	TOTAL OF SUBCONTRACT ITEMS			
	PROFIT MULTIPLIER	X		
	ADJUSTED TOTAL		→	

TOTAL JOB PRICE → $

Index

ABOUT THE AUTHORS

C. Kenneth Kolstad, now retired, was a partner in the firm of Kolstad and Kohnert, Consulting Engineers, in Colorado Springs, Colorado. He was a member of the National Society of Professional Engineers, the Consulting Engineers Council of Colorado, the Illuminating Engineering Society, and the International Association of Electrical Inspectors. He holds a degree in electrical engineering from Northeastern University.

Gerald V. Kohnert is the owner of Kohnert Engineering, Inc., in Colorado Springs, Colorado. He was formerly employed by Electrical Construction Co. and Mayfield Engineering Co. Mr. Kohnert is a graduate of the Illinois Institute of Technology. He is a member of the Consulting Engineers Council of Colorado and the Construction Specification Institute.